PETER NORMANTON has edited and published the horror comics fanzine, *From the Tomb*, for eight years and has recently published the 23rd issue. He is widely admired for supporting the work of horror artists and small publishers. He lives in Rochdale.

Also available

The Mammoth Book of 20th Century Science Fiction
The Mammoth Book of Best New Erotica 7
The Mammoth Book of Best New Horror 18
The Mammoth Book of Best New Manga
The Mammoth Book of Best New Manga 2
The Mammoth Book of Best New SF 20
The Mammoth Book of Best War Comics
The Mammoth Book of Bikers
The Mammoth Book of Celtic Myths and Legends
The Mammoth Book of Comic Fantasy
The Mammoth Book of Comic Quotes
The Mammoth Book of CSI
The Mammoth Book of the Deep
The Mammoth Book of Dickensian Whodunnits
The Mammoth Book of Dirty, Sick, X-Rated & Politically Incorrect Jokes
The Mammoth Book of the Edge
The Mammoth Book of Erotic Women
The Mammoth Book of Extreme Science Fiction
The Mammoth Book of the Funniest Cartoons of All Time
The Mammoth Book of Great Detective Stories
The Mammoth Book of Great Inventions
The Mammoth Book of Haunted House Stories
The Mammoth Book of Insults
The Mammoth Book of International Erotica
The Mammoth Book of IQ Puzzles
The Mammoth Book of Jacobean Whodunnits
The Mammoth Book of Jokes
The Mammoth Book of Killers at Large
The Mammoth Book of King Arthur
The Mammoth Book of Lesbian Erotica
The Mammoth Book of Modern Ghost Stories
The Mammoth Monsters
The Mammoth Book of Mountain Disasters
The Mammoth Book of New Jules Verne Adventures
The Mammoth Book of New Terror
The Mammoth Book of On the Road
The Mammoth Book of Perfect Crimes and Impossible Mysteries
The Mammoth Book of Pirates
The Mammoth Book of Polar Journeys
The Mammoth Book of Roaring Twenties Whodunnits
The Mammoth Book of Roman Whodunnits
The Mammoth Book of Secret Code Puzzles
The Mammoth Book of Sex, Drugs & Rock 'n' Roll
The Mammoth Book of Sorcerers' Tales
The Mammoth Book of Space Exploration and Disasters
The Mammoth Book of Special Forces
The Mammoth Book of Special Ops
The Mammoth Book of Sudoku
The Mammoth Book of Travel in Dangerous Places
The Mammoth Book of True Crime
The Mammoth Book of True War Stories
The Mammoth Book of Unsolved Crimes
The Mammoth Book of Vampires
The Mammoth Book of Wild Journeys
The Mammoth Book of Women Who Kill
The Mammoth Book of the World's Greatest Chess Games

The Mammoth Book of

Best Horror Comics

Edited by Peter Normanton

ROBINSON
London

Constable & Robinson Ltd
3 The Lanchesters
162 Fulham Palace Road
London W6 9ER
www.constablerobinson.com

First published in the UK by Robinson,
an imprint of Constable & Robinson Ltd 2008

A copy of the British Library Cataloguing in Publication Data is available from the British Library.

ISBN 978-1-84529-641-4

Printed and bound in the EU

3 5 7 9 10 8 6 4

CATG-PEFC-052
www.pefc.org

Contents

7 Foreword

I The Dark Age of Comics – 1940s and 1950s

14 Famous Tales of Terror
22 Hitler's Head
30 No Rest for the Dead
37 He
44 The Secret Files of Dr Drew
53 The Corpse That Wouldn't Die!
61 Bride of Death
68 Dungeon of Doom
74 Terror of the Stolen Legs
81 Den of Horror
89 The Living-Dead
97 Marching Zombies
106 Grave Rehearsal
113 A Glimpse of the Pit
122 The Horror of the Walking Corpse
130 The Thing That Walked at Night
137 Partners in Blood
148 Dead Man's Revenge
155 The Hand of Glory
164 The Man Who Would Be Fate

II The Terror Returns – 1960s and 1970s

177 The Monster of Dread End
189 Santa's Claws
198 The Game Keeper
206 Fatal Scalpel
214 The Weirdest Character I've Ever Known!
222 Now... Another Maniac!
229 Through a Glass Darkly
238 Ghouls Walk Among Us
246 Tradition of the Wolf
255 Sea of Graves

III The Faithful Few – 1980s and 1990s

269 Killer Planet

281 Over His Head

291 Christmas Carol

302 Mr Monster: His World

314 Home Ties

323 One of these Days

352 The Dunwich Horror

364 Dream Snake

377 Purgation

IV A New Millennium for the Macabre – 21st century

412 Dread End

421 The Festival

427 The Crawlspace

435 Immortal: A Vampire Tale

447 There Was an Old Woman

459 Cal McDonald: A Letter from B. S.

469 Luna's Story Little Red Riding Hood

503 The Graveswellers

525 Shuteye

Acknowledgments

Foreword

My first discovery of horror came at an all too tender age with the fairy tales of childhood and the strange illustrations that went with them. But it was not until an oppressively hot afternoon in the August of 1974, when I was twelve years old, that I became hooked by the horrors lurking in the pages of comic books. In the window of my local newsagent's I caught sight of a magazine with a beautifully illustrated cover: a partially naked female draped before a gorilla-like beast. It wasn't the bare flesh that got me excited, it was the beast looming in the background and the threat this moody scene evoked.

The cover was the work of Sebastia Boada, and the magazine was Skywald's *Nightmare 17*; my life was forever changed. I savoured every last morsel of its content, convinced I would never see anything of its ilk again. That same summer, an afternoon television show with comedian Bob Monkhouse also revealed his love of comics. It was one of those treasures in the attic type of programmes, which dominate so much of today's daytime viewing. These particular treasures held my attention for the duration of the show; they were EC horror comics, the ultimate prize for any comic book collector with a craving for terror. Try as I might, I couldn't get them out of my mind.

Time passed and I became a huge fan of Marvel's horror comics, along with their black-and-white magazines, which to my young eyes seemed so much more mature in their outlook than the regular colour comics. Names such as Frank Brunner, Mike Ploog, Gene Colan, Tom Palmer, Steve Gerber, Tom Sutton and Val Mayerik filled my mind. I loved the artwork, but Steve's rebellious tales never failed to capture my imagination.Then, as soon as they seemed to come into my life, horror comics disappeared. I never understood why, but as a collector there were still plenty of back issues to be sought.

I could never stop hunting for those missing issues. It was akin to an addiction. I satiated my craving by searching market stalls, second-hand shops and then going to comic fairs. It was a very wet January in 1985, soon after I had started work, before I was in a position to purchase my first EC, *Haunt of Horror 12* with its classic Ingels cover. For some reason – probably the expense – it completely killed the desire to acquire more. However, I continued to pick up the new horror comics that came out during the middle years of the 1980s which, while enjoyable, were few and far between.

Comics began to take second place for a while. I had met my wife and life was good. Then I got married and within a short time was hooked all over again. I was mortgaged up to the eyeballs but within a short time of saying

"I do" managed to afford two EC science fiction titles, *Weird Science 8* and *11*. Up until then I had been happy to buy reprints. What came over me I don't know, but before the end of the year I had picked up my first pre-Code Atlas titles, *Suspense* and *Astonish* plus an ACG *Forbidden Worlds*. They were quite good, but the ECs were so much better and there was something about having the original copies.

As my collection started to grow, it was no longer enough just to own these comics and digest the stories; I wanted to learn all I could about the creative minds behind these publications. For most of the 1990s, while adding to my collection – largely thanks to Ken Harman – I tracked down every book and magazine that I could. I began to piece together the tale behind the boom in horror comics during the early 1950s, the crusade against them and subsequent ban on their explicit and gory content. I also learned of the history and characters involved in my early years of collecting during the 1970s. The history behind these comics is fascinating but it is the stories that make it so worthwhile.

Although I have a passion for the pre-Code years, it is impossible to ignore the talent that has followed. Even as I type these words there is much exciting new material coming into the comic shops. For this anthology I have selected from the full range of horror comics, from the 1940s to the present day. While editing my own horror comic fan publication *From the Tomb* and working alongside the likes of Frank Motler, Doc Garriock and Barry Forshaw, my knowledge of and love for these comics and their creators have grown. To be asked to put together a book of this kind is like being a kid all over again. You won't find anything by Marvel, DC, Warren or EC in these pages – they have published their own collections – but what you will find is a rich array of talent spanning over sixty years.

Before you tuck into this Mammoth tome I would like to thank Pete Duncan for asking me to edit this project and my wife Mary for putting up with the insanity of a comic book collector.

Peter Normanton

THE DARK AGE OF COMICS

1940s and 1950s

In the years immediately after the Second World War, the warm glow that permeated the golden age of the superhero comic slowly began to fade. Those colourful comics could no longer command the enormous sales they had a few years before; in their wake came a variety of new genres. Almost side by side came the violence of the crime comic and the sugariness of teenage romance, then at the very end of the decade a handful of horror comics clawed their way onto the distributors' schedules. Each spawned an abomination, the like of which had never before been seen in a comic book. Within a matter of years outrage followed upon outrage as the contents of these so-called comics emerged to become the most notorious in the industry's short-lived history. While these publications did everything they could to entertain the youth of America, there were gatherings of morally inclined campaigners who looked upon their gaudy content with grave concern. The machinations of well-meaning groups were inevitably to bring ruination on the comic book industry.

As early as 1943 Classic Comics released an interpretation of Dr Jekyll and Mr Hyde. This adaptation is now acknowledged to be the first fully fledged horror comic, although it was never intended as a guinea pig for a new frightful phase in comics. Only a few characters of a supernatural persuasion managed to creep into other stories from these early years. Continental's *Suspense* has long been looked upon as a precursor to the horror comic, as are Harry A. Chesler's *Dynamic, Punch Comics* and *Red Seal Comics*, which contained elements of horror. Eight of the ten issues of *Yellowjacket Comics* contain "Tales of Terror" narrated by an Old Witch, but each of these titles were completely overshadowed by the towering might of the superhero comic.

It was not until Avon ventured into the realm of terror with the aptly named *Eerie*, cover dated January 1947, that the entire content of a comic book was first dedicated to horror. Sadly, it didn't act as a catalyst for the first wave of comic book terror. *Eerie* may well have been an early victim of the axe, or more likely was only ever scheduled for the kind of one-off appearance Avon seemed to favour. All was not lost though, for the title would be resurrected four years later.

The first comic book publisher to launch an ongoing series committed to the weird and supernatural was the American Comics Group, a largely wholesome enterprise. They debuted *Adventures into the Unknown* in the autumn of 1948 – a fitting time of year if ever there was one to release a title of this chilling kind. Whether the American Comics Group was more patient than their counterparts at Avon, or their timing was more apt, *Adventures into the Unknown* proved successful and regularly appeared until 1967.

Hidden away in the pages of its third issue were the stylized renderings of the then unknown Al Feldstein. Al may have had designs to progress his career in comics, but not even his wildest imaginings could have prepared him for what was to follow. Before the end of 1949, working alongside the legendary Bill Gaines, he introduced the Crypt Keeper into the pages of EC's *Crime Patrol 15*, and similarly brought the Vault Keeper to *War Against Crime!* with its tenth issue. It proved the beginning of a new direction for what had become a desperately flagging line of titles, ushering in a never-to-be-forgotten phase in comic book creativity. *The Crypt of Terror*, soon to become the notorious *Tales From the Crypt*, and *The Vault of Horror* were EC's first hideous tomes. *The Haunt of Fear* would follow in their shadow just a month later. By the end of 1951 the news-stands were beginning to overflow with this deranged phenomenon.

The part played by *Adventures into the Unknown* in arousing interest in this ghoulish form of entertainment should not be underestimated, but the real credit for what was to happen lies with EC. Rival publishers had always perused one another's products to keep up with the latest trend, but their attitude towards EC bordered on plagiarism.

Long-time editor of Marvel Comics, Stan Lee, has gone on record demeaning his line of Atlas horror titles as nothing more than copies of EC's comic books. Their underlying premise was indeed inspired by EC, but Stan shouldn't have been so quick to undervalue what became a healthy assemblage of weird and wonderful books. From the latter part of 1952 through until early 1954, the boom period for the horror craze, Atlas's portfolio included over a dozen titles tailored to shock the senses. Among these were the long-running *Journey into Mystery* and *Strange Tales,* but it was the macabre delights in the pages of *Adventures in Terror*, *Adventures into Weird Worlds* and *Menace* that the youngsters most craved.

Other comic publishers followed, each in turn evolving a unique approach. Fawcett, the esteemed publishers of *Captain Marvel Adventures*, released titles such as *Worlds Beyond* and *This Magazine is Haunted*. Their titles didn't languish in the exploitation associated with their contemporaries; instead they pursued a form of storytelling which sought to chill using carefully plotted stories to focus the element of tension. Their team of resident artists included the versatile talents of Kurt Schaffenburger, Bob Powell and George Evans, names that assured the highest standards. Fawcett could also boast the talent of Norman Saunders, who produced several beautifully painted covers for *Strange Stories from Another World*.

Stanley P. Morse was responsible for a series of shameless entries during these years, *Mr Mystery*, *Weird Mysteries*, *Weird Tales of the Future* and *Weird Chills*. Over half a century after they first appeared, these now rate amongst the most prized in any horror enthusiast's collection. Violence, decapitation and even a suggestion of sex were no strangers to their pages.

Amongst paperback publisher Ace's horror titles were *Baffling Mysteries*, *The Beyond*, *Hand of Fate* and *Web of Mystery*. Their approach was usually restrained, resorting to more conventional themes such as haunted castles, vampires and ghosts. Once every so often they included a hidden gem of the most despicable kind.

Harvey Comics is fondly remembered for their loveable character Casper but their line of horror comics rivalled virtually anything on the news-stand. *Witches' Tales*, the notorious *Chamber of Chills*, *Black Cat Mystery* and *Tomb of Terror* each revelled in an array of grisly covers, which left you with a pretty good idea as to what lay waiting in their pages. The deranged artistry of Howard Nostrand, Bob Powell, Lee Elias and Rudy Palais all appeared in this flesh-creeping range of comics.

Comic Media only ever published two horror titles, *Horrific* (later to become *Terrific*) and *Weird Terror*. It's perhaps as well, for they contained a depravity that defies belief. The dark vision of the aspiring Don Heck epitomized their covers. His unique portrayals continue to attract the interest of many collectors of the genre, as do these titles' interior pages. Issue 6 of *Weird Terror* promised "Shrunken Skulls, Decapitations, Cemeteries, Murders" and didn't disappoint.

Jack Kirby and Joe Simon had already become giants in the comic book industry a decade before. In the employ of Prize Comics they created a very particular brand of horror in what became the long-running title *Black Magic*.

They refused to wallow in the gruesome carryings-on readily enjoyed by their peers, but were amply proficient in terms of plot and characterization.

There was always at least one publisher prepared to go to that extra step further to shock and ultimately boost their sales figures. Charlton's *The Thing!* grew steadily more debauched from its fifth issue, with panels revelling in an excess of violence, dismemberment and that great favourite of the day, severed heads. Master's *Dark Mysteries* along with Story's *Mysterious Adventures* and *Fight Against Crime* (all believed to have been the property of the same publisher) took on a decidedly darker guise as the years went by. They began to swipe EC's mocking style – not always, I might add, with the same penchant for sardonic humour.

For the publishers of the horror comic it was a boom period, but there were those who felt the youth of America was becoming a little too preoccupied with these dissolute delights. As more and more unsavoury titles appeared in the stores and the youngsters became increasingly enamoured with these dark tales, an appreciable sense of alarm spread across the United States. Critics of both the horror genre and the preceding reign of crime in the comic books considered them a menace to society.

Most eminent amongst the opponents of the comic book publishers was psychologist Dr Fredric Wertham, whose work maligning horror and crime comics appeared in an assortment of women's journals during the late 1940s and on into the early 1950s. His research into the damaging effect of these so-called comics on juveniles and their impact on the spiralling problem of delinquency culminated in his highly influential book *Seduction of the Innocent*. Shortly afterwards, the almost farcical Senate Subcommittee to Investigate Juvenile Delinquency hearings of 1954, held amidst the paranoiac fear of Communist infiltration, effectively put an end to the activities of the horror publishers, diluting the entire medium with a succession of stipulations formalized in the Comics Code. It meant that from March 1955 the words weird, horror and terror were no longer permitted to appear in comic titles. Excessive bloodshed, gore, depravity, lust and scenes of a sado-masochistic nature were forbidden. The force of evil prevalent in these dark comic books could not be presented in an alluring manner but had to be imbued with a due sense of morality. Furthermore, the walking dead, torture, vampires, ghouls, cannibals and werewolves were all banished. The new comic books of America became a sanitized version of what had gone before. If we are to describe the years leading up to then – the pre-Code years – as the Dark Age of comics, then the years following 1955 were a darker age still for many talented artists and writers.

Now you know the gory bits, let's make sure we keep things in perspective. For the most part these tales were written in a darkly humorous vein; even the most wretched of scenes could raise a chuckle. If their creators had wanted these tales to be taken too seriously, they would have been on a one-way ticket to the asylum, if not the state penitentiary. The cackles accompanying the macabre puns were intrinsic to the charm of EC's line of morbid tales. Harvey's *Witches' Tales* in particular, along with the outrageous *Mr Mystery* from Stanley P. Morse, preferred to use this method of narration for their misbegotten yarns. And it is nigh on impossible to read many of Atlas's chilling fables without being aware of a distinctly tongue-in-cheek tone.

But the dark humour was not enough to save them. The graphic extremities so gleefully orchestrated by the creators of these comics as a means of making a quick buck ironically precipitated their death knell. The comic books of fifty years ago marched the damned unceremoniously to the hangman's noose, the electric chair or Madame Guillotine. Corpses crawled from the graves that once preserved their eternal sleep, while creatures from the depths of our own world, and beyond, ran amok destroying towns and cities across the globe. In hidden laboratories deranged scientists reanimated the dead and gave life to abominations they never should have given life to. On far away islands and deep in the darkest jungles, lost tribes shrank their victims' heads while their cannibal cousins consumed the bodies. Could you ever be sure the man in the next room was who, or what, he said he was? This was the age of the Cold War and pandemic paranoia – a paranoia the publishers sought freely to exploit before finding themselves caught in the path of its insufferable wake. Eventually, the Senate Committee hearings of 1954 and the Comics Code doomed the four-colour books of terror and numerous companies with them.

Famous Tales of Terror

Yellowjacket Comics 1, September 1944

This, our earliest entry, comes from a time before horror had captured public imagination. *Yellowjacket Comics* was one of numerous anthology titles that allowed its editors to test certain genres; for the première it was Edgar Allan Poe's unsettling narration of "The Black Cat" rendered for a first interpretation in the comic book format. These tales of terror would appear in all but two of *Yellowjacket Comics*' ten issue run, through until June 1946. It was published by E. Levy; a company which later evolved to become Charlton Comics.

FAMOUS TALES of TERROR
IN THESE PAGES OF YELLOWJACKET COMICS, WE PRESENT WITH PRIDE AN OLD MASTERPIECE ADAPTED TO COMIC CONTINUITY... THE FIRST IN THE SERIES OF FAMOUS SHORT MYSTERY STORIES IS EDGAR ALLEN POE'S, The BLACK CAT!
"THE STORY I MUST TELL YOU, IS ONE WHICH I CAN HARDLY HOPE YOU WILL BELIEVE. BUT, AS YOU CAN SEE, I AM GOING TO DIE-- TOMORROW, AND TODAY I WOULD UNBURDEN MY SOUL!

"IN MY CHILDHOOD, I WAS KNOWN FOR MY DOCILITY AND KINDNESS TOWARD ANIMALS...
NICE PUPPY! YOU WANT ME TO PLAY WITH YOU, EH?
"THEN, WHEN I GREW UP, I MARRIED A GIRL WHOSE DISPOSITION WAS VERY LIKE MY OWN! WE LOOKED FORWARD CONFIDENTLY TO YEARS OF HAPPINESS!
I PRONOUNCE YOU MAN AND WIFE!
"OUR HOME WAS A SMALL ZOO -- BUT MY FAVORITE PET WAS A BEAUTIFUL BLACK CAT WHOM I NAMED "PLUTO"!
"PLUTO FOLLOWED ME ABOUT THE HOUSE LIKE A LITTLE BLACK SHADOW--
HERE, PUSS--TASTE THIS! GOOD, ISN'T IT?
"OUR HOME CONTINUED TO BE A VERY HAPPY ONE UNTIL I FELL INTO INTEMPERANCE...
DEAR, I-I WISH YOU WOULDN'T DRINK ANY MORE TONIGHT! PLEASE!?
WIFE, DON'T NAG ME! I'LL DRINK AS I PLEASE--WHEN I PLEASE!
"IN MY DRUNKEN FITS, I WOULD BECOME UNBEARABLE! ONLY PLUTO ESCAPED MY VILE, UNREASONABLE RAGES!
STUPID PESTS--GET AWAY FROM ME!
AWRR!
CHEEE!
"THEN, ONE NIGHT WHEN I STAGGERED HOME, PLUTO REFUSED TO COME TO ME...
PLUTO--COME HERE! COME, I SAY! WHAT, YOU DISOBEY ME?
REOWRRR!

"I GRABBED HIM UP, BUT...
OWW! YOU BIT ME!
YEOWRR!
"A BLINDING RAGE SEIZED ME -- I DREW OUT MY POCKET KNIFE AND CORNERED HIM!
YOU FOUL BEAST-- YOU'LL NEVER BITE ME AGAIN!
HISSSSSS!

"DELIBERATELY, I CUT ONE OF HIS EYES FROM ITS SOCKET!
YEOWRRR!
"THE CAT RECOVERED BUT ALWAYS IT WOULD FLEE ME IN COMPLETE TERROR!
"HOWEVER, MY CONSCIENCE WAS TROUBLED AT EACH SIGHT OF HIM -- FINALLY, I COULD STAND IT NO LONGER...

"MY REMORSE WAS TERRIBLE BUT I HAD TO DESTROY THE ANIMAL.. DESTROY IT, BECAUSE IT LOVED ME AND I KNEW I HAD NOT BEEN WORTHY OF THAT DEVOTION! I KNEW IT WAS I WHO SHOULD BE HANGING FROM THAT ROPE ---

"I HAD FINALLY FALLEN ASLEEP THAT NIGHT WHEN I WAS AROUSED BY THE CRY OF
FIRE!
3

"MY WIFE, OUR SERVANT GIRL, AND I WERE LUCKY TO ESCAPE! THAT FIRE DESTROYED EVERYTHING... MY ENTIRE FORTUNE WAS SWALLOWED UP IN FLAMES!
OUR WEALTH-- OUR HOME ALL GONE IN A SHORT HOUR!

"WE FOUND REFUGE FOR THE NIGHT, BUT THE NEXT DAY AS I WALKED PAST THE SMOKING RUINS---
THOSE PEOPLE! WHAT ARE THEY DOING AROUND MY HOUSE?

"THEN I SAW IT!! UPON THE SURFACE OF THE STANDING WALL, AS IF ENGRAVED IN BAS RELIEF, WAS THE SILHOUETTE OF A GIGANTIC CAT... HANGING BY A NOOSE AROUND HIS NECK!

"FROM THAT TIME FORWARD, I COULD NOT RID MYSELF OF THE BLACK CAT!

"AS THE DAYS WENT BY, I FOUND MYSELF SEEKING FORGETFULNESS MORE AND MORE. ALWAYS, I SEEMED TO BE LOOKING FOR SOMETHING...

"THEN, ONE NIGHT I FOUND A BLACK CAT, VERY LIKE PLUTO-- HE WAS CURLED UP ON A HOGSHEAD.

"WHEN I LOOKED CLOSER, I FOUND THIS ANIMAL HAD A LARGE, INDEFINITE SPLOTCH OF WHITE ON HIS BREAST! I DECIDED THEN AND THERE THAT I MUST OWN HIM!
4

"THE CAT FOLLOWED ME HOME MOST WILLINGLY!"

"IT DOMESTICATED ITSELF AT ONCE AND BECAME A GREAT FAVORITE WITH MY WIFE!"

"BUT I SOON CAME TO HATE THE ANIMAL — FOR, LIKE PLUTO, HE HAD BUT ONE EYE!

"AND, AS MY HATE GREW, IT BECAME AN ACTUAL DREAD OF THE BEAST! MY FEAR ALONE KEPT ME FROM DESTROYING HIM!

"AND FINALLY, ONE DAY, I NOTED THAT THE SPLOTCH OF WHITE ON THE ANIMAL'S CHEST HAD COME TO ASSUME THE SHAPE OF A GALLOWS!!"

"IT WAS SOME TIME LATER THAT MY WIFE AND I DESCENDED INTO THE CELLAR ON SOME HOUSEHOLD ERRAND! THE CAT FOLLOWED ME DOWN THE STEEP STAIRS -- CLOSE ON MY HEELS!

"I TRIPPED OVER HIM AND TUMBLED HEADLONG! I WAS NOT SERIOUSLY HURT BUT THE INCIDENT INFURIATED ME!
5

"I GRABBED UP AN AXE AND AIMED A BLOW AT THE CAT!
NO! DON'T!

"MY WIFE STOPPED ME--HER INTERFERENCE ONLY ENRAGED ME MORE!

"IN A BLIND FURY, I BURIED THE AXE DEEP IN HER HEAD! SHE FELL DEAD ON THE SPOT WITHOUT A SOUND!

"I FORTHWITH SET MYSELF THE TASK OF CONCEALING HER BODY! I USED A CROWBAR TO DISLODGE THE BRICKS IN THE CELLAR WALL!

"I PROPPED HER BODY AGAINST THE INNER WALL AND RELAID THE BRICKS WITH MINUTE CARE!

"MY NEXT STEP WAS TO HUNT FOR THE HORRIBLE BEAST WHICH HAD BEEN RESPONSIBLE FOR SO MUCH WRETCHEDNESS! HOWEVER, I COULD NOT FIND HIM.- THE CAT MUST HAVE FLED THE HOUSE! FOREVER, I PRESUMED!

"I SLEPT SOUNDLY THAT NIGHT–EVEN WITH THE BURDEN OF MURDER UPON MY SOUL!

"ON THE FOURTH DAY AFTER THE EVENT, THE LAW OFFICERS CAME TO MY HOUSE. I FELT NO EMBARRASSMENT WHATSOEVER, CONFIDENT IN MY PLACE OF CONCEALMENT!

"I FELT QUITE SAFE AS THEY DESCENDED INTO THE CELLAR.

"THE POLICE, THOROUGHLY SATISFIED, PREPARED TO DEPART BUT I COULD NOT LET WELL ENOUGH ALONE--

WE'LL GO NOW!

GENTLEMEN, I THANK YOU FOR YOUR TROUBLE! I AM SORRY NOT TO BE ABLE TO HELP YOU!

"IN SHEER BRAVADO, I RAPPED MY CANE HEAVILY AGAINST THE WALL – AT THE VERY SPOT WHERE MY WIFE'S BODY WAS HIDDEN!

YOU SEE WHAT AN EXCELLENT CONSTRUCTION THERE IS IN THIS HOUSE?

RAP! RAP!

"TO MY COMPLETE HORROR, I WAS ANSWERED FROM THAT STONY TOMB BY A CRY THAT GREW AND SWELLED INTO ONE CONTINUOUS INHUMAN SCREAM!

AYIEEEEE

"THE OFFICERS IMMEDIATELY TORE OPEN THE BRICKWORK-- AND THERE STOOD THE BODY OF MY WIFE! ON HER HEAD PERCHED THAT HIDEOUS BEAST— THE BLACK CAT!"

Hitler's Head

Weird Terror 1, September 1952

Don Heck excelled in his time with Comic Media, so much so that he became the regular cover artist for both *Weird Terror* and its companion *Horrific*. He was able to play with the light and dark in a way that made him perfect for these ghastly comics. When "Hitler's Head" was published the Nazi spectre had been vanquished, but it still inspired a paranoiac dread, one the comic book publishers regularly seized on. Like many of its contemporaries, this dark tale was unashamed in its exploitation of those fears, bringing Adolf and his newly found demonic minions back from the very depths of hell.

Don Heck had begun life in the production department at Harvey Comics before moving on to work for Quality, Hillman and Toby Press. After Comic Media, he moved to Atlas, latterly known as Marvel Comics, where he came to be revered for his work on The Avengers.

EX-GESTAPO COLONEL ERIC HAUSNER FLED TO SOUTH AMERICA TO ESCAPE THE HORROR AND MADNESS THAT WAS ADOLPH HITLER AND NAZI GERMANY--BUT HE MADE THE MISTAKE OF NOT LISTENING TO OR BELIEVING THE TERRIBLE CURSES OF A DYING MAN. WHEN THE WEIRD HORDES OF HELL SPEWED FORTH TO CLAIM HIM--NOTHING ON THIS EARTH COULD STOP HIM FROM SEEING...

HITLER'S HEAD!

HAUSNER! YOU'RE COMING BACK WITH ME! DO YOU HEAR ME, HAUSNER? YOU'RE JOINING ME AND MY DEMONS IN HELL! HA, HA, HA!
N-NO! GET BACK TO YOUR ROTTING TOMB! THIS IS A HORRIBLE NIGHTMARE! SHOOT THEM, MEN! SHOOT THEM! SHOOT THEM!
RATATATAT
DON HECK

THE PLACE-A HUGE CASTLE COURTYARD IN THE JUNGLES OF SOUTH AMERICA FAR FROM THE BIG CITIES. THE TIME--EARLY MORNING NOT SO LONG AGO...TWELVE MEN FACING A SINGLE TARGET...
READY---FIRE!!

GOOD! YOU HAVE NOT LOST YOUR AIM! THAT IS A GREAT CONSOLATION! DISMISSED!

ERIC--WHAT HAS COME OVER YOU? YOU ARE FRIGHT-ENED OF YOUR OWN SHADOW! WHY SHOULD YOUR BODYGUARD NEED TARGET PRACTICE!
SOMETHING HORRIBLE HAS HAPPENED, DOCTOR! ORDINARILY-I AM A BRAVE MAN! BUT--NOW I I'M NOT SURE!

YOU KNOW WHY WE ARE HERE, GERHARDT! WE ARE ALL NAZIS--AND WE ESCAPED INTO THIS COUNTRY! BUT WHAT IF I WERE TO TELL YOU THAT SOMEONE--SOMETHING ELSE FOLLOWED US...

WHO COULD THAT BE, ERIC? WE BOTH KNOW ALL WHO ARE HERE! ALL OF US HAVE TAKEN ASSUMED IDENTITIES!
YES! I'M KNOWN AS EMILIO HARODA, THE WEALTHY IMPORTER--INSTEAD OF ERIC HAUSNER, THE GESTAPO COLONEL! BUT LAST NIGHT--WELL--LET ME TELL IT TO YOU FROM THE BEGINNING...

"YOU KNOW WHAT HAPPENED THOSE LAST DAYS IN GERMANY! THE ALLIES AND THE RUSSIANS HAD SURROUNDED BERLIN. WE WERE BOMBARDED FOR DAYS--AND DEATH AND DESTRUCTION WERE EVERYWHERE..."

"HITLER WAS IN HIS SECRET VAULT UNDER THE REICH CHANCELLERY. ALL THE TOP NAZIS WERE THERE--GOEBELS, HIMMLER, SCHULTZ, KRAMER... AND I! HE SHRIEKED AND CURSED, ME...
YOU HAVE NOT KILLED ENOUGH, HAUSNER! YOUR CONCENTRATION CAMP REPORTS HAVE NOT BEEN GORY ENOUGH! MURDER IS WHAT I ORDERED. I WANT MORE DEAD!
BUT THE WAR IS LOST... I CAN'T KILL ANYMORE!

LIE! TREACHERY! COME BACK HERE, YOU PIG! I'M NOT DONE WITH YOU. YOU DIE WITH ME FOR YOUR CHICKEN-HEARTED SQUEAM-ISHNESS! COME BACK! YOU CANNOT ESCAPE!
I CAN AND I WILL! YOU'RE DYING AND I'M NOT AFRAID OF THE DEAD! GOOBYE FOREVER, FUHRER!

YOU KNOW THE REST! WE ESCAPED BY SUBMARINE AT A SECRET DOCK ON THE SEACOAST-! YOU MET ME THERE--AND WITH OUR MEN, WE ESCAPED! SO FAR, WE HAVE REMAINED UNDETECTED BUT--
YES--? GO ON!

"LAST NIGHT, I AWAKENED SUDDENLY TERROR-STRICKEN! I IMAGINED A FIGURE IN BLACK STANDING IN THE SHADOWS OF MY ROOM... HOVERING OVER ME..."

UH--I--OH...WHAT A NIGHTMARE! WAIT! THERE IS SOMEONE IN MY ROOM! W-WHO ARE YOU? WHAT DO YOU WANT?

IT IS YOUR FUHRER, HAUSNER! DID YOU THINK YOU COULD REALLY ESCAPE ME? I CAME BACK FROM HELL FOR YOU!
AIIIEEEEE! HELP! CARL--HANS! HELP!

"IT CAME FOR ME WITH OUTSTRECHED CLAWS--SOMEHOW, IT HAD CHANGED INTO AN EVEN MORE EVIL MONSTER! IT'S FETID BREATH AND BLOODSHOT EYES WERE CLOSE TO MY FACE! I SPRANG BACK FRANTICALLY--SCREAMING WITH MORTAL HORROR..."

COME ERIC! DO YOU NOT RECOGNIZE ME? WHERE IS YOUR LOYALTY? WHERE IS YOUR LOVE? HA, HA!
YAAAAH! GET BACK! D-DON'T TOUCH ME! I-I'LL KILL YOU!

I'LL CHOKE THE EVIL BREATH OUT OF YOUR ROTTED THROAT! I--I'LL SMASH YOUR FACE IN! LEAVE ME ALONE! LEAVE ME ALONE!
HA HA HA HA

HA HA HA HA HA

"I MUST HAVE FAINTED. THE NEXT THING I KNEW I WAS LYING PROPPED UP AGAINST THE WALL OF MY ROOM, GLIBBERING WITH HORROR. IT WAS DAWN. OF THAT WEIRD APPARITION, THERE WAS NO TRACE..."

THIS WAS NO DREAM! IT WAS REAL--REAL...MUST WARN EVERYONE... MUST BE PROTECTED...

HOW DOES ONE TELL HIS MEN--MEN WHO HAVE BEEN THROUGH BITTER WAR CAMPAIGNS WITH HIM -- THAT OUR FUHRER IS HERE? WAS IT A NIGHTMARE--OR AM I INSANE?

A FEW HOURS LATER ERIC HAUSNER, NOW RELAXED AFTER RELATING HIS TERRIBLE EXPERIENCE TO DR. GERHARDT, SITS IN HIS LIBRARY WRITING...

WHAT IS IT HANS? WHAT'S THE MATTER?
COME QUICKLY, MY COLONEL! CARL--HE... HAS HANGED HIMSELF!

THE TWO MEN RACED DOWN THE CASTLE THROUGH A CORRIDOR TO THE DUNGEONS USED CENTURIES AGO FOR PRISIONERS -- NOW LIVING QUARTERS FOR THE MEN. ERIC HAUSNER TRIED TO KEEP CALM...

WHY--DO YOU ASK, ERIC HAUSNER? YOU WERE OUR MASTER'S CHIEF HANGMAN! HAVE YOU FORGOTTEN SO SOON?

HANS--! DO YOU SEE THEM? THEY ARE WAITING TO GRAB ME!

THIS SHALL BE YOUR FATE! ONE AFTER ANOTHER WILL DIE! DEATH WILL COME CLOSER AND CLOSER --AND YOU WILL NOT ESCAPE! OUR MASTER WARNED YOU LONG AGO...TAKE HEED! HA, HA, HA!
AAAIIIIEEEE! I'M GETTING OUT OF HERE!

COLONEL! WHERE ARE YOU GOING! WHAT ARE YOU TALKING ABOUT? SURELY YOU ARE JOKING--?
N--NO! BAR THAT DOOR, HANS! DON'T LET ANY OF THOSE CREATURES OUT OF THERE ON YOUR LIFE! KEEP THEM AWAY FROM ME!

HOURS PASSED, AND ERIC HAUSNER MADE PREPARATIONS TO LEAVE THE CASTLE FOR GOOD. BUT THE NIGHT OF THE LAST DINNER, THE MANY GRUESOME EXPERIENCES CONTINUED...
YOU LOOK PALE TONIGHT, ERIC! HAS ANYTHING ELSE STRANGE HAPPENED?
NOT SINCE HANS FOUND CARL HANGING DEAD IN HIS ROOM... I'M LEAVING THIS CURSED PLACE, DOCTOR! WE'RE ALL LEAVING!

SUDDENLY ALL THE LIGHTS IN THE ROOM WERE SNUFFED OUT...
ERIC HAUSNER! WE HAVE COME FOR YOU! YOUR TIME DRAWS NEAR! OUR MASTER CALLS! HA, HA, HA!
HA
HA
HA
EEEEEEEEEE!!
HA HI

EXCELLENCY-- ARE YOU ALL RIGHT?
Y-YES...BUT--GERHARDT! OH, GOTT IN HIMMEL! LOOK AT GERHARDT!

HORRORS! THE DOCTOR HAS BEEN GARROTED! COLONEL--THAT WAS YOUR OWN PERSONEL METHOD FOR STRANGLING YOUR PRISONERS! BUT WHO HAS DONE THIS DEED?

DIDN'T YOU SEE? ARE YOU BLIND? IT WAS--THE FUHRER! HE HAS COME BACK FOR ALL OF US! HE AND HIS CREATURES WAIT FOR US! HURRY LET'S GET OUT OF HERE!
COLONEL--! KARLSON AND ANDERS ARE DEAD OUTSIDE! THEY'VE BEEN GARROTED!
CRASH

MINUTES LATER THE TERRIFIED GROUP RUSHED HEADLONG, TOWARDS THE CASTLE GATES, DETERMINED TO FLEE-- BUT NOW AN EVEN GREATER MENACE THREATENED THEM!

SIR--! THE BRIDGE TO THE MAINLAND HAS BEEN WASHED OUT! WE CANNOT LEAVE. WE SHALL ALL DROWN!
THEN INSIDE-- QUICK! I KNOW WHERE WE CAN FIND SHELTER FROM THIS FLOOD!

THE DESPERATE GROUP NOW RUSHED BACK DOWN THE CASTLE STEPS INTO A CAVERN OF WEIRD SURROUNDINGS --A CAVERN THAT HAD ONCE BEEN THE BURIAL GROUNDS FOR THE ENTIRE COUNTRYSIDE...
FOLLOW ME--AND WE WILL WAIT HERE UNTIL MORNING. WE SHALL BE SAFE FROM THE FLOOD!
NOT EVEN THE DEMONS CAN GET THROUGH THIS RING OF GUNS!

HOURS LATER, THE MEN SAT QUIETLY IN SMALL, TENSE GROUPS, TALKING IN LOW UNDERTONES. OVERHEAD, THE EVERCONSTANT MOISTURE DRIPPED AND OOZED THROUGH WALLS GREEN WITH SLIME AND AGE... THEN--
I DON'T LIKE THE WAY HE'S BEEN ACTING LATELY! LISTEN TO HIM!
MEN--IT IS HE! DON'T YOU SEE HIM! HITLER'S HEAD APPROACHES US, LOOK!!

HA, HA, HA... YOU HAVE TRIED TO FLEE FROM ME AGAIN, HAUSNER! WHEN WILL YOU AND YOUR MEN LEARN THAT IT IS HOPELESS?
YAAAAH! ADOLPH HITLER--! COLONEL HAUSNER WAS RIGHT! IT IS THE FUHRER!

NO! DON'T BE DECEIVED! THIS IS SOME HORRIBLE SUPERNATURAL CREATURE MASQUERADING AS THE FUHRER! SHOOT IT DOWN, YOU FOOLS! IF YOU CAN NOW SEE IT--SHOOT!
BANG!
BANG

BUT BULLETS DID NOT AFFECT THE HORRIBLE MONSTERS THAT ROSE ROTTED AND NAUSEATING FROM THE GRAVES OF THE BURIAL GROUND! HITLER LEADS A NEW ARMY OF THE DAMNED --BUT THIS ARM! CAME FROM THE BEYOND...
HAUSNER--! I HAVEN'T FORGOTTEN! YOU'RE COMING WITH ME!-- BACK TO WHERE YOU BELONG! HA! HA! HA!
KILL THEM! KILL THEM!
RATATATATATATA
BANG! BANG

SO THE SCREAMS DIED DOWN--AND THE HELLISH NOISES SUBSIDED ALONG WITH THE WAILING OF THE WIND AND THE WHINING OF TREE-BRANCHES BENT DOUBLE, CEASED. NEXT MORNING, THE LOCAL POLICE RODE TOWARDS THE CASTLE...

No Rest for the Dead

Journey into Fear 12, March 1953

Journey into Fear was published by Canada's Superior Comics. Their portfolio of titles included some of the most bizarre tales from this, or any other period, and their use of the Iger studio gave their comics a sense of uniformity artistically. Connoisseurs have often maligned Iger's assemblage as lacking character, but as you will see from these pages this is far from the truth. Only a few years before they had included on their payroll EC's Al Feldstein and Jack Kamen as well as the esteemed Matt Baker.

NO REST for the DEAD
PEOPLE ARE DEATHLY AFRAID OF GHOSTS, IT'S SAID BUT READ NOW THE SHOCKING TALE OF THE MAN WHO REVERSED THIS EERIE SITUATION... THE MAN WHO TORTURED GHOSTS!
AND NOW FOR "THE BOOK"!
NOT "THE BOOK"
P-PLEASE, N-NOT "THE BOOK"!!
WEREDOLF CEMETERY... OF A MIDNIGHT... WHERE RESTLESS SOULS SEEK A FEW HOURS RE-SPITE FROM THE MOULDERING GRAVE...
MOAN
WAA-AAOOO... WHERE IS MY BABY?
EEEAAAA... I DIED... TOO YOUNG...
URRR-RRROWWW...

IN HIS DREARY, DILAPIDATED SHANTY, OLD JAKE CRONER, THE CEMETERY'S CARE-TAKER, VAINLY SEEKS TO SNATCH SOME SLUMBER...
MOAN-NNN!
THEY'RE AT IT AGAIN, BLAST 'EM!
EVERY NIGHT... THE SAME DANGED THING! SCREECHES ...MOANS... WAILS... SOBS. BLAST THE SCUMMY LOT! I HATE 'EM!!
LAY OFF, WILL YA? SHUT YOUR DECAYING MOUTHS AND LET A MAN SLEEP! I'M WARNIN' YA... CLAM UP!!
BUT AS THE UNFORTUNATE SPECTRES PERSIST...
DON'T SAY I DIDN'T WARN YA...
CRONER'S COMING!
HE'S CARRYING "THE BOOK"!!
NO!! N-NOT "THE BOOK"!!
I WARNED YA TO QUIT THAT INFERNAL WHIMPER-ING AND YAMMERING! YA DIDN'T... AND SO NOW I'M GONNA THROW "THE BOOK" AT YOU!!

CACKLING, CRONER LEAFS THROUGH HIS BOOK ON ANCIENT WITCHCRAFT...
ZARPF! SEND YOUR FIENDS FROM BEYOND THE UNHOLY VEIL OF DARKNESS TO TORMENT "THEM"! ZGYGYG! FNFGYTK! PKTZYP!!!
AND AS THE BLASPHEMOUS CURSE CORRUPTS THE NIGHT, EVIL MONSTERS CRAWL OUT OF THE EARTH AND TEAR AND CLAW AT THE PANICKY GHOSTS!
HEE-HEE! RIP 'EM! TEAR 'EM!
ALICE PEARCE
REST IN PEACE
MERCY! MERCY!
CALL OFF THE FIENDS, CRONER!!
SAVE US, CRONER!!!
BACK! RETURN TO ZARPF! PZYTKP! KTYGFNF!! GYGYZ!!!
THANK YOU FOR YOUR MERCY, CRONER!
MERCY? HA! I'VE BARELY BEGUN TO TORTURE THE GHOSTS!—
ALICE
LISTEN. I'VE GOT SAD NEWS FOR YOU FROM... THE OUTSIDE WORLD!
SAD NEWS?
3

YOU — SWANSON! YOU KILLED YOURSELF SO YOUR WIFE WOULD GET THE INSURANCE MONEY! WELL... HA-HA!... I'VE GOT A SURPRISE FOR YOU!
TELL ME!
SHE'S BEEN CHEATED OUT OF THE MONEY BY A CONFIDENCE MAN! YOUR WIFE IS STILL PENNILESS! AND WITHOUT YOU ALIVE TO LOOK AFTER HER, SHE'LL GO TO THE POORHOUSE!
MOAN! OH... NO! MARY! MARY!
YOU—KENNEDY! I LEARNED FROM A LITTLE VULTURE THAT YOUR WIFE HAS REMARRIED... YOUR BROTHER! IN FACT, SO THIS VULTURE SAID, YOUR BROTHER POISONED YOU SO HE COULD GET HER!
MOAN!
YOU—DESKIN! YOUR...
NO! DON'T TELL ME! I—I DON'T WANT TO HEAR...!
YOUR SON HAS STOLEN HIS WIFE'S SAVINGS AND RAN AWAY WITH HER SISTER!
AAA—AAAOOWWW!
ALICE PEARCE
HERE RE HENRY

HAA-HA-HA-HA-HA-HA.!!
WHY DO YOU LAUGH AT OUR MISERY, CRONER?

I LAUGH... BECAUSE ALL THESE CRUEL THINGS I'VE BEEN TELLING YOU FOR MONTHS HAVE BEEN LIES!
LIES?
WHY DID YOU DO IT, CRONER?

WHY? I'LL TELL YOU WHY! BECAUSE YOU RUIN MY SLEEP WITH YOUR NOISY CARRYINGS-ON! BECAUSE I CAN'T GET A BETTER JOB THAN LIVING IN THIS FILTHY OLD CEMETERY CARING FOR YOUR MOULDERING BONES...!

AND MAYBE I DID IT JUST BECAUSE I ENJOY TORTURING YOU! AND YOU'VE REALLY GOT SOMETHING TO MOAN ABOUT! HA! HA!
YOU'LL BE SORRY CRONER!!!

THEIR THREATS DON'T SCARE ME! ANYTIME THOSE GHOSTS TRY TO GET TOUGH WITH ME, I'LL GIVE THEM THE BOOK-TREATMENT!

BUT... THE NEXT NIGHT...
IT'S QUIET! TOO QUIET! THIS IS THE FIRST TIME IN YEARS THEY'RE NOT MOANING! HOW COME? I'D BETTER INVESTIGATE!

THEY'RE DIGGING A HOLE IN THE GROUND! AND THERE'S A NEW GRAVESTONE IN FRONT OF THE HOLE... ONE I NEVER SAW BEFORE! WHAT'S GOING ON HERE??
JAKE CRONER
MY NAME... ON THE GRAVESTONE!
YES CRONER... YOUR NAME!!
DROPPING HIS BOOK ON WITCHCRAFT, CRONER SEEKS TO FLEE, IN TERROR. BUT HE TRIPS ON THE BOOK, AND...
YAAA-AAAAA!
NO! PLEASE STOP! YOU'RE... BURYING ME... ALIVE... AGGHHH-HHH...
NOW YOU'RE ONE OF US, CRONER!
WH-WHAT ARE YOU GOING TO DO WITH M-ME??
NOW IT'S OUR TURN TO TORTURE YOU!!!
AAA-AAA-
JAKE CRONER
The End

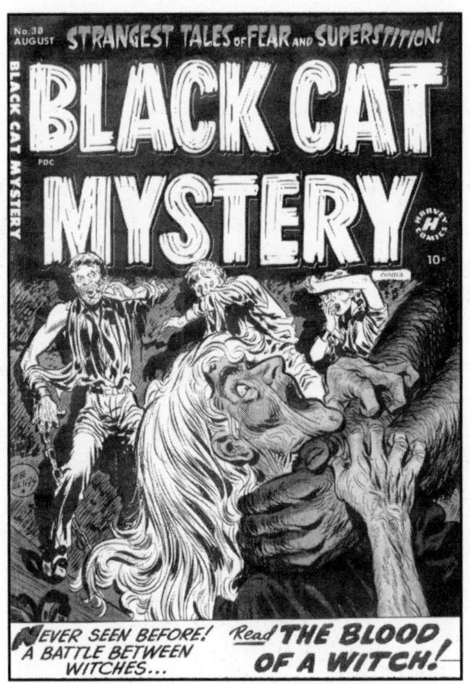

He

Black Cat Mystery 38, August 1952

The foul machinations of a bloodthirsty device, akin to the imaginings of Edgar Allan Poe's "*The Pit and the Pendulum*", were brought to life here by the brushstrokes of Rudy Palais. If ever an artist was made for the fiendish domain it was Rudy. For him horror availed itself to creativity; the scripts laid before him were enmeshed in both atmosphere and drama and if it needed a little more, well he wasn't averse to his interpretation of the proceedings. Take a look at the characters in this or any of his horror stories: they sweat profusely. These were people thrust to the very edge.

HE SEEMED POLITE AND FRIENDLY, THIS INN-KEEPER, BUT THERE WAS SOMETHING ABOUT HIM--SOMETHING THAT WAITED FOR THAT DREADFUL, HORRIBLE MOMENT WHEN HE WOULD EAT AGAIN--GORGING, TEARING, BITING AT HIS FOOD WITH GHOULISH APPETITE--WITH SCREAMING, SLAVERING, SMIRKING LEER UNTIL THE VERY ROTTED RAFTERS OF HIS CRYPT ECHOED AND RE-ECHOED THEIR WAILING PLEA: *FLEE--RUN! RUN*...FROM...

HE

IT WAS A TERRIBLE WINDSWEPT NIGHT--THE HIGHWAY WAS DESERTED EXCEPT FOR NEWLYWED MR. AND MRS. JAMIE WINTERS, CAUGHT IN THE STORM...
IT'S NO USE, HONEY! THE CAR'S STALLED IN THIS FLOOD!
THERE'S A HOUSE NEARBY! MAYBE THEY CAN GIVE US SOME HELP!
BBBRR...
BBRR...SPUTTER
PUTTER...BRRRR

MAKING THEIR WAY THROUGH THE TORRENTIAL DOWNPOUR, THE YOUNG COUPLE FINALLY STOOD BEFORE A STRUCTURE WHOSE UGLY, SHAPELESS ARCHITECTURE WAS STARKLY OUTLINED IN THE SUDDEN FLASHES OF LIGHTNING THAT CRACKLED OVERHEAD...
SORRY TO BOTHER YOU, SIR--BUT WE'RE STRANDED ON THE HIGHWAY... CAN WE USE YOUR PHONE?
COME IN--COME IN!

WELCOME TO THE INN OF SIMON MORIARTY! UNFORTUNATELY, THE STORM HAS PUT OUR PHONE AND LIGHTS OUT OF ORDER, BUT WHY NOT REMAIN HERE?
I GUESS WE'D BETTER WE CAN'T STAY IN THE CAR!
THEN AS THEIR HOST LED THEM UP A FLIGHT OF RICKETY STAIRS, THE CONFINES OF THE INN FOCUSED SLOWLY INTO VIEW, WEIRDLY-ILLUMINATED BY THE GHOSTLY FLICKERING LIGHT OF THE CANDLE...
OH, JAMIE... IT... IT'S SO STRANGE-LOOKING--!
SHH, ANNE... HE'LL HEAR YOU! WE'RE LUCKY WE EVEN FOUND THIS PLACE.
HERE WE ARE! YOU'LL FIND IT VERY COMFORTABLE, I ASSURE YOU! I'LL LEAVE YOU THIS CANDLE... OH--AND YOU CAN PAY ME--IN THE MORNING!! HA-HA--GOODNIGHT!
UH--GOOD-NIGHT-!
I KNOW I SOUND FOOLISH, DEAR--BUT--THIS ROOM--THIS ENTIRE HOUSE FRIGHTENS ME! LET'S GO BACK TO THE CAR!
NONSENSE, ANNE! WE'LL CATCH OUR DEATHS OF COLD OUT THERE! THERE'S NOTHING TO BE WORRIED ABOUT!
THE YOUNG COUPLE PREPARED FOR SLEEP, BUT IT WAS A TROUBLED, PUZZLING SLEEP--INTERRUPTED CONSTANTLY BY THE CREAKING OF STRANGE SOUNDS AND MOANING WIND. THEN IN THE WEE HOURS OF THE MORNING...
RATTLE
SQUEEAAK
WHAT WAS THAT-?
JAMIE--THE DOORKNOB--! IT..IT'S TURNING--! OHH-H...
THERE'S NO-ONE OUTSIDE, DEAR! THE WIND PROBABLY CAUSED A DRAFT IN THE HALLWAY AND MADE THE KNOB RATTLE, THAT'S ALL--! NOW GO BACK TO SLEEP.
BUT WINTERS HAD SEEN THE DOORKNOB MOVE TOO FIRMLY TO BE A FREAK OF EXTERNAL CIRCUMSTANCE! AS HE LAY DOWN...
THERE IS SOMEONE OUTSIDE! JAMIE--WHO CAN IT BE?
I--I DON'T KNOW--BUT I'M GOING TO FIND OUT!

THE YOUNG MAN FLUNG OPEN THE DOOR PREPARED FOR THE WORST-- BUT THE SIGHT THAT CONFRONTED HIM STUNNED HIM BEYOND WORDS!

THANK HEAVEN YOU HEARD! PLEASE SAVE ME-- PLEASE! SAVE ME FROM *HIM! HE-HE'S* COMING FOR ME--!

WHO ARE YOU? WHAT IS ALL THIS?

I--I CAN'T EXPLAIN, BUT YOU MUST TAKE ME OUT OF HERE-! WE'LL ALL BE KILLED! WE'LL-- OHHH...

THERE YOU ARE! I'M SORRY HE DISTURBED YOU. MR. COREY ISN'T WELL. HIS DOCTOR TOLD ME TO LOOK AFTER HIM! NOW GO BACK TO YOUR ROOM, SIR.

WITHOUT WAITING FOR HIS GUESTS TO REPLY, THE INN-KEEPER QUICKLY LED THE CRINGING MAN DOWN THE STEPS INTO THE DARKNESS BELOW...

JAMIE-- I WON'T STAY HERE A MOMENT LONGER!

YOU'RE RIGHT! SOMETHING FUNNY IS GOING ON HERE. PACK YOUR THINGS ANNE. WE'RE LEAVING!

JAMIE WINTERS DRESSED QUICKLY AND WENT DOWN-STAIRS TO FIND THE INN-KEEPER WHILE ANNE FINISHED HER PACKING. MOMENTS LATER...

NOW WHERE IS HE? I COULD ALMOST SWEAR HE JUST CAME DOWN HERE MOMENTS AGO!

EEEEEEE

ANNE--WHAT'S WRONG, HONEY? UH--WHERE ARE YOU-?
SHE'S GONE! GREAT SCOTT! THERE--BEHIND THE BED--IT LOOKS LIKE A SECRET PASSAGEWAY-!

THE YOUNG HUSBAND ENTERED THE PASSAGE-WAY. FROM ALL SIDES OF HIM THE ROTTEN WALLS OOZED A WET SLIME THAT GURGLED OUT IN FETID ODOR CLEARLY WARNING HIM THAT HE HAD DESCENDED INTO A LABYRINTH OF HELL!

THE MAN THAT TRIED TO WARN US-- HE'S HANGING FROM THAT HOOK LIKE A SHANK OF BEEF!

3

THEN WINTERS SAW HIS TERRIFIED WIFE TIED TO A CHAIR AND LEERINGLY POISED OVER HER WAS THEIR HOST--A MEAT CLEAVER IN HIS HANDS AND LICKING HIS RED LIPS IN ANTICIPATION-!
HA, HA... SUCH PRETTY FOOD! SUCH TENDER FLESH-!
H-HE'S A GHOUL! I..I'VE GOT TO DO SOMETHING --AND FAST!

AAARRGHH!
YOU MONSTER-- YOU HORRIBLE MONSTER!

YOU DARE ATTACK ME!
UGH-H-H! LET GO--! I CAN'T BREATHE... UGH--HH--

DARKNESS OVERCAME WINTERS IN BLACK FOLDS OF TERROR. HE REGAINED CONSCIOUSNESS TO FIND HIMSELF IN A WORST NIGHTMARE-!
I'LL START THE KNIFE SWINGING! IT SLICES SO MUCH BETTER THAN I CAN! YOU'LL LIKE IT-! IT WON'T HURT A BIT-- AT FIRST! HA, HA...
TIC TOK TIC
SSSSS SWISH

LOWER AND LOWER IT SANK UNTIL THE RANCID AIR FROM ITS WELL-OILED, GLEAMING STEEL EDGE SENT A MESSAGE OF DOOM THROUGH HIS NUMBED BRAIN AND A SHIVER OF TERROR THROUGH HIS SPINE--!
IT--IT'S ALMOST UPON ME... I CAN FEEL IT--! JUST A FEW MORE SWINGS--ANNE--ANNE--NEVER TO SEE YOU AGAIN--!
TIC TOC
SSSSSW/SSHHHHHHHHH
OH, STOP IT--PLEASE--PLEASE!!
HA, HA... BITE DEEP, MY PET! SINK INTO THE YIELDING FLESH--CUT YOUR CRIMSON PATH QUICKLY! HA, HA, HA...
SSSSS
SSSSSS
AAAAAAA
THE KNIFE HUNG PRECARIOUSLY ON THE CREST OF ITS FINAL SWING--THEN IT SWUNG BACK PONDEROUSLY--READY FOR THE KILL! SUDDENLY--!
STOP THAT HORRIBLE CONTRAPTION --QUICK!
NO! I'LL KILL--!
YOU'LL NOT KILL ANYONE AGAIN, YOU FIEND!
BANG!
BANG!
OH, JAMIE, JAMIE--!
IT'S ALL OVER, FOLKS! HE BROKE OUT OF THE ASYLUM A FEW DAYS AGO. WE FIGGERED HE MIGHT COME BACK HERE...THIS USED TO BE HIS PLACE! THEN WHEN WE SAW YOUR CAR NEARBY ON THE HIGHWAY, WE KNEW WE DIDN'T HAVE MUCH TIME!
COME ON, DARLING--! WE'RE GETTING OUT OF HERE! FORGET THERE EVER WAS SUCH A CREATURE--!
BUT BOTH KNEW SECRETLY HOW FORTUNATE THEY WERE! THE UNKNOWN DOES NOT OFTEN SPARE ITS PUNY TRANSGRESSORS--FOR SOMEWHERE DEEP WITHIN THE CRUMBLING SLIME OF HIS OWN MIND MAY BE ANOTHER GHOUL WHO IS CHOOSING A VICTIM--AND NOTHING BUT MERCIFUL FATE CAN THWART HIS WAITING--YES, WAITING NOW--PERHAPS EVEN FOR YOU!!
THE END

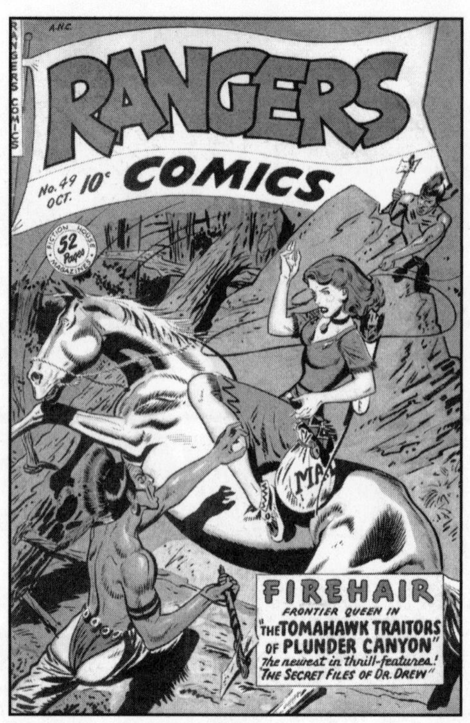

The Secret Files of Dr Drew

Rangers Comics 49, October 1949

Fiction House acquired a formidable reputation for their range of anthology titles, specifically from the War and Good Girl stables, but they were also the publishers of the esteemed *Planet Comics*. *Rangers Comics* played host to their first attempt to enter this domain, with a series of Dr Drew stories running consecutively from issue 47 through until 60. Artist Jerry Grandenetti's style is reminiscent of Will Eisner in each of the stories up to issue 56. This is hardly surprising as he worked in Will Eisner's studio when he first entered comic books in 1948, following advice from the publisher of *Quality Comics*, "Busy" Arnold. He freely admits he looked up to Eisner as "a god". This tale was later reprinted in *Ghost Comics 11*.

THE SECRET FILES of DR. DREW
STALKER OF THE UNKNOWN!
Who can estimate the power of the human mind to exert its force on matter... ignoring the laws of time and space...? Science has proven that extra-sensory perception exists... that there is an uncharted dimension of the mind. But is this mind force powerful enough to CAUSE UNTOLD ANGUISH!
The ancients said it was... and they called it witchcraft...!
Case no. 105 B The Witch's Doll!
The winding road to my castle atop Bone Hill has been traveled by many a desperate person seeking my aid... but one of the most terrifying encounters with the unknown was heralded by the breathless arrival...
DR. DREW... QUICK! AN EMERGENCY.. NO TIME TO EXPLAIN..!
of a little man...
ROYAL HOTEL, DRIVER.. HURRY!
who thought I was..
I HOPE WE'RE IN TIME.. SHE'S SINKING RAPIDLY..
IS THERE A DOCTOR IN ATTENDANCE ??
somebody else!
DOCTOR ?? BUT YOU... Y'MEAN YOU AIN'T DESMOND DREW, THE M.D.
GRANDENETTI

WHAT'LL I DO NOW? DON'T YA KNOW ANYTHING ABOUT MEDICINE?
I'M NOT A MEDICAL PRACTITIONER, BUT I CAN TELL YOU WHAT'S WRONG WITH THIS GIRL!
HELP ME- HELP ME! I CAN'T STAND ANY MORE OF THIS PAIN!
SHE'S NOT ILL.. THIS IS WITCHCRAFT!
I was taking a chance...but the symptoms matched with those I had read in ancient records of persons bewitched ...I muttered a few words of white magic.
WHAT'S THAT GIBBERISH?
OH, THANK YOU, DOCTOR...I DON'T KNOW WHAT YOU DID...BUT IT HELPED!
AN ANCIENT SPELL...IT'LL BRING YOU TEMPORARY RELIEF ONLY.. NOW, WHO ARE YOU?
Her name, she said, was Jennie Paris. She was an actress with a travelling stock company. She knew no one in town.
TELL ME, MISS. PARIS...DO YOU HAVE ANY ENEMIES... ANYONE WHO WOULD WISH YOU HARM ??
ENEMIES?? NO... NOT THAT I CAN THINK OF...
AND THEN I SAW IT... IT WAS A DOLL...BUT SO PERFECTLY DID IT DUPLICATE EVERY FEATURE OF JENNIE PARIS' FACE, THAT IT MIGHT HAVE BEEN HERSELF IN MINIATURE!
2

The witch's doll... an ancient hex in which the sorcerer procures a replica of his victim... and on it spews his hated evil, all the while muttering his fearful incantations which cause his victim to feel that hate...

This sort of magic is known in the depths of Africa, but seemed incredible in present-day America. Nevertheless, I took the manufacturer's name..if a duplicate of this doll existed, I would find my sorcerer!

DOLLS OF EVERY SIZE AND DESCRIPTION FILLED THE SHOP... STARING WITH SIGHTLESS EYES AS I RANG THE BELL.

I FOLLOWED HIM DOWN A LONG CORRIDOR...
THIS WAY, PLEASE...
WHEN I WOKE UP, I WAS AT HOME.
HIGGINS... WHAT TIME IS IT ?
WHY, IT'S NOON, SIR.
OH.. MY HEAD... WHAT TIME DID I COME IN LAST NIGHT ?
I'M SURE I DON'T KNOW, SIR. I WAS ASLEEP BY MIDNIGHT.
BY THE WAY, SIR.. A MESSENGER LEFT THIS PARCEL FOR YOU.
THE SAME GRISLY WARNING THAT HAD BEEN SENT TO JENNIE PARIS... BUT I KNEW ITS MEANING!
WHY, IT'S YOU, SIR.. WHOEVER COULD HAVE MADE IT ?
NEVER MIND THAT.. GET ME MY CLOTHES.. AND A REVOLVER!
4

I knew what I had to do... I set out for the doll shop...
AND SUDDENLY
I FELT STABS OF ANGUISH IN MY LEGS AND ARMS...
INVISIBLE FINGERS CLUTCHING AT MY THROAT...
IN VAIN DID I INVOKE THE WHITE MAGIC I KNEW...
THE RANGE WAS TOO CLOSE, FOR POWERFUL BLACK MAGIC WAS EMANATING FROM THAT TINY SHOP... AND DIRECTED TOWARD ME!

BUT I MADE IT... STRUGGLED INTO THE SHOP, PAST THE STARTLED PROPRIETOR... INTO THE BACK ROOM...
...AND THE PAINS CEASED AS ABRUPTLY AS THEY HAD BEGUN!
DR. DREW...I TRIED TO PREVENT YOUR COMING... BUT SINCE I FAILED...WON'T YOU SIT DOWN? ER... PERMIT ME TO INTRODUCE MYSELF.. LEANDER MILES.
BUT I THOUGHT YOU DIED IN AFRICA!
MOST PEOPLE THINK SO.. I FIND IT CONVENIENT TO MAINTAIN THAT ILLUSION BUT I RETURNED FROM AFRICA WITH THE SECRET OF THE KAFFIR WITCH DOLL. I AM THE ONLY MAN ALIVE WITH THAT SECRET!
AND I SHALL DEMONSTRATE IT TO YOU... YOU WILL FORGIVE ME IF I FIRST RENDER YOU INCAPABLE OF MOTION...
HE BOUND THE ARMS OF THE DOLL IN MY IMAGE WITH WIRE... AND AS HE DID SO, I LOST ALL FEELING IN MY ARMS...
YOU WERE VERY CLEVER TO FIND ME, DR. DREW... AND YOUR CLEVERNESS WILL PROVE YOUR UNDOING!
!! NO NO.. STOP!
BUT BEFORE THAT HAPPENS, YOU ARE GOING TO WATCH WHAT HAPPENS TO JENNIE PARIS.. BY WITCHCRAFT!

IT'S SUCH A SIMPLE WAY OF GETTING REVENGE.. OLD PAPA BERTRAND MAKES ME THE DOLLS..THE REST IS THE SECRET OF AFRICA.
OBSERVE, DR. DREW! WHAT I AM ABOUT TO DO TO THIS IMAGE WILL BE FELT BY JENNIE PARIS, MILES AWAY!
STOP, YOU FIEND! [НОВШМОС КАПОП]
YOUR ATTEMPTS AT WHITE MAGIC ARE FUTILE, DR. DREW. MISS JENNIE PARIS REFUSED MY LOVE.. THEREFORE SHE MUST PAY THE PENALTY!
UGH!!
HE WAS SO INTRIGUED WITH HIS OWN ELOQUENCE THAT HE FORGOT TO WATCH ME ... I SAW MY CHANCE.. I SIEZED THE REPLICA OF MYSELF AND SMASHED IT ON THE TABLE...
THE CURSED IMAGE SPLINTERED INTO A THOUSAND PIECES.
I WAS FREE!
AND NOW FOR THIS DOLL!
NO!
WITH ALL MY STRENGTH I HURLED THE IMAGE OF JENNIE PARIS AGAINST THE WALL!
AND TEN MILES AWAY...
MARY..FRED.. THE PAINS.. THEY'VE STOPPED!
7

DREW! YOU'LL PAY FOR THIS— I SWEAR IT!
PERHAPS, BUT YOU'LL NOT FIND IT QUITE SO EASY WITHOUT YOUR BLACK MAGIC!
In the melee, shelves of dolls were smashed and overturned!
AND FROM THE DEBRIS OF PLASTER, STRAW, AND COTTON CAME SMOKE... THEN FLAMES....
I FLED...
...AND NONE TOO SOON! AS I REACHED THE STREET, THE BUILDING BURST INTO FLAMES... A MONSTROUS FUNERAL PYRE FOR THE LAST PRACTITIONER OF THE DEADLIEST ART THE WORLD HAS EVER KNOWN...
LATER...
DR. DREW.... I DON'T KNOW HOW TO THANK YOU.
I SHOULD THANK YOU, MY DEAR... YOU BROUGHT MILES' ACTIVITY TO LIGHT... WE CAN BOTH BE GLAD THE AFFAIR IS FINISHED, EXCEPT THAT I DO WISH WE COULD HAVE PREVENTED THAT FIRE...
WHY?? UGH! WE'RE WELL RID OF HIM AND HIS WITCHCRAFT!
BUT STILL, I WOULD HAVE LIKED TO KNOW JUST HOW HE DID IT! ..ER.. PROFESSIONAL REASONS, OF COURSE..

The Corpse That Wouldn't Die

Web of Evil 2, January 1952

Rendered by Jack Cole and later reprinted in the pages of *Intrigue 1* on the eve of the Comics Code, this tale can only be described as hideous. Quality, a company of repute, was somewhat cautious in seizing on the horror bandwagon, yet they produced some memorable stories in their solitary horror title *Web of Evil* (that is until the one-off appearance of *Intrigue*). This is one of their more macabre offerings and is strangely reminiscent of H. P. Lovecraft's "Herbert West – Reanimator".

Jack Cole's fluid panels would grace the pages of 102 appearances of Plastic man in *Police Comics*. Many more stories flowed from his resourceful brushes, including the daily *Spirit* strip in 1942 and later work for *Playboy* when the comic book industry imploded in 1955. Sadly, all was not well with this immensely talented artist; at the age of forty-four he took a pistol to his head and ended his life.

THE CORPSE THAT WOULDN'T DIE!
ANDREW GRANGER WAS ONE WEEK DEAD... BUT NOTHING COULD KEEP HIM LYING IN HIS GRAVE ...NOTHING EXCEPT A MYSTIC PHRASE THAT LAY BURIED WITHIN THE MOULDY COVERS OF A BOOK.. A BOOK THAT CONTAINED THE FEARFUL SECRET OF RAISING THE DEAD!
LATE ONE COLD AUTUMN DAY, CHARLES VENABLE TURNED UP THE CRACKED, PUDDLE-FILLED DRIVEWAY OF A NEGLECTED ESTATE... THE HOME OF CARL GRANGER!
GRANGER
EVERYTHING ABOUT THE PLACE LOOKED DECAYED, MOULDY, DEAD! THE GROUNDS, THE STONE MANSION, THE STAINED MARBLE TERRACE.. EVERYTHING!
THEY'VE LET EVERYTHING GO TO RUIN! WHY? IT MUST HAVE BEEN A BEAUTIFUL PLACE...ONCE!

CHARLES VENABLE SOON FOUND SOMETHING HERE THAT REVOLTED HIM, SOMETHING THAT RAN A COLD SHIVER DOWN HIS SPINE! VENABLE DIDN'T KNOW WHAT IT WAS, BUT IT WAS THERE JUST THE SAME! SOMETHING EVIL! SOMETHING ABNORMALLY EVIL!

IT EVEN SMELLS BAD! THE SMELL OF DECAY, OF THINGS ROTTING! I OUGHT TO TURN AROUND AND GO BACK... BACK WHERE I CAME FROM! BACK TO REALITY!

BUT "REALITY" MEANT NO JOB SO CHARLES VENABLE KNOCKED ON THE THICK DOOR AND WAS ADMITTED TO A ROOM WHICH HAD NOT KNOWN A MOP OR A DUSTER IN TWENTY YEARS!

YOU MUST BE THE MAN THE EMPLOYMENT AGENCY WROTE ABOUT! EXCUSE THE APPEARANCE OF THE PLACE! I'M NOT FUSSY ABOUT APPEARANCE!
YES! THE GROUNDS ARE BADLY NEGLECTED!

EVERYTHING IS BADLY NEGLECTED! WHAT DOES IT MATTER? THE THINGS OF THE FLESH, OF THE MATERIAL WORLD DO NOT COUNT! LET IT ROT! THIS WAY, PLEASE!
WILL THE STAIRCASE CARRY MY WEIGHT, MR. GRANGER?

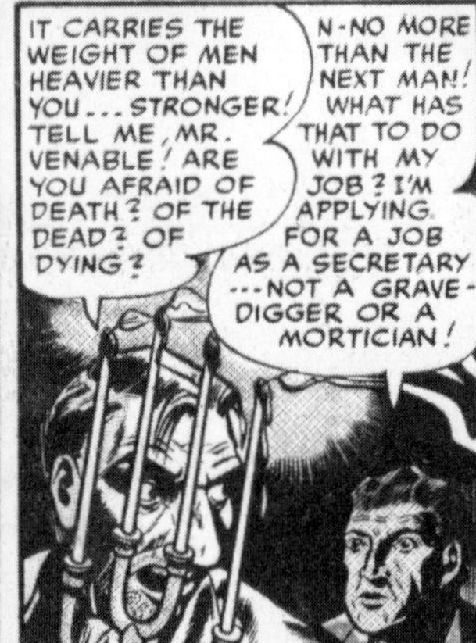

IT CARRIES THE WEIGHT OF MEN HEAVIER THAN YOU... STRONGER! TELL ME, MR. VENABLE! ARE YOU AFRAID OF DEATH? OF THE DEAD? OF DYING?
N-NO MORE THAN THE NEXT MAN! WHAT HAS THAT TO DO WITH MY JOB? I'M APPLYING FOR A JOB AS A SECRETARY ---NOT A GRAVE-DIGGER OR A MORTICIAN!

CORRECT! BUT BE PREPARED FOR ANYTHING! STRANGE THINGS! THINGS THE MIND OF MAN CANNOT EXPLAIN! THIS WAY, PLEASE! TO MY STUDY!

Y-YOUR STUDY? WHAT ARE... THOSE, MR. GRANGER?
CORPSES! I USE DEAD MEN IN MY RESEARCH! DID THE AGENCY TELL YOU I NEED A MAN WHO CAN READ SANSKRIT?

I MUST HAVE CERTAIN PASSAGES TRANSLATED IN ORDER TO COMPLETE MY STUDIES! SELECT ANY PORTION OF THIS BOOK AND TRANSLATE IT, IF YOU PLEASE!
2

WHY, T-THIS BOOK... IT'S ABOUT RAISING THE DEAD! ABOUT BRINGING THE DEAD BACK TO LIFE!
AND AS YOU WILL SOON LEARN, VICE VERSA! READ ALOUD, IF YOU PLEASE!

"SOME SAY THE DEAD CANNOT RETURN! THAT WHEN THEY ARE ABROAD IN THE LAND THEY CANNOT BE SENT BACK TO THEIR GRAVES! THIS IS FALSE! WE KNOW A MAGIC SAYING THAT CAN MAKE THE DEAD LIE STILL!"
THAT'S WHAT I WANT! I MUST HAVE THE FORMULA! IT IS BURIED IN THAT OLD BOOK ON SORCERY!

I MUST HAVE IT, YOU HEAR? IT IS SOMEWHERE IN THIS BOOK! YOU MUST TRANSLATE DAY AND NIGHT, TO FIND THE WORDS, YOU HEAR?
BUT WHY, MR. GRANGER? WHY DO YOU NEED A MAGIC FORMULA FOR RETURNING THE DEAD TO THEIR GRAVES?

THERE! YOU HEAR IT? THAT SLITHERING SOUND ALONG THE HALLWAY!
YES! WHAT IS IT? WHAT'S OUT THERE?
SSSSHHHH!

I DON'T KNOW! I'M AFRAID TO LOOK! I-I CAN ONLY GUESS! EVERY NIGHT I HEAR THAT WHISPERING, SLITHERING SOUND, AS IF SOMETHING WERE DRAGGING ALONG THE FLOOR!
I'LL OPEN THE DOOR! WE'LL SEE WHAT IT IS!
SSSSHH

NO! NOT YET! NOT UNTIL I HAVE THAT MAGIC FORMULA!
BUT WHAT DO YOU EXPECT TO FIND OUT THERE?

I..I DON'T KNOW! BUT IF YOU FIND THE MAGIC FORMULA...THEN I CAN OPEN THE DOOR! THEN I CAN DARE FACE WHATEVER IT IS!

TIME GROWS SHORT! THE SOUND GROWS LOUDER! THAT'S WHY YOU MUST FIND THAT PASSAGE! ONLY THAT MAGIC FORMULA CAN SAVE ME NOW! SAY YOU WILL FIND IT, VENABLE! SAY IT!
I'LL DO MY BEST, MR. GRANGER!
SSSSHHH
3

AND SO, OUT OF PITY, VENABLE TOOK THE JOB! HE BEGAN TO READ! HE READ DAY AND NIGHT! HE DID NOTHING BUT TRANSLATE!

NOR COULD HE STOP TRANSLATING FOR AN INSTANT! GRANGER REFUSED TO LET HIM OUT OF SIGHT!
YOU'RE STOPPING! YOU MUSTN'T! YOU MUST GO ON! READ ON! YOU MUST FIND THAT MAGIC PHRASE! IT'S BURIED SOMEWHERE IN THE BOOK!
BUT MY EYES HURT! THE PRINT IS SO FINE! THE LANGUAGE IS SO DIFFICULT! IT MUST HAVE BEEN WRITTEN 4,000 YEARS AGO!

WHAT DIFFERENCE DOES IT MAKE? MY LIFE'S AT STAKE! I... GASP! THE SOUND! IT'S BACK AGAIN!
THIS IS CRAZY! WHY DON'T WE SEE WHAT IT IS? I'M GOING TO HAVE A LOOK!
SSSSSSS
SSSHHHHHH

NO! NO! YOU CAN'T LET IT INTO THE ROOM! YOU'VE GOT TO STAY HERE! YOU'VE GOT TO KEEP TRANSLATING!
BUT HOW CAN I WITH THAT THING CRAWLING AROUND? IT'S ENOUGH TO DRIVE A MAN INSANE!

NOW IT'S POUNDING ON THE DOOR!
GO AWAY! GO AWAY, I TELL YOU! LEAVE ME ALONE! LEAVE ME ALONE!
KNOCK! KNOCK! KNOCK!

THE POUNDING IS LOUDER! STRONGER! WHAT AM I GOING TO DO? VENABLE, HELP ME! HELP ME!
KNOCK! KNOCK! KNOCK!

BUT THERE WAS NOTHING TO DO... EXCEPT WAIT FOR THE POUNDING TO STOP AND TO HEAR THE SLITHERING SOUND GO DOWN THE HALL, GROWING FAINTER... FAINTER... TILL THERE WAS DEAD SILENCE AGAIN!
ONE NIGHT THE POUNDING WOKE VENABLE UP! HE FLUNG A BATHROBE ACROSS HIS SHIVERING SHOULDERS AND OPENED THE DOOR OF HIS ROOM!
I'VE GOT TO FIND OUT WHAT IT IS!
WHO'S THERE? ANSWER! WHO'S THERE?

SUDDENLY, VENABLE SPIED SOMETHING MIS-SHAPEN, INHUMAN CRAWLING ABOUT IN THE DARKNESS!
GET AWAY FROM HERE! GO... OR I'LL KILL YOU!
EEEAA! YIIIII!
WHACK! CRACKKK!

A FEW WHACKS WITH THE SWORD AND VENABLE DROVE THE SHRIEKING THING FROM THE DOOR OF HIS EMPLOYER...
HAS IT GONE? VENABLE, ANSWER ME! DID IT GO AWAY?
YES! BUT YOU KNOW WHAT IT IS! YOU'RE GOING TO TELL ME NOW ONCE AND FOR ALL!
I CAN'T! I MUSTN'T! IT'S SOMETHING I CANNOT TELL ANYONE!
YOU'LL TALK, GRANGER, OR I WALK OUT OF THIS HOUSE RIGHT NOW... TONIGHT! IF YOU WANT ME TO STAY, I'VE GOT TO KNOW WHAT'S GOING ON HERE?

COME INSIDE MY STUDY, VENABLE! I CAN'T BEAR TO REMAIN OUT HERE! EACH TIME HE RETURNS HE GETS STRONGER, BOLDER, MORE IMPATIENT!
HE? WHO ARE YOU TALKING ABOUT?

"MY BROTHER... ANDREW! I WAS JEALOUS OF ANDREW! WE WERE BOTH STUDENTS OF SORCERY! WE WERE STUDYING HOW TO BRING BACK THE DEAD! ANDREW WAS BRILLIANT, I WAS NOT! I WAS JEALOUS, VERY JEALOUS...
I'VE JUST DISCOVERED SOMETHING, CARL! COME HERE!
YOU'RE ALWAYS DISCOVERING SOMETHING! YOU ALWAYS WERE THE BRILLIANT ONE IN THE FAMILY!

"ONE NIGHT, I COULDN'T STAND IT ANY LONGER! THE IDEA THAT ANDREW WAS SMARTER THAN I WAS DESTROYING ME! SO ONE NIGHT, I TOOK UP A KNIFE AND WITH A CURSE...
DIE! DIE, YOU GENIUS! SEE WHERE YOUR BRILLIANCE HAS TAKEN YOU! TO THE GRAVE!
EEEEAHH!

"I STABBED HIM AGAIN AND AGAIN! I STABBED HIM TILL I WAS ARM WEARY! THEN I BURIED HIM IN THE GARDEN! NO ONE KNOWS WHERE ANDREW IS... OR WHAT HAPPENED TO HIM EXCEPT ME!

THIS HAPPENED A WEEK AGO... AND FOR ONE WEEK... HE'S DRIVEN ME OUT OF MY MIND! EACH NIGHT HE RETURNS... FROM HIS GRAVE! THAT'S WHY YOU'VE GOT TO FIND THAT FORMULA! WE MUST KEEP ANDREW IN HIS GRAVE!
WELL, COUNT ME OUT! I WON'T HELP A MURDERER! I'M LEAVING THIS HOUSE NOW! AS SOON AS I CAN DRESS AND PACK!
5

BUT AS VENABLE PACKED, HE HEARD A SLOW, DELIBERATE TREAD IN THE HALLWAY! HE WENT FEARFULLY TO THE DOOR OF HIS ROOM AND LOOKED OUT...
THE CORPSE! GRANGER! GRANGER! LOCK YOUR DOOR! THE CORPSE IS COMING BACK!
THUMP! THUMP! THUMP!

I CAN'T LOCK THE DOOR! IT WOULDN'T DO ANY GOOD! YOU'VE GOT TO FIND THAT FORMULA, VENABLE! PLEASE! PLEASE!
ALL RIGHT! GIVE ME THE BOOK! BUT FOR HEAVENS' SAKE, SHUT THE DOOR!
THUMP! THUMP!

THERE! THE DOOR IS LOCKED AND BOLTED! HE CAN'T GET IN! READ, VENABLE! READ AS YOU NEVER READ BEFORE!
CLICK! SLAMM! PLOCK!

GASP! HE'S BREAKING THROUGH!
CRASH! CRACKKK!

YOU MURDERING WRETCH! FOR ONE MINUTE YOU LOST YOUR HEAD LAST WEEK! NOW YOU SHALL LOSE IT PERMANENTLY!
NO! STAY AWAY! ANDREW, PLEASE! VENABLE, HELP ME!
IT'S TOO LATE NOW! I'LL GET THE POLICE!
CRASHHH!

NOTHING WILL HELP! YOU'RE DOOMED, CARL! DOOMED!
EEEIII!

WHEN THE POLICE CAME, THEY GAPED AT THE SIGHT! ONE BODY WAS DECAPITATED! THE OTHER LYING NEARBY WITH A SURGICAL SAW IN ITS CLAMMY HAND...
ONE CORPSE IS A WEEK OLDER THAN THE OTHER! BUT HOW COME IT'S GOT AN ARM AROUND THE FRESH STIFF?
THE WHOLE THING GIVES ME THE CREEPS, CORONER! WHAT'S THE ANSWER?

THE ANSWER IS A MAGIC FORMULA! IT'S IN THIS BOOK.. IF YOU CAN FIND IT!

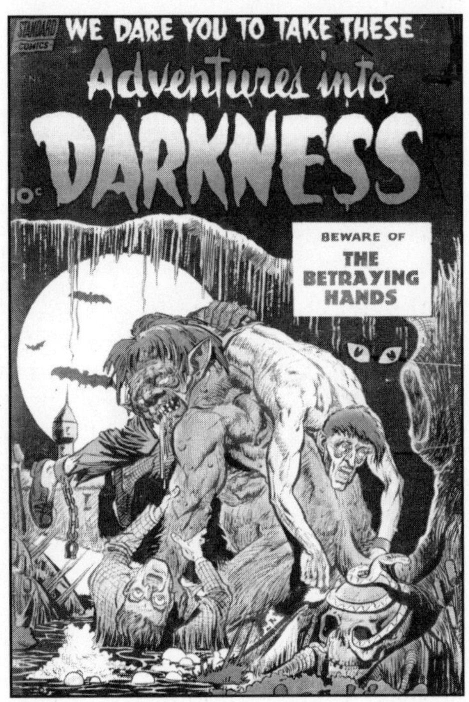

Bride of Death

Adventures into Darkness 7, December 1952

Standard's line of horror comics only occasionally shocked, though they could boast some spine-tingling cover art. However, when they let Jack Katz loose at the drawing board they were guaranteed something special. "Bride of Death" is beautifully reflective of Katz's creative spirit. It's a ghastly tale of exhumation, obsession and, once again, reanimation. While Delores is resplendent in her revived state, it is Jack's depiction of the deranged Joseph that will live with you.

BRIDE OF DEATH

B-1322

IT IS THE DEAD OF NIGHT IN THE SMALL MOUNTAINOUS COUNTRY OF MALGOA, AND AN EERIE SCENE IS LIT UP BY THE FITFUL SPUTTERING OF A CANDLE IN THE BASEMENT OF DR.SERO'S HOME...
FOOLS! THE BODY YOU HAVE BROUGHT ME IS DECOMPOSED! I TOLD YOU I NEED A FRESH BODY FOR MY EXPERIMENT!
WE TOOK A GREAT CHANCE TO BRING YOU THAT CORPSE! YOU KNOW THE PENALTY FOR ROBBING GRAVES!

GET OUT! GET OUT!
I'VE HAD ENOUGH! THE MAN IS MAD!

MAD... AM I? GIVE ME A FRESH BODY AND I WILL PROVE TO THE WORLD THAT I CAN BRING THE DEAD BACK TO LIFE! MY STIMULANT CAN START THE HEART AGAIN! IT WORKED WITH ANIMALS... AND IT WILL WORK WITH A HUMAN!

THERE WAS LITTLE SLEEP FOR THE BROODING DOCTOR THAT NIGHT, AND EARLY NEXT MORNING HE HAD A CALLER...
MY GOOD FRIEND, JOSEPH, HOW LONG WILL YOU STAY COOPED UP IN HERE? ALL THESE MONTHS... HIDING YOURSELF... WORKING ON SOMETHING SO SECRET YOU DARE NOT REVEAL IT EVEN TO ME... YOUR BEST FRIEND!
SOON... SOON THE WORLD WILL KNOW WHAT I HAVE BEEN DOING!
BUT WHERE ARE YOU GOING IN THOSE CLOTHES? HAVE YOU COME TO MOURN FOR ME?
NOT YOU, JOSEPH, I GO TO WITNESS THE LAST ACT OF A TRAGEDY... TODAY WAS TO BE THE WEDDING DAY OF THE BEAUTIFUL DOLORES MARTIZ. INSTEAD... I GO TO HER FUNERAL!
THE EXCITEMENT OF HER APPROACHING WEDDING TO HER BELOVED MARIO WAS TOO MUCH FOR HER WEAK HEART. SHE IS TO BE BURIED TODAY.
DOLORES MARTIZ! I HAVE HEARD OF THE GIRL'S BEAUTY! YOU SAY SHE HAS RECENTLY DIED?
IT IS BUT TWO DAYS... A TERRIBLE TRAGEDY TO LOSE ONE SO YOUNG... SO BREATHTAKINGLY BEAUTIFUL! BUT HOW WOULD YOU KNOW, HIDING YOURSELF HERE... FROM EVERYONE!
PERHAPS YOU ARE RIGHT, MY FRIEND! THIS PLACE IS GETTING ON MY NERVES! I THINK I WILL JOIN YOU!
AT THE CEMETERY...
LOOK... HERE COMES THE FUNERAL PROCESSION NOW...
AND AT THE GRAVE, PREPARED TO RECEIVE THE LAST REMAINS OF THE BEAUTIFUL GIRL...
THAT IS MARIO... THE MAN SHE WAS TO MARRY! HE IS TAKING IT VERY HARD...
MY BEAUTIFUL ONE! DO NOT TAKE HER FROM ME! (SOB)

THAT NIGHT DR. SERO RETURNS TO THE GRAVE, AND...

AT LAST... A FRESH BODY!

I WILL SHOW THE WORLD! I'LL SHOW THEM ALL!

LUCK IS WITH ME! NO ONE IS ABOUT! ANOTHER MINUTE AND I SHALL HAVE HER SAFELY IN MY HOME.

BACK AT HIS HOME...
SHE IS EVEN MORE BEAUTIFUL THAN THEY SAID!

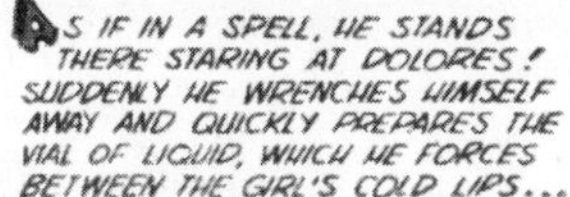
AS IF IN A SPELL, HE STANDS THERE STARING AT DOLORES! SUDDENLY HE WRENCHES HIMSELF AWAY AND QUICKLY PREPARES THE VIAL OF LIQUID, WHICH HE FORCES BETWEEN THE GIRL'S COLD LIPS...

DRINK, MY LOVELY! DRINK! IT WILL BRING BACK THE WARM BREATH OF LIFE!

FOR A BRIEF MOMENT, THE GIRL LIES MOTIONLESS. THEN COLOR SUFFUSES HER FACE AND A GROAN BREAKS FROM HER LIPS...
I DID IT! I DID IT! SHE'S BREATHING! SHE'S ALIVE!
(MOANNN) M-MARIO!

IT WAS I WHO BROUGHT YOU BACK TO LIFE, MY DEAR! NOT MARIO...
WH...WHO ARE YOU?

QUICKLY DR. SERO EXPLAINS...
SO YOU SEE... IT IS ME YOU BELONG TO NOW! ME!
NO...NO! IT IS MARIO I LOVE... MARIO...!

CURSED BE MARIO! YOU WILL BE MINE!

AND A BRIDE YOU WILL BE, MY BEAUTIFUL ONE! MY BRIDE! BUT SINCE WE CANNOT BE MARRIED HERE, WE WILL DRIVE TO THE NEXT TOWN, WHERE THE PADRE WILL MAKE US ONE IN THE MORNING! BUT COME...WE MUST HURRY!

WE SHOULD BE THERE AT SUN-UP! AND THEN YOU'LL HAVE YOUR WEDDING, AFTER ALL!

AS THE CAREENING CARRIAGE SPEEDS PAST THE GRAVEYARD...
IT IS... MARIO...!

DOLORES...! YOU CALLED MY NAME! I AM HERE!

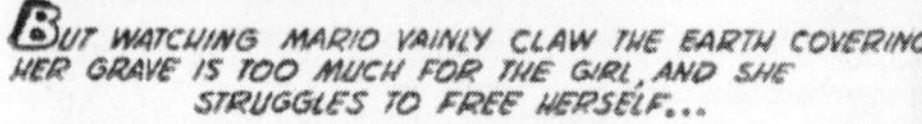
BUT WATCHING MARIO VAINLY CLAW THE EARTH COVERING HER GRAVE IS TOO MUCH FOR THE GIRL, AND SHE STRUGGLES TO FREE HERSELF...

LET ME GO...(GASP) LET ME GO!
QUIET!

AGHH...GHH!
SHE FIGHTS LIKE A THOUSAND DEMONS!

SUDDENLY DOLORES SLUMPS IN DR. SERO'S ARMS...
DOLORES..! DOLORES! SPEAK TO ME..!

GOOD HEAVENS! SHE'S HAD ANOTHER HEART ATTACK! SHE... SHE'S DEAD!

BACK! BACK TO MY HOUSE! I MUST HAVE THE VIAL!

THE CARRIAGE SCREECHES TO A STOP, AND IN A WILD FRENZY THE DOCTOR CLUTCHES HIS VIAL OF SERUM! ALREADY DOLORES' BODY IS GROWING COLD!

HERE, MY DEAR! DRINK THIS..! DRINK!

IT WAS MORE THAN HER HEART COULD TAKE! IT...WON'T...RESPOND!

BUT IT MUST! IT MUST! COME BACK TO ME, DOLORES!

SUDDENLY... THE COLD HANDS OF THE GIRL TIGHTEN AROUND HIS THROAT!

GAHH..GHHH! NO..! IT'S..RIGOR MORTIS! SHE'S TAKING ME TO THE GRAVE WITH HER!

YES... RIGOR MORTIS HAD SET IN AND THE GIRL HAD INVOLUNTARILY STRANGLED DR. SERO. BUT WHO CAN TELL? PERHAPS SOMETHING FROM THE BEYOND HAD DICTATED THE PUNISHMENT!

Dungeon of Doom

Chamber of Chills 6, March 1952

Alfred Harvey's team of editors was becoming a little unnerved at the level of sadistic glee prevalent in their tales; the content in this one will give you an idea why. Yet such misgivings never entirely put paid to the machinations of their fiendish creators. The editorial line appeared to be that these comics had to be horrible, but not too horrible! "Dungeon of Doom" was unrelenting in its sadistic portrayal, made all the more disturbing because it occurred beneath the streets of what would have been modern-day New York. It's not for the squeamish.

DUNGEON OF DOOM!
AM I THE ONLY MAN IN THE WORLD WHO SEES THEM AS THEY REALLY ARE? AM I THE ONLY MAN WHO KNOWS THE DANGER AND THE HORROR OF THE MONSTERS AROUND US?
HOW DOES A SUBWAY MOTORMAN GET TO WORK? HE RIDES THE SUBWAY!
JEENSBORO LINE
TO
RIA CORONA & FLUSHING
WHEW! NOT SO BAD TO DRIVE THESE BUGGIES, BUT RIDING IN ONE--OFFF--IS NO CINCH! WISH I COULD AFFORD A CAR. BUT I CAN'T AFFORD ANY-THING... EXCEPT A DULL ROUTINE...
BUT IN THE NEXT INSTANT LARRY FROST'S "DULL ROUTINE" VANISHED. THE CAR LURCHED VIOLENTLY AND LARRY TRIPPED—
WHAT THE-- ONHHH!
OWWW-- MY HEAD--!

HEY--Y'ALL RIGHT, MAC?
YES...YES. JUST A FUNNY WHIRRING IN MY EYES...
OHHH... MY HEAD. WHAT A BUMP... OHH...
THE INCIDENT PASSED. NEXT STOP THE GIRL GOT OFF; THREE STOPS LATER, LARRY LEFT. BUT THEN IT BEGAN...
GASP! GOOD LORD! LOOK AT THAT--THAT MONSTER! WHO IS HE--WHAT IS IT? DOESN'T ANYONE ELSE SEE IT---
LARRY SAW A SUBWAY GUARD. HE RAN FRANTICALLY TO HIM...
LOOK--LOOK AT THAT! WHAT IS IT, MAN--WHAT IS IT?
WHAT IS WHAT? YOU MEAN THAT GUY WALKING DOWN THE RAMP? WHAT ABOUT HIM? JUST ANOTHER GUY, AIN'T HE?
YOU MEAN HE LOOKS LIKE AN ORDINARY MAN TO YOU? WHAT'S THE MATTER WITH ME? I--I SAW A MONSTER!!
THAT GUY--A MONSTER? HA-HA-Y'OUGHT T'GET MORE SLEEP. HAVE YOUR NIGHT-MARES THEN! HA-HA-HA-HA--
IN A DAZE, LARRY MADE HIS WAY TO THE CAR-BARN. HE BARELY HEARD THE DISPATCHER SPEAK TO HIM...
MAYBE IT WAS A NIGHTMARE, SOME-THING I IMAGINED. NO ONE ELSE SAW IT, SO HOW--
WAKE UP, BOY! I'VE BEEN TELLING YOU--YOU GOT THE MILK RUN TONIGHT, THE EAST SIDE TUNNEL UP TO 90TH STREET.
I--OH--HUH?
"THE MILK RUN"--LARRY FROST HAD PLENTY OF TIME TO PONDER HIS PROBLEM FOR THERE WERE FEW, IF ANY, RIDERS ON THAT ROUTE LATE AT NIGHT. IT WAS A LONELY, WILD STRETCH OF TUNNEL, WHERE ANYTHING MIGHT HAPPEN...
THAT "WHIRRING" IN MY EYES. WISH IT WOULD STOP. MAYBE THAT'S WHAT MADE ME SEE THAT--THAT "MONSTER". BRRR...WHAT A SCARE I GOT...
CLOSED

WHEN THE ABANDONED WEST-SIDE SUBWAY TUNNEL'S DARK MOUTH LOOMED AHEAD, LARRY'S MUSINGS WERE CUT SHORT...
ANOTHER ONE! ANOTHER MONSTER! GOING DOWN THE CLOSED-OFF TUNNEL! I'M CRAZY-- I MUST BE GOING CRAZY!

LARRY STOPPED THE PASSENGER-LESS TRAIN. HE HAD TO SEE WHERE THE MONSTER HAD GONE... IF, INDEED, HE HAD SEEN A MONSTER!
THIS'LL THROW ME OFF SCHEDULE. BUT I'M ALONE ON THE TRACK,.. AND I'VE GOT TO FOLLOW THAT--THAT "THING"...

THE ABANDONED TUNNEL WAS DARK AND DANK, AND THE SLIME UNDER-FOOT SEEMED TO WHISPER TO LARRY OF THE HORROR THAT LAY AHEAD...
THERE! A LIGHT UP AHEAD! THEN I'M NOT CRAZY! I DID SEE SOMETHING! THERE IS SOMETHING-- SOMEONE--UP AHEAD---

SUDDENLY LARRY SAW A SCENE OF HORROR THAT ROOTED HIM TO THE SPOT.
WE MUST WORK FAST--KILL THE TWO HUMANS WHO SEE US AS WE REALLY ARE! OTHERWISE THEY WILL LEARN THAT WE GROUNDINGS ARE TAKING OVER THE WORLD.
BUT ARE YOU SURE THEY CAN SEE THROUGH THE HYPNOTIC SCREEN WE HAVE THROWN OVER THE EARTH?

OF COURSE! DID I NOT SEE THE FREAK ACCIDENT? THEY BUMPED THEIR HEADS TOGETHER--ATTUNED THEIR SIGHT MECHANISMS TO SEE US AS WE REALLY ARE!
THEN THEY MUST DIE! DEATH TO THEM! AIII, KILL, KILL!

WE HAVE THE GIRL NOW--IN THE DISINTEGRATING TOP! WE SHALL HAVE THE MAN BEFORE THE NIGHT IS OUT!
PLEASE... PLEASE LET ME OUT!

THEY'RE GIBBERING ABOUT MYSELF AND THAT GIRL--THE ONE I BUMPED INTO! AND THEY'VE GOT HER IN THAT CONTRAPTION! I'VE GOT TO RUN FOR HELP!
YAAAAA--HELLLLLP--!

SPURRED BY TERROR, LARRY RAN FROM THE ABANDONED TUNNEL, WHILE THE GROUNDINGS DANCED FIENDISHLY ABOUT THE MACHINE, WHICH NOW GAVE OFF AN EERIE, OMINOUS HUMMING SOUND...
YAAAAA! THE HEAT I'M BURNING--HELP--YAAA--
SHE DISINTEGRATES! AIIII--FROM FLESH TO BONES--DEATH--DEATH--

AHHHHHH--
MELT--MELT! THUS WILL WE RID OURSELVES OF ALL WHO DISCOVER OUR PLANS--OUR PLOT TO CONQUER THE WORLD--HA-HA-HA---

THE GIRL'S TERRIBLE SCREAMS WERE STOPPED ABRUPTLY AS THE HUMMING BECAME A HIGH WHINE. THEN, SUDDENLY...
THE SMILE OF LIFE IS NOW THE GRINNING OF A SKULL--HA-HA-HA-HA!
AIII--SHE IS NO MORE!

MEANWHILE, LARRY FROST DASHED MADLY BACK TO HIS CAR...HE HAD TO GET TO THE POLICE...TAKE THEM TO THE ABANDONED TUNNEL...
OH, HURRY, HURRY! WHERE HAVE YOU BEEN! I'M SCARED--TERRIBLY SCARED--HURRY--GET THE CAR MOVING--PLEASE--
WHA--GASP--I--I THOUGHT THE CAR WAS EMPTY--I DIDN'T SEE YOU--

WITH FEVERISH HASTE LARRY FROST THREW THE CAR INTO MOTION...AND THEN THE LONE PASSENGER MADE A STARTLING STATEMENT--
OH, HURRY, HURRY, MOTORMAN! WE'VE GOT TO GET POLICE--I--I SAW MONSTERS ON THE TRACK! HURRY!
WHAT--YOU--YOU SAW THEM TOO? BUT THEY DON'T KNOW THERE'S A THIRD PERSON WHO CAN SEE THEM!
MOTORMAN

OH, WHAT ARE THEY? WHAT ARE THEY DOING?
THEY'RE KILLING ANOTHER GIRL BACK THERE--AND PLANNING TO TAKE OVER THE WORLD! AND THEY CAN DO IT TOO! BECAUSE THEY LOOK LIKE HUMANS TO EVERYONE ELSE! HEY--I--I CAN'T MOVE---I CAN'T MOVE TO STOP THE TRAIN---

HA-HA-HA WHY KEEP UP THE GAME ANY LONGER! OF COURSE YOU CANNOT MOVE, FOOL! I'VE HYPNOTIZED YOU! HA-HA-HA!
WHA--AHNNH! YOU--YOU'RE A MONSTER! A GROUNDING! YAAAA!

YES! BUT YOU COULD NOT SEE ME AS I REALLY AM UNTIL I CHOSE TO LET YOU! WE KILLED THE GIRL AND NOW--YOU! THEN NOTHING SHALL STOP US FROM CONQUERING THE WORLD! HA-HA-HA-HA--

NO!! I'LL STOP YOU! I'LL--AHHHH--THE HEAT--I'M BURNING--YAAAAH!
YOU'LL DO NOTHING, FOOL--EXCEPT DIE--HAHAHA---

YOU REMEMBER THE STORIES IN THE NEWSPAPERS THE NEXT MORNING. "THE UNSOLVABLE MYSTERY" IT WAS CALLED. HOW WHEN THE SUBWAY TRAIN STOPPED, GUARDS LOOKED IN AND SAW--
GLORY BE! A SKELETON AT THE CONTROLS OF FROST'S TRAIN!
GASP--SAINTS PROTECT US! WILL Y'LOOK AT THE THING! WHAT IS IT--WHAT DOES IT MEAN---

YOU KNOW WHAT IT MEANS! SO YOU BE CAREFUL! LOOK CAREFULLY--SCRUTINIZE YOUR NEIGHBORS, THE PEOPLE ON THE STREETS! ARE THEY WHAT THEY SEEM TO BE--OR ARE THEY MONSTERS? PERHAPS, IF YOU WATCH, THERE IS STILL TIME TO SAVE THE WORLD FROM ENSLAVEMENT BY THE MONSTERS ABOUT YOU!!

The End.

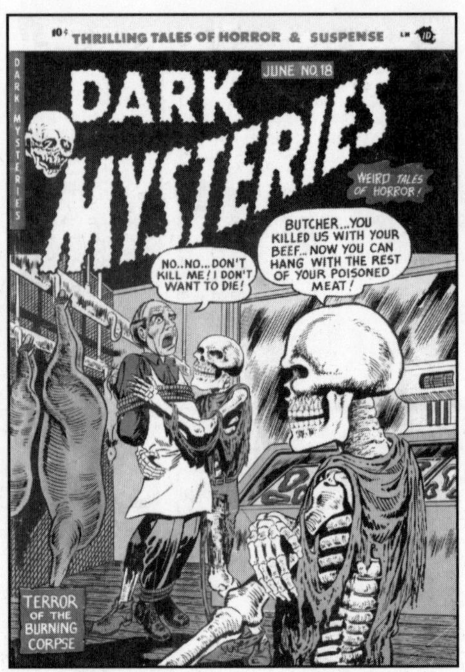

Terror of the Stolen Legs

Dark Mysteries 18, June 1954

It was only after eight issues of *Dark Mysteries* that the editors at Master Comics turned their gaze on their competitors at EC whose creations *Tales from the Crypt*, *Vault of Horror* and *Haunt of Fear* had made such a terrifying impact. In terms of storytelling they were never quite EC's peer; but when it came to sanguinary delectation Master Comics were rarely surpassed. Nazi experimentation was at the fore of these pages, a theme all too familiar to the genre at the time. Altman's deft brushstrokes regularly appeared in this title and it is easy to see why when you look at the opening panel to this tale; it just might turn your stomach again.

WOULD YOU BELIEVE IT, MY VORACIOUS READERS - HA HA HA! I'M HYSTERICAL JUST THINKING ABOUT IT - A MURDERED CORPSE, DOWN TO HIS LAST LEGS, JUST A BONY, SKELETAL, COLLECTION OF CLANKING VERTEBRAE, LOSES THOSE LEGS - BUT CONTINUES TO WALK THE EARTH CREATING THE...

THE STENCH OF HUMAN BLOOD, THE REEK OF MOLDERING FLESH AND BONE, FILLS DR. FRANZ BURCH'S LABORATORY AT THE LINZ CONCENTRATION CAMP! TO HIS INSPIRED MIND THESE ARE AS THE ESSENCES OF PERFUMES - FOR HE HAD FINALLY DISCOVERED THE FORMULA FOR RESTORING THE DEAD TO LIFE! BUT ROLFE, THE ONE GUINEA-PIG ON WHOM HIS FORMULA HAS WORKED HAS TO BE BURIED, ALIVE, - BUT ROLFE WON'T STAY IN HIS GRAVE! SCRAPE, SCRAAAAPE! THE SAW GOES THROUGH THE BONES, SEVERING THE LEGS THE GHOST CANNOT PURSUE HIM... OR CAN IT?
THIS TAKES CARE OF YOU, MY DEAR ROLFE! MINUS YOUR LEGS YOU'LL HAVE TO SETTLE DOWN IN THAT GRAVE OF YOURS... AND STAY THERE ONCE AND FOR ALL! PERHAPS NOW I CAN GET SOME SLEEP! WITHOUT WONDERING THROUGH WHAT WINDOW YOU'LL BE PEERING AT ME NEXT!

DARK NIGHT - THIN, COLD MOONLIGHT - SETTLES ON THE NAZI CONCENTRATION CAMP AT LINZ! A WHISTLING WIND BREAKS THE AWFUL STILLNESS AND THE TREAD OF THE ARMED GUARD! THEN A PIERCING SHRIEK RENDS THE AIR, EMENATING FROM THE LIGHTED WINDOW, THE LABORATORY OF SURGEON DR. FRANZ BURCH!

A LOUD SHRIEK... AND ONCE MORE, STILLNESS! THE RATTLE OF DEATH IS OVER! DR. BURCH, BRILLIANT NAZI SCIENTIST, IS EXPERIMENTING WITH LIFE AND DEATH, WITH THE LIVING INMATES OF THE LINZ CONCENTRATION CAMP AS HIS GUINEA-PIGS!

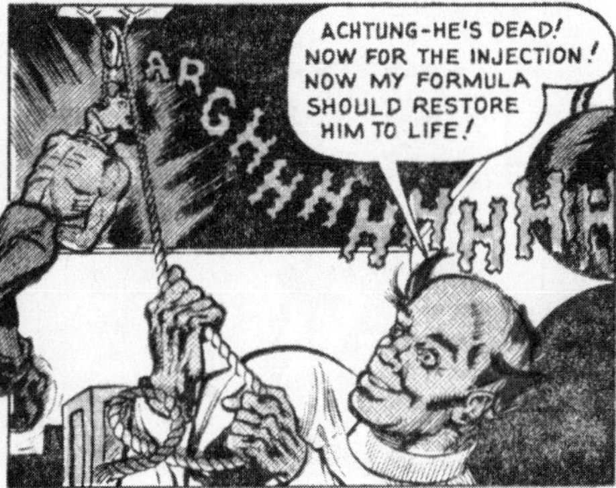

ACHTUNG - HE'S DEAD! NOW FOR THE INJECTION! NOW MY FORMULA SHOULD RESTORE HIM TO LIFE!

AN ANGRY CURSE BREAKS FROM THE COMPRESSED LIPS OF DR. BURCH! THE FORMULA FAILED TO WORK- FOR THE TENTH TIME!

SCHWEINERAI! THEY SEND ME SPECIMENS HALF DEAD TO BEGIN WITH! THEY LACK VITALITY TO RESPOND TO THE SERUM!

BURCH KEEPS HIS NERVES UNDER CONTROL WHEN HE CALLS ON COMMANDANT PAULUS! ONLY ONE THING IS AS IMPORTANT TO HIM AS HIS FORMULA... THE COMMANDANT'S DAUGHTER, MARGARET!

THAT DUMKOPF, THE COMMANDANT! SUCH STUPIDITY! SENDING ME THE WEAKEST PRISONERS FOR MY EXPERIMENTS

TAKE ME TO THE BARRACKS, COMMANDANT! I WANT TO LOOK OVER THE INMATES!

THEY'RE ALL IN A LOW PHYSICAL STATE, DOCTOR!

NO PITY, ONLY DISGUST- FILLS THE EYES OF BURCH INSPECTING THE STILL LIVING PROSPECTIVE VICTIMS FOR HIS EXPERIMENTS!

PAH! AREN'T THERE ANY ROBUST, HEALTHY SPECIMENS FOR ME, COMMANDER PAULUS?

RATIONS ARE LIMITED FOR PRISONERS, AND THEY DO HARD LABOR!

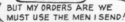

TEA TIME IN THE COMMANDANTS PARLOR!

I AM ON THE THRESHOLD OF THE GREATEST SCIENTIFIC DISCOVERY! I MUST HAVE HARDY SPECIMENS TO WORK ON! WHEN I PUT THEM TO DEATH, WOUNDED, I INJECT THEM WITH MY SERUM I CAN *BRING THEM BACK TO LIFE*, HEALED! GIVE ME ONE REALLY HEALTHY MAN AS HEALTHY AS OUR SOLDIERS!

BUT MY ORDERS ARE WE MUST USE THE MEN I SEND!

HIS EYES GLEAM WITH STRANGE FIRE, HIS LONG, DELICATE FINGERS TWITCH WITH NERVOUS IMPATIENCE, AS DR. BURCH TALKS OF HIS GREAT DISCOVERY! UNTIL MARGARET PAULUS ENTERS....

THE WORLD WILL KNEEL BEFORE OUR ARMIES WHEN... OH, MISS MARGARET, YOU LOOK LOVELY!

HOW DO YOU DO, DR. BURCH? HELLO, FATHER!
LIEBCHEN!

THIS, HERR DOCTOR, IS THE APPLE OF MY EYE...MY MARGARET!
NOW, NOW, FATHER!
I CAN HARDLY BLAME YOU, SIR! I COULD DOTE ON HER MYSELF!

A DISCREET COUGH INTERRUPTS THIS PLEASANT SCENE...
COUGH!
I BROUGHT THE LIST YOU WANTED, SIR!
ROLFE'S A MODEL PRISONER, THE BEST TRUSTEE WE'VE EVER HAD!
2

THAT ROLFE... HE DOESN'T LOOK LIKE A PRISONER!
HE'S A POLITICAL RENEGADE! INTELLIGENT MAN- ER- I MEAN, HE'S MISGUIDED, BUT HE'S GOT BRAINS! HE'S USEFUL IN MY HOUSE!

DESPITE BURCH'S PASSION FOR MARGARET, HE GETS SMALL ENCOURAGEMENT!

WHEN WILL YOU HAVE DINNER WITH ME, MARGARET? ANY EVENING YOU SAY...
SORRY, FRANZ, I'M BUSY THESE DAYS... PERHAPS SOMETIME...

BURCH LEAVES MARGARET, UNABLE TO ADMIT THAT HE IS BEING REBUFFED! AN EGOIST, HE FINDS OTHER EXCUSES...

MARGARET IS SO YOUNG, SO SHY... SHE CAN'T BELIEVE THAT I, DR. BURCH, AM IN LOVE WITH HER! I'LL HAVE TO CONVINCE HER...

IN HIS LABORATORY, BURCH FINDS TWO SPECIMENS AWAITING HIM... AND HE SETS TO WORK, THROWING OFF HIS FANTASIES OF MARGARET!

READY, DOCTOR, FOR THE NEEDLE! I'VE JUST SEVERED THE WRIST... HE'S DYING!
PAH! THIS ONE WON'T RESPOND! TOO WEAK... LET'S TRY YOURS...

I'LL HAVE TO CRACK DOWN ON PAULUS! HE MUST SEND ME ROBUST SPECIMENS! I'LL WALK OVER TO HIS HOUSE...
YES, SIR!

PUTRID ODORS CLING TO BURCH- EVEN WHILE A WIND BLOWS! HE CANNOT WALK OFF HIS TWO FRUSTRATIONS... HIS SCIENTIFIC FAILURE AND HIS ROMANTIC ONE - MARGARET!

JUST ONE HEALTHY SPECIMEN AND I'LL STARTLE THE WHOLE WORLD! THEN MARGARET WILL BE EAGER TO MARRY ME...

VOICES... SOFT, WHISPERING, SECRET... PENETRATE THROUGH BURCH'S DREAMS...

SOUNDS LIKE-MARGARET! THIS IS HER HOUSE- I MUST SEE...

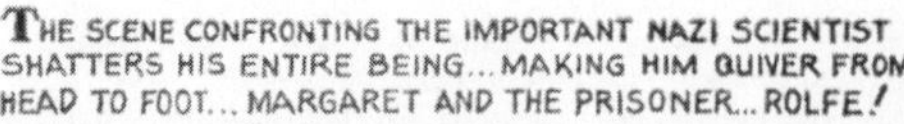
THE SCENE CONFRONTING THE IMPORTANT NAZI SCIENTIST SHATTERS HIS ENTIRE BEING... MAKING HIM QUIVER FROM HEAD TO FOOT... MARGARET AND THE PRISONER... ROLFE!

I'LL FIND A WAY TO SAVE YOU, MY DARLING! I LOVE YOU SO...
IT'S DANGEROUS FOR YOU, SWEET!
THE SILLY FOOL! PREFERRING HIM TO... ME! NOW I KNOW WHY PAULUS PROTECTS HIM!

THE NEXT DAY THE AGILE MIND OF BURCH IS QUICK TO FIND A WAY TO HANDLE THE IMPASSE... AND HE SENT FOR PAULUS!
THANK YOU FOR COMING TO MY LABORATORY, COMMANDANT! YOU MUST BELIEVE IT IS URGENT!
CERTAINLY, CERTAINLY, HERR DOCTOR! I AM GLAD TO COME...

THERE IS ONE PRISONER WHO IS IDEAL FOR MY EXPERIMENT! I MUST HAVE HIM AT ONCE!
GLADLY, GLADLY, HERR DOCTOR! WHICH ONE!

WITH SINISTER RELISH, BURCH SLOWLY ENUNCIATED THE PRISONER'S NAME TO THE SHOCKED COMMANDANT...
R-O-L-F-E!
YOU'RE - NOT SERIOUS? WHY - HE'S - TO - BE - PARDONED!

PLAYING HIS TRUMP CARD, BURCH PASSES OFFICIAL ORDERS FROM THE HOME OFFICE TO THE TREMBLING COMMANDANT!
DO YOU STILL WISH TO ARGUE, PAULUS?
ACH - NO, NO! BUT, PLEASE, DO ME A FAVOR! NOT A WORD TO MARGARET! I - I THINK SHE LIKES HIM! FEELS SORRY FOR THE FELLOW!

PERHAPS THE KEENEST SATISFACTION COMES TO BURCH WHEN THE DEFIANT, HANDSOME ROLFE IS BROUGHT BEFORE HIM-IN CHAINS
WHAT DO YOU WANT OF ME?
YOU ARE THE LUCKIEST MAN IN THE WORLD! I'VE SELECTED YOU TO TEST MY SERUM FOR RESTORING YOU TO LIFE-AFTER DEATH! YOU WILL BE A HERO!

YOU'RE INSANE... YOU'RE NOT HUMAN... ARRRRRGHH...
STEP ASIDE, HANS... I'M READY WITH THE NEEDLE...
GENTLEMEN, THIS PRISONER IS NOW DEAD!

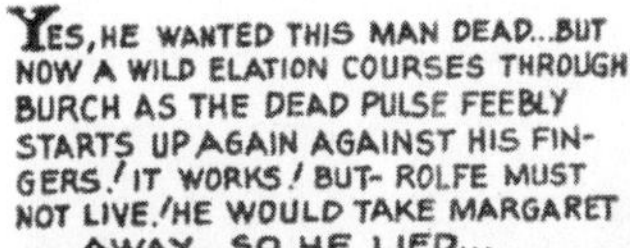

YES, HE WANTED THIS MAN DEAD...BUT NOW A WILD ELATION COURSES THROUGH BURCH AS THE DEAD PULSE FEEBLY STARTS UP AGAIN AGAINST HIS FINGERS! IT WORKS! BUT- ROLFE MUST NOT LIVE! HE WOULD TAKE MARGARET AWAY... SO HE LIED...

BEFORE ROLFE CAN REACH CONSCIOUSNESS, HE MUST BE BURIED! BURCH ORDERS THE DIGGERS TO HURRY, HURRY...

I'VE DONE IT!
HANS, GET SOME MEN TO TAKE AWAY THE BODY- IT STILL HASN'T WORKED!
DIG FASTER... DUMP THE BODY IN!

WELL, I'M RID OF HIM! AND AT LAST MY SERUM IS A SUCCESS! AS SOON AS I GET ANOTHER SPECIMEN I'LL SHOW THE ENTIRE WORLD!

THE FIELD IS NOW CLEAR FOR BURCH- AND HE HURRIES TO MARGARET...

MARGARET, I HEARD YOU HAD BEFRIENDED ROLFE! TERRIBLE ABOUT HIS SUICIDE! I WANTED TO TELL YOU HOW SORRY...

I CAN'T UNDERSTAND IT, DR. B- I MEAN, FRANZ! YOU'RE SO KIND TO CALL!

THE NEXT FEW WEEKS ARE BUSY, HAPPY ONES FOR BURCH! MARGARET IS KINDER... AND SOME NEW SPECIMENS ARE BEING BUILT UP FOR HIS EXPERIMENT... BUT ONE NIGHT HE IS AWAKENED BY A QUEER SOUND- AT THE WINDOW...

WHO'S THERE? WHAT- IS- THAT? A- SK- SKELETON! I MUST BE DREAMING!
TAP TAP TAP TAP

AND AT THE LONELY GRAVE NEAR THE WILLOW, THE NEXT NIGHT AGAIN THE EARTH STIRS... BONY LIMBS PROTRUDE!

AGAIN THE CLANKING BONES STIFFLY WEND THEIR WAY TOWARD DR. BURCH'S LIGHTED OFFICE WINDOW AS HE SITS IN HIS LABORATORY LISTENING... LISTENING TO THE UNWORLDLY SOUND...

EVERY NIGHT, FROM THEN ON, BURCH RECEIVES A GHOSTLY VISITATION FROM THE WALKING SKELETON! NO MORE CAN HE SPEND THE EVENING HOURS AT HIS WORK, NOR CAN HE SLEEP, NO MORE CAN HE FIND PEACE!

GO BACK TO YOUR GRAVE, ROLFE!

YOU WERE BURIED DEEP... WHY DON'T YOU STAY THERE?

GO BACK! YOU ARE DEAD!

THE DESPERATE SLEEPLESS MAN HAS ORDERED THE GRAVE EXHUMED AND IS NOW FRANTICALLY SEVERING THE LEGS OF ROLFE'S SKELETON...

AND BURCH MADE SURE THE LEGS WERE BURNED... HE DID THE JOB HIMSELF...

NOW YOU'LL HAVE TO STAY IN YOUR GRAVE... MINUS LEGS YOU'LL WALK NO MORE! YOURS SHALL BE BURNED!
AHHHH! I'VE OUTSMARTED HIM THIS TIME! HA HA HA!

MINUS HIS LEGS ROLFE WAS AGAIN BURIED! NOW BURCH ENJOYS REFRESHING SLEEP, FOLLOWED BY A DELICIOUS BREAKFAST BUT IT IS INTERRUPTED BY TWO CALLERS...

...THE CAMP IS ALARMED! GHOULS HAVE ROBBED THE CEMETERY... A GRAVE HAS BEEN OPENED...
SPEAK UP, MAN! WHAT WAS TAKEN?

VERY ODD, SIR! ONLY A PAIR OF SKELETON LEGS!
UH...UH... L-LEGS!

THE END

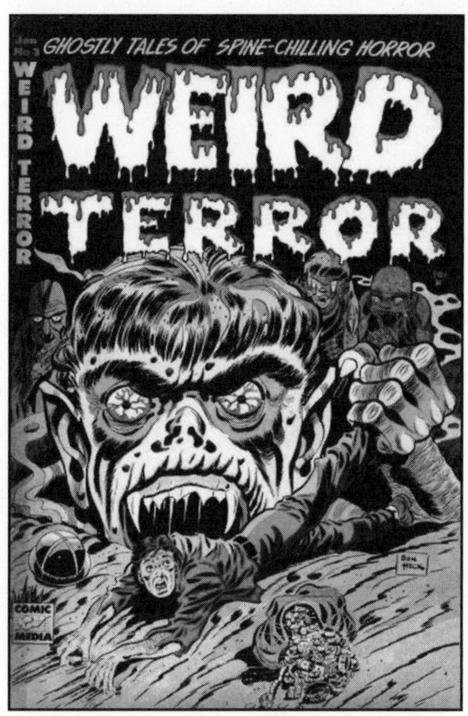

Den of Horror

Weird Terror 3, January 1953

If yours is the pursuit of reasons behind the introduction of the debilitating Comics Code, then look no further. While it isn't cited in any of the inflammatory anti-comic book texts of the time, "Den of Horror" encapsulates every fear espoused by the crusaders. No one can say with any certainty how these pages gained the approval of Comic Media's editors; it was almost as if they were deliberately taking the sordid to untold limits. The scenes of flagellation and torture defy belief. But surely this sort of thing could not be going on in a kid's comic book? It begs the question whether these creators had more than just a prepubescent market in mind; after all, many of these people had served in the forces during the Second World War and the comic book had been a staple source of escapism. This entry in *Weird Terror* is extreme, but the title rates among the darkest of an infamous phase in comic book publishing.

ROBERT BAKER, AN EVIL PLAYBOY, WAS INTENT UPON TURNING HIS ANCIENT ANCESTRAL CASTLE INTO A PERSONAL CIDATEL OF FRIVOLITY! BUT HIS OWN TYRANNY TRANSFORMED HIS LAVISHLY DECORATED DRAWING ROOM INTO A...

DEN OF HORROR

ROBERT BAKER, SOON AFTER ARRIVING IN ENGLAND TO RE-OPEN THE LEGENDARY CASTLE THAT HAS BEEN IN HIS FAMILY FOR CENTURIES, LOOKS UPON THE IMPOSING STRUCTURE FOR THE FIRST TIME...

WELL--NOT TOO BAD AT THAT! IT'LL TAKE SOME DOING TO FIX UP THIS PLACE, BUT MONEY IS NO OBJECT!

AND THE SOONER I GET IT DONE, THE SOONER I CAN START THROWING SOME PARTIES AND ENJOYING MYSELF HERE! IT SHOULD RELIEVE MY BOREDOM!!

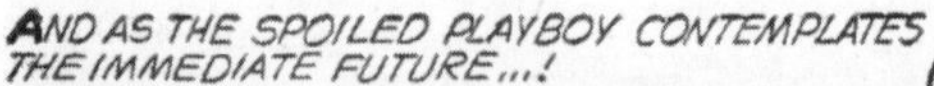

BAKER RELEASES THE OLD WOMAN HEAVILY AND THEN LISTENS TO HER WIERD TALE!!

BUT THE EVIL TEMPERED MILLIONAIRE SOON LOSES PATIENCE WITH HIS STRANGE AND WIERD VISITOR...!

DISREGARDING THE STRANGE WORDS OF THE OLD CRONE, BAKER HURRIES THE CASTLE'S RENOVATIONS TO COMPLETION AND, AFTER HIRING A STAFF OF LOCAL SERVANTS, INVITES HIS WEALTHY FRIENDS TO HIS FIRST PARTY!

BOB, OLD MAN! I SAY, THIS PLACE IS REALLY SOME-THING NOW!!
YES, YOU'D NEVER DREAM THIS VERY ROOM WAS ONCE A FEARED TORTURE CHAMBER!

BUT AT THE HEIGHT OF THE FESTIVITIES...
ANOTHER DRINK, MR. BA---OHHH.. I'M SORRY--!!
YES, I'D-- --WHA--!

YOU CLUMSY IDIOT!!
BUT I-- OOHHH!!

BOB, SHE DIDN'T MEAN--
KEEP BACK!! I HEAR SERVANT-BEATING RUNS IN MY FAMILY!! HA-HA-HA!!

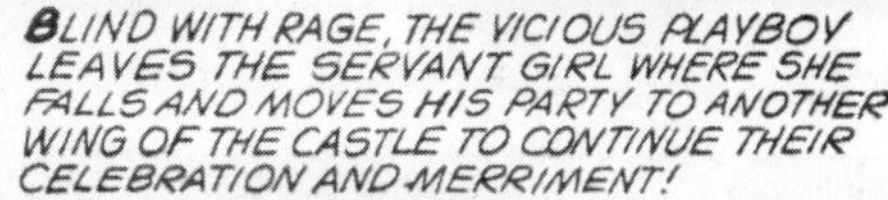

BLIND WITH RAGE, THE VICIOUS PLAYBOY LEAVES THE SERVANT GIRL WHERE SHE FALLS AND MOVES HIS PARTY TO ANOTHER WING OF THE CASTLE TO CONTINUE THEIR CELEBRATION AND MERRIMENT!

-SOB..- -SOB..-

AND THAT NIGHT, AS HIS GUESTS SLEEP, BAKER IS AWAKENED BY A PIERCING, AGONIZED, BLOOD-CURDLING SHRIEK!!

IT... IT CAME FROM THE DRAWING ROOM!

BAKER GOES TO THE DRAWING ROOM.....TO WITNESS A FANTASTIC SIGHT THAT MAKES HIS BLOOD RUN COLD!!

A TORTURE CHAMBER! CENTURIES OLD! WHERE... WHERE MY DRAWING ROOM WAS AN HOUR AGO!

THEY'VE SEEN ME!! KEEP AWAY!!

NO!! NOOO...!!
WE'VE WAITED A LONG TIME, BAKER!!

OVERPOWERED BY HIS HIDEOUS PURSUERS AND COMPLETELY HELPLESS IN THEIR DIABOLICAL GRIP, BAKER IS DRAGGED BACK INTO THE GRUESOME CHAMBER!

YOUR TIME HAS COME, ROBERT BAKER!
NO!

AAAIIEEEEE
DIE, BAKER! DIE AS YOUR GREAT-GRANDFATHER KILLED OTHERS!
YOU HAVE FOLLOWED THE WAYS OF YOUR EVIL ANCESTORS--NOW YOU SHALL PAY FOR BOTH OF YOU!!
STOP!...I-I'LL GIVE YOU ANYTHING... I'LL--GASP--MONEY--GASP-!
GASP-...I...I'LL PAY YOU ANYTHING ..ANY--THING... UUGGHHRRR!!
HIS BODY WRACKED WITH PAIN, BAKER SAGS IN EXCRUCIATING AGONY!
.....AND DIES DISMALLY... AS THE BLOOD DRIPS STEADILY FROM HIS TORN BODY!

THE NEXT MORNING, BAKER'S GUESTS GATHER FOR BREAKFAST... UNAWARE OF THE MACABRE EVENTS THAT HAD TRANSPIRED DURING THE NIGHT!
BOB'S NOT IN HIS ROOM!!
AND NONE OF THE SERVANTS SAW HIM LEAVE!... NO ONE'S SEEN HIM SINCE ..... LAST NIGHT!!

SEARCHING THE RAMBLING CASTLE FOR THEIR MISSING HOST, BAKER'S GUESTS COME UPON THE PLUSH DRAWING ROOM .... SCENE OF THE PREVIOUS EVENING'S PARTY!
NO!!..IT CAN'T BE!
IT'S BOB!
GOOD LORD!

WHAT DOES IT MEAN...? THIS WHIP WITH BOB'S GREAT-GRANDFATHER'S NAME ENGRAVED ON IT!
AND THIS LOCKET! THIS LOCKETON WAS MY GREAT-GRANDFATHER! WHO HAD BEEN LASHED TO DEATH BY MR BAKER'S GREAT-GRANDFATHER!!
HAVING ACHIEVED HIS STRANGE AND ALMOST UNBELIEVABLE REVENGE, THE SERVANT GIRL'S ANCESTOR WALKS THE EARTH NO MORE! FOR ROBERT BAKER'S EVIL LIFE HAS BEEN FORFEITED AS JUST PAYMENT FOR HIS GREAT-GRANDFATHER'S TYRANNY! AND HIS OWN!!
THE END

The Living-Dead

Dark Mysteries 20, October 1954

Here is a title that just didn't know when to stop. The crusade against this style of comic was reaching fever pitch. Comic book burnings were common, but *Dark Mysteries* carried on regardless. "The Living-Dead" were the children of another ignoble strain of Nazi experimentation. Artist John D'Agostino conspired with the shadows to breathe life into a truly hideous tale, one that revealed he was another artist whose style suited this unsettling genre.

THE LIVING-DEAD

THE CRISP, SMOOTH, SNOW CRACKLED UNDER IVOR BLAU'S SKIIS AS THEY SKIMMED OVER THE SURFACE--WEAVING EXPERTLY, DANGEROUSLY, IN AND OUT OF THE TALL, THICK TREES! NIGHT WAS FALLING RAPIDLY LIKE A DARK CURTAIN AND A SUDDEN CHILL PENETRATED TO THE BONES AS THIS MAN REALIZED HE WAS LOST IN THE BLACK FOREST! READ ON, FELLOW STUDENTS OF HORROR--HEH, HEH, HEH...

IT CAN'T BE... NO! NO!!
John D'Agostino

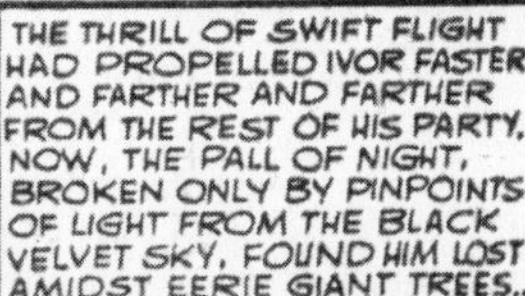

THE THRILL OF SWIFT FLIGHT HAD PROPELLED IVOR FASTER AND FARTHER AND FARTHER FROM THE REST OF HIS PARTY. NOW, THE PALL OF NIGHT, BROKEN ONLY BY PINPOINTS OF LIGHT FROM THE BLACK VELVET SKY, FOUND HIM LOST AMIDST EERIE GIANT TREES..

WHAT LUCK - A HOUSE!

BUT IVOR'S RELIEF AT FINDING A HAVEN VANISHED ABRUPTLY AS IT DAWNED ON HIM THAT THERE WAS SOMETHING STRANGE ABOUT THIS HOUSE SET IN THE THICK OF A FOREST! THE OPEN DOOR, THE STRONG INDEFINABLE ODOR--STRANGE BUT NOT UNPLEASANT..
I'D RATHER TAKE MY CHANCES IN THE FOREST...

HE HAD NOT GOTTEN FAR WHEN A SOFT, MELLOW VOICE STOPPED HIM IN HIS TRACKS! STARTLED BY THE UN-EXPECTED APPEARANCE OF A GIRL IN THE DOOR-WAY AND STRUCK BY HER UNUSUAL BEAUTY! FEAR AT THE MOMENT DEPARTED...

DON'T LEAVE... ARE YOU LOST?
...YES! I THOUGHT NO ONE LIVED HERE...

UP WINDING STAIRS THEY WENT AND IVOR FELT AN INTENSE WEARINESS ASSAIL HIS LIMBS, WELCOMING IN HIS HEART THE PROSPECT OF A BED TO LIE ON...
YOU LOOK TIRED! I'LL SHOW YOU TO A ROOM... WE CAN TALK IN THE MORNING...
YOU'RE SO KIND... AND SO BEAUTIFUL!

THE FLICKERING CANDLE CAST MISSHAPEN SHADOWS ACROSS THE MUSTY BEDROOM AND THE MASSIVE FOUR-POSTER BED LOOMED UP LIKE A HUGE UGLY SARCOPHOGUS...
WE ONLY HAVE CANDLELIGHT OUT HERE IN THE WOODS-- I'LL BRING YOU A TRAY...
THANK YOU...

IVOR STOLE OUT OF HIS ROOM TO WATCH THE GIRL DESCEND THE WINDING STAIRWAY! HOSPITABLE AS SHE WAS, AN UNEASINESS SEEPED THROUGH HIS BEING.
WONDER IF ANY-ONE ELSE LIVES HERE?

WITH THE GIRL DOWNSTAIRS, IVOR STEALTHILY OPENED THE DOOR NEXT TO HIS ROOM AND AGAIN MET WITH THE STRANGE SWEET ODOR...
WHAT A STRANGE SWEETNESS, JUST LIKE THAT GIRL...

EMBOLDENED TO LOOK IN, IVOR WAS ASTONISHED TO SEE A ROOM WITH YOUNG PEOPLE FAST ASLEEP...
WHAT DOES THIS MEAN? THEY'RE ALL SLEEPING...YET THEY'RE SO STILL...
2

A NAMELESS FEAR STIRRED THROUGH IVOR'S BLOOD AS HE LEFT THE MYSTERIOUS ROOM JUST IN TIME TO SEE THE GIRL COMING UP THE STAIRS WITH A TRAY...
MAYBE SHE'LL TELL ME ABOUT THOSE YOUNG PEOPLE...

AFTER A SURPRISINGLY DELICIOUS REPAST, IVOR FELT MORE RELAXED AS HE PLACED A KISS OF APPRECIATION ON THE GIRL'S HAND! HE WAS AWARE OF IT'S UNUSUAL SOFT COOLNESS AND A DESIRE TO HOLD HER CLOSER...

IMPULSIVELY, IVOR CAUGHT THE SLENDER FORM IN HIS ARMS! HER NEARNESS INTOXICATED HIM...
PLEASE--LET ME KISS YOU, YOUR BEAUTY IS MADDENING...
YES--YOU MAY...

WHAT A WONDERFUL END TO HIS ADVENTURE! OUT OF THE FRIGHTENING DISCOVERY THAT HE WAS LOST IN THE THICK WOODS, AND THE STRANGE EXPERIENCE OF FINDING THIS LONELY HOUSE WITH IT'S SLEEPING OCCUPANTS, IVOR HAD FOUND THE EXCITINGLY BEAUTIFUL GIRL--AND LOVE...

THE NEXT MORNING IVOR HURRIED DOWN EAGER TO SEE HIS NEW LOVE--AND EXPECTING TO FIND THE SLEEPING OCCUPANTS OF THE NEXT ROOM UP AND ABOUT AFTER THEIR LONG SLEEP...
OH, GOOD MORNING, SLEEP WELL?
DARLING, I DREAMED OF YOU!

HIGH SPIRITED AS IVOR FELT THE THROES OF HIS NEW LOVE, THE IMAGE OF THE SLEEPING PEOPLE HAUNTED AND TAUNTED HIM... BESIDES, THE PUNGENT SMELLS SEEMED MORE PERVASIVE THAN EVER... SICKENING IN FACT...
THERE'S SOMETHING I MUST CONFESS! I--I LOOKED INTO THAT BED-ROOM WHERE THOSE PEOPLE ARE SLEEPING! I WONDERED...

THEY ARE MY GUESTS! THEY ARE VERY WEARY AND ARE STILL SLEEPING!
3

IVOR WANDERED FROM ROOM TO ROOM WHILE THE GIRL WAS BUSY! SHE HAD ANSWERED HIM CURTLY-- SHUT OFF ALL DISCUSSION OF HER STRANGE GUESTS BUT IVOR OBEYED A SUDDEN IMPULSE...
THIS NOISE SHOULD AWAKEN THEM--
BANG
PLING
BAM

THE BANGING ON THE PIANO KEYBOARD HAD NO EFFECT ON THE SLEEPERS AND IVOR, IN AN EXCESS OF HIDDEN ANXIETY PUSHED ON A HEAVY TABLE TILL IT TURNED OVER IN A CRASH BUT STILL THEY SLEPT...
NOW WILL YOU WAKE UP? THIS SHOULD WAKEN THE DEAD!!
CRASH

LIKE A NIGHTMARE, WILD FAN-TASIES GREW WILDER AS IVOR BECAME OBSESSED WITH THE DESIRE TO STIR THE SLEEPERS.
WHAT'S WRONG WITH THEM?

BUT THIS TIME IVOR TOUCHED THEM AND THEY WERE ASLEEP NO LONGER...
UGE... TH--THEY'RE BECOMING SKELETONS... YET THEY MOVE... THEY'RE GETTING UP...

IN A DAZE, IVOR FOUND HIM-SELF BACK IN HIS ROOM! THIS STRANGE, LOVELY GIRL WAS TALKING TO HIM IN HER SOFT, SWEET VOICE...
IT IS TIME FOR ME TO EXPLAIN-- BUT FIRST, TELL ME YOUR NAME... MINE IS VANIA...
MINE IS IVOR BLAU, SON OF DR. KLAUS BLAU, THE NAZI SCIENTIST WHO DISSAPPEARED!

IMMEDIATELY VANIA'S SOFTNESS CHANGED TO HORROR...
OH, NO! NOT YOU! NOW YOU MUST HEAR THE STORY-- YOUR FATHER IS INVOLVED--AND YOU TOO!

DURING WORLD WAR II IN YOUR FATHER'S LABORATORY, AN EXPERIMENT WAS TAKING PLACE--HE WAS SO DEDICATED TO THE NAZI CAUSE, DR. BLAU WAS WILLING TO USE YOU, HIS OWN SON, TO PROVE HIS THEORY...

YES, YOUR IDEA COULD HELP US VIN THE VAR... BUT YOUR FORMULA IS POISONOUS...
SEE, I VILL INJECT MY OWN SON, IVOR, TO PROVE YOU ARE WRONG, HERR GENERAL...
4

ALL RIGHT, YOU MAY HAVE SIX PRISONERS FROM THE CONCENTRATION CAMP!

THOSE YOUNG PEOPLE IN THE NEXT ROOM WERE BROUGHT HERE FOR THE CRUEL EXPERIMENT UNDER-TAKEN SECRETLY BY YOUR FATHER, DOCTOR BLAU...

SCHWEIN! MOVE FASTER--FASTER!

YES, YOUR FATHER WAS SURE HE COULD DRAW BLOOD FROM LIVING PEOPLE INJECTED WITH HIS FORMULA AND RESTORE WOUNDED GERMAN SOLDIERS DYING FROM LOSS OF BLOOD TO LIFE...

IS THIS THE LAST ONE? WE MUST WORK FAST! DRAW ALMOST ALL HER BLOOD--THEN, REINJECT HER...

THERE WAS ONE LEFT--A GIRL, DR. BLAU HAD ALREADY DRAWN HALF HER BLOOD WHEN AN EXCITED MESSENGER ARRIVED..

SOON, WE'LL HAVE THESE SCUM BACK TO LIFE WITH MY FORMULA! NOW, THEY ARE HALF-DEAD, 'ZOMBIES,' WHO CANNOT DIE...
HERR DOCTOR BLAU... I BRING ALARMING NEWS!

THE ALARMING NEWS WAS THAT AMERICAN SOLDIERS WERE RAPIDLY ADVANCING... THE NAZIS HAD FALLEN...

DR. BLAU, YOU MUST LEAVE.. WE HAVE LOST THE WAR! THE AMERICANS ARE CLOSE...
SCHWEINEREI, JUST WHEN I WAS PROVING MY EXPERIMENT!

AND SO, YOUR FATHER, THE GREAT SCIENTIST MADE HIS ESCAPE, LEAVING HIS GUINEA PIGS ON THEIR BEDS--NOT ALIVE, YET NOT QUITE DEAD, AWAITING THE INJECTED BLOOD DR. BLAU PROMISED...

DON'T GO... YOU MUST RESTORE... US...

THESE YOUNG PEOPLE HOVERING BETWEEN LIFE AND DEATH, NEED ONLY A SMALL SUPPLY OF BLOOD INJECTED WITH YOUR FATHER'S FORMULA! AS FOR THE GIRL... SHE COULD WALK, AND TALK AND ONLY WAIT...

5

AT THE BEGINNING OF VANIA'S STORY, IVOR FELT PRIDE IN THE COURAGE AND BRILLIANCE OF HIS FATHER, FAMOUS NAZI SCIENTIST, EXPERIMENTING TO AID THE SUPER RACE, BUT A SUBTLE CHANGE IN VANIA'S VOICE--AND NOW, IN HER APPEARANCE--FROZE HIS BLOOD.

WHO.. WHO WAS THAT LAST GIRL?

AND HIS WORST SURMISE BECAME TRUE AS HE HEARD HER VOICE CACKLE AND SQUEAK...
YES, HEH, HEH, YOU'VE GUESSED IT-- IT WAS I, VANIA! NOW I CAN GROW OLD AND HOPE FOR RELEASE!

IVOR MADE HIS WAY TO THE DOOR! ESCAPE WAS ALL HE DESIRED--FROM THIS PLACE OF DECAYING CREATURES AND A VENGEFUL MONSTOR WHOSE FORM WAS CHANGING BEFORE HIS EYES...
COME, PAY YOUR FATHER'S DEBT! GIVE US YOUR INJECTED BLOOD TO REPLACE WHAT HE TOOK!
NO, NO!

THE SOUND OF CLANKING BONE LIKE WEIRD CASTANETS PURSUED HIS MAD RUSH DOWN THE STAIRS! HIS LIMBS SEEMED TO FREEZE INTO IMMOBILITY...
COME BACK! GIVE US YOUR BLOOD! YOU WERE INJECTED WITH YOUR FATHER'S FORMULA!
MY LEGS... HARD TO MOVE THEM!

BONEY ARMS ENVELOPED THE TERROR-STRICKEN EX-NAZI YOUTH...

I HAD NOTHING TO DO WITH MY FATHER'S EXPERIMENT--SPARE ME...AAGHHHHH!

AGAIN THE SOUND OF VANIA'S LAUGHTER ECHOED THROUGH THE HALL! HE FELT STRANGELY EMPTY AND EXHAUSTED AS HE SAW VANIA'S UGLY FORM COMING TOWARDS HIM...

AAEEEE... NO!!
HEEEHEEE! THEY HAVE THEIR REVENGE-- AND NOW THEY'RE GONE UP TO FIND THE PEACE OF DEATH...

AND VANIA... NOW A REAL ZOMBIE, HAD HER WAY OF IVOR AND SHE WATCHED HIM SINK TO THE FLOOR AS HIS SCREAMS GREW FAINT AND SHE KNEW HE BREATHED HIS LAST AGONIZING BREATH...

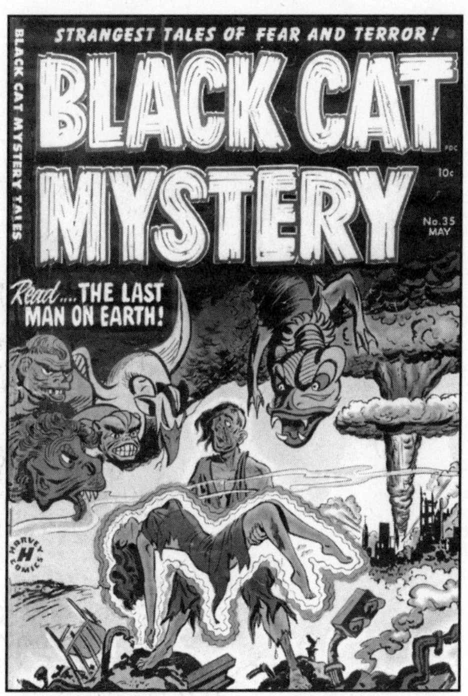

Marching Zombies

Black Cat Mystery 35, May 1952

Zombie comics may dominate the modern horror market, but in the 1950s they found themselves overrun by the fangs of leather-winged vampires and the howl of werewolves. When presented with a script describing the insane rampage of a zombie collective, Rudy Palais had his hapless heroes sweat all the more before having them hurled into a pit of razor-sharp knives. Rudy seemed to revel in their anguish, pouring himself into each panel as this tale mounted to its sadistic climax. Once again the scenes defied Harvey's editorial line, but their readers just couldn't get enough.

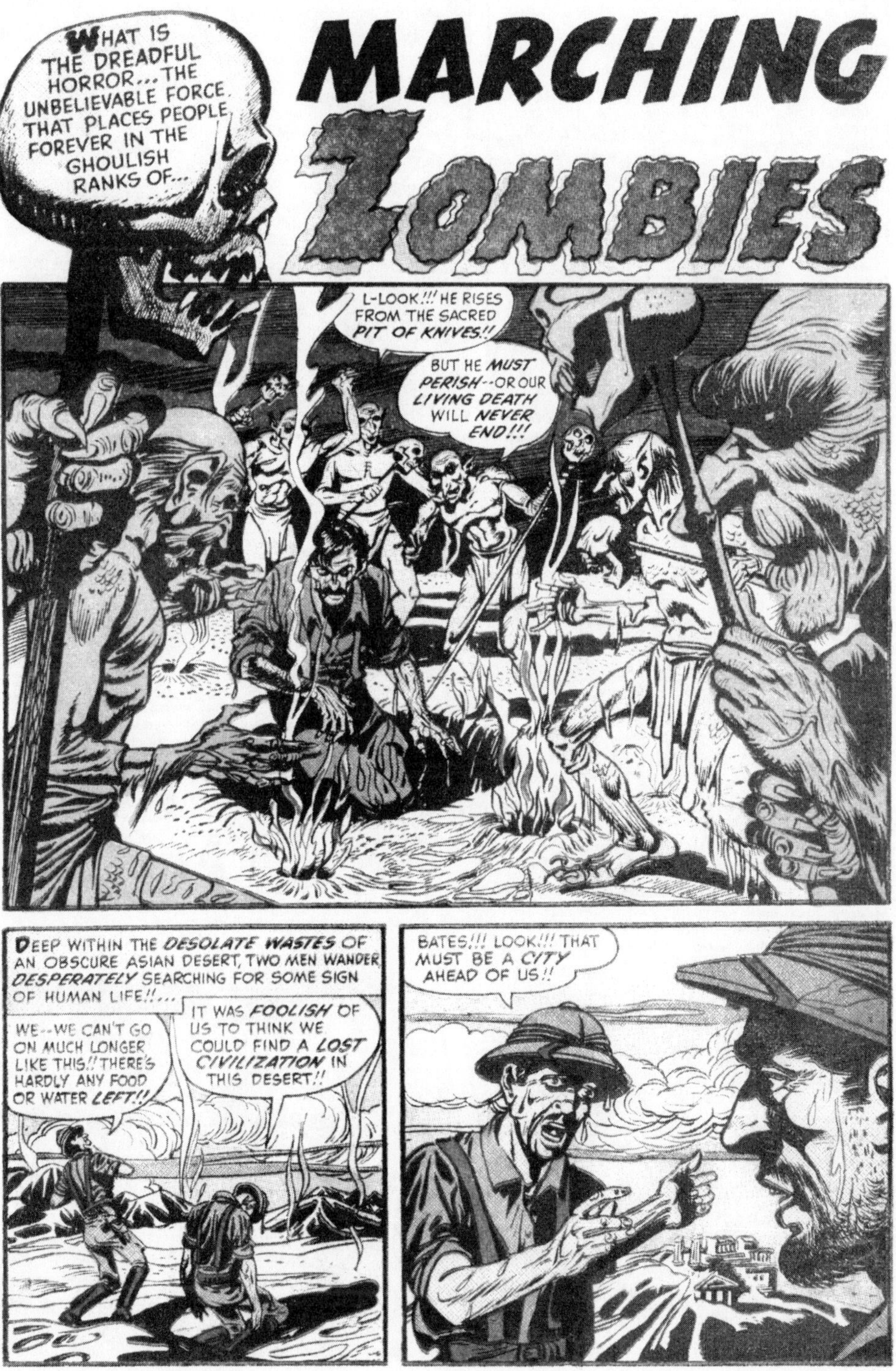

WHAT IS THE DREADFUL HORROR... THE UNBELIEVABLE FORCE THAT PLACES PEOPLE FOREVER IN THE GHOULISH RANKS OF...

MARCHING ZOMBIES

L-LOOK!!! HE RISES FROM THE SACRED PIT OF KNIVES!!

BUT HE MUST PERISH--OR OUR LIVING DEATH WILL NEVER END!!!

APPROACHING THE CITY IN THE DESERT, THE MEN FIND ONLY DECAY AND A DEATHLY SILENCE THAT STRIKES THEM WITH AN UNEXPLAINABLE TERROR!...
WHY, THERE'S NO-BODY HERE!! IT SEEMS TO BE THE RUINS OF SOME ANCIENT CITY!!
THERE'S A STRANGE FEELING IN THE AIR--AS IF DEATH HAD NEVER LEFT!!! LET'S--

SANDERS!! LOOK!
YAA-HH

AS THE REPULSIVE SILENT CREATURES APPROACH, A LOOK OF HORRIFIED RECOGNITION FREEZES ON THE FACES OF THE MEN!!...
THEY--THEY SEEM LIKE MEN WHO HAVE WANDERED FROM THE DEPTHS OF THE GRAVE!!
LIKE--- ZOMBIES!

WHAT DO YOU WANT WITH US??? WE MEAN YOU NO HARM!!
THAT MUST BE THEIR CHIEF APPROACHING!

YOU WISH TO KNOW WHO WE ARE!! WE ARE AN ACCURSED TRIBE-- DEAD THESE MANY YEARS--DOOMED BY OUR GOD KALU TO WANDER THE RUINS OF OUR CITY!!
WE CAN RETURN TO OUR BURIAL MOUND BEYOND THE HILL ONLY WHEN WE HAVE SHED THE BLOOD OF A LIVING HUMAN!!...

AS THE HIDEOUS FEATURES OF THE LIVING DEAD BECOME DISTORTED WITH UNHOLY EVIL, A NUMBING FEAR GRIPS THE TWO MEN!...
...AND ONE HAS COME TO US AT LAST!!!
KALU MUST BE APPEASED!! WE MUST RETURN TO OUR GRAVES!!

SEIZE HIM!!
NO! NO! LET ME GO!!!

WHERE ARE YOU TAKING HIM??? WHAT ARE YOU GOING TO DO???
KALU CALLS HIM TO HIS SACRED PIT OF KNIVES!!! HE MUST BE ANSWERED!!
THE SHARP KNIVES HAVE WAITED MANY YEARS FOR YOUR BLOOD!! THEY ARE HUNGRY TO PIERCE YOUR FLESH!!!
NO-O-O!!

KALU!! HE IS YOURS!!
NO!! OO DON'T!! D---

SCREAMING WITH THE WILD AGONY BEFORE SUDDEN DEATH, SANDERS IS FLUNG INTO THE DEADLY PIT...
AAARGH-H!

AND NOW WE DESTROY HIM, TOO!!! KALU WILL BE PLEASED!!

WAIT! WE HAVE BROKEN THE CURSE WITH THE BODY OF HIS FRIEND!! THERE IS NOTHING MORE THAT CAN BE ASKED OF US NOW!!

SUDDENLY, AN ANGUISHED MOAN FROM THE PIT OF KNIVES BREAKS UPON THE VOICES OF THE LIVING DEAD---AND A TERRIFYING SIGHT FALLS UPON THEIR GLAZED EYES!
THE PIT!! A HAND IS RISING FROM THE PIT!!!

IT IS HE WHOM WE HAVE JUST THROWN INTO THE PIT!!
WHY DOES HE RETURN THIS WAY??? IS NOT KALU SATISFIED??

MY EYES CANNOT GAZE ON HIM!!
YET HE IS NEITHER LIVING NOR DEAD--AS WE ARE!! SPEAK TO US!! WHAT IS THE WILL OF OUR GOD???

SUDDENLY, A BOLT OF LIGHTNING ANNOUNCES THE COMING OF THE FEARED ONE, THE APPROACH OF A GIANT FROM THE PAGAN WORLD OF DARKNESS!...

KALU!! WE HAVE SHED THE BLOOD OF A LIVING HUMAN-- AND YET HE RISES FROM HIS DEATH. WHY IS OUR CURSE NOT ENDED???

MY PIT OF KNIVES IS SACRED!! I WILL NOT HAVE IT SOILED BY THE BODY OF THIS MAN!! HE MUST GO WITH YOU TO YOUR BURIAL MOUND!!

WHAT DOES HE SAY? HIS BLOOD IS TO STAIN OUR EARTH!!
NO! NO! THIS CANNOT BE!!!

KALU, OUR BURIAL MOUND IS SACRED TO US!! THE BODY OF THIS MAN MUST NOT REST THERE! WE CANNOT DO AS YOU SAY!!

AS THE ANGRY MUMBLINGS OF THE ZOMBIES INCREASE, SO DOES THE WRATH OF THEIR LEADER BECOME LIKE A STORM ABOUT TO BURST WITH WILD FURY UPON THE SCENE!!...
YOU FOOLS!! I DEMAND THAT YOU OBEY ME!! I AM YOUR GOD AND YOUR LEADER!!

SHOW YOUR OBEDIENCE TO ME!! FLING HIM INTO THE PIT OF KNIVES!! THIS IS MY WILL!!

WE WILL NOT DO THIS IF WE MUST BURY HIM IN OUR SACRED GROUND!!
NO! NO! WE MUST RETURN ALONE TO OUR GRAVES BEYOND THE HILL!!

THEN I WILL SHOW YOU WHAT IT MEANS TO DEFY ME!!
YAAAH-H-H!!! DON'T! DON'T!!!

AGAIN A BODY IS TOSSED TO ITS BLOODY DOOM IN THE LOATHESOME PIT--AND AGAIN A SHRIEK OF AGONY RENTS THE AIR!!...
YAARGH-H-H-H!!!

KALU!! WE KNOW YOUR POWER-- AND WE BEG FORGIVENESS!!! WHAT WILL YOU DO NOW???

RISE UP FROM THE PIT, MAN OF A DISTANT LAND!!! RISE WITH YOUR DEATH WOUNDS FRESH AND BLEEDING!!!

AS BEFORE, A GHASTLY BEING EMERGES FROM THE PIT, DEAD AND YET NOT DEAD-- A KNIFE-RIDDEN MASS OF HUMAN FLESH!!...
UGH-H-H!!! AARGH-H!!!

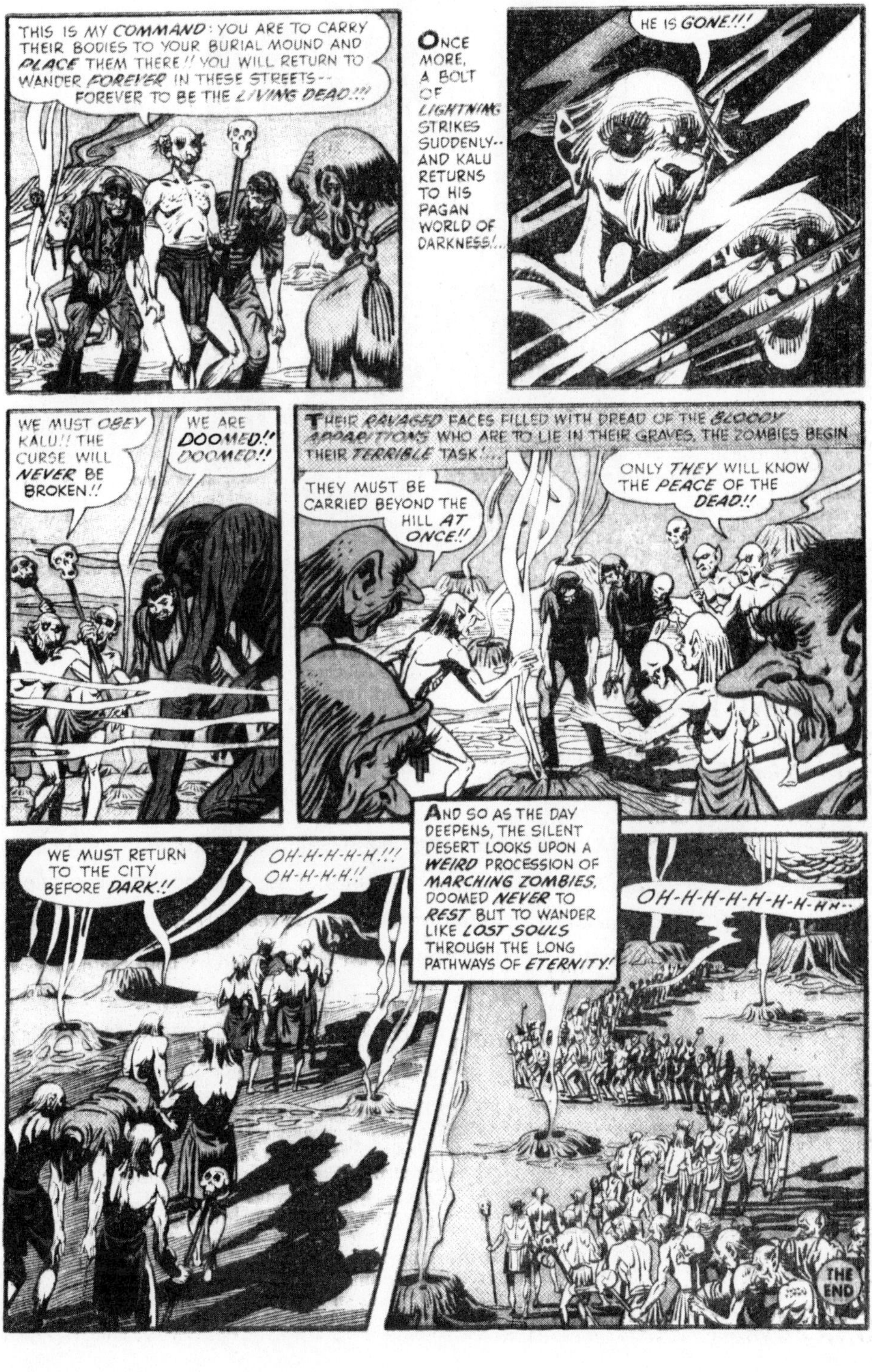

ONCE MORE, A BOLT OF LIGHTNING STRIKES SUDDENLY.. AND KALU RETURNS TO HIS PAGAN WORLD OF DARKNESS!..

WE MUST OBEY KALU!! THE CURSE WILL NEVER BE BROKEN!!

WE ARE DOOMED!! DOOMED!!

THEIR RAVAGED FACES FILLED WITH DREAD OF THE BLOODY APPARITIONS WHO ARE TO LIE IN THEIR GRAVES, THE ZOMBIES BEGIN THEIR TERRIBLE TASK!...

THEY MUST BE CARRIED BEYOND THE HILL AT ONCE!!

ONLY THEY WILL KNOW THE PEACE OF THE DEAD!!

WE MUST RETURN TO THE CITY BEFORE DARK!!

OH-H-H-H-H!!! OH-H-H-H!!

AND SO AS THE DAY DEEPENS, THE SILENT DESERT LOOKS UPON A WEIRD PROCESSION OF MARCHING ZOMBIES, DOOMED NEVER TO REST BUT TO WANDER LIKE LOST SOULS THROUGH THE LONG PATHWAYS OF ETERNITY!

OH-H-H-H-H-H-H-HH..

THE END

Grave Rehearsal

Strange Fantasy 7, August 1953

The whip-wielding Madam Satin could only have plied her trade in a title by the name of *Strange Fantasy*. There are hints of sadomasochism in a tale that savoured the macabre delight of premature burial and the rejuvenating stimulus of a mud bath. An odd combination and a far cry from Edgar Allan Poe's original, but nonetheless disturbing. The Ajax Farrell group employed the production-line approach endorsed by the Iger Studios; in fact Jerry Iger served as art director to Ajax-Farrell Publications for a couple of years when his studio closed down in 1955. While there are those who criticize their often prosaic art, there was no doubt that their team was adept in the delineation of beautiful women.

IT WAS ONE EASY STEP FOR B. S. FITTS, EGOMANIACAL YELLOW TABLOID PUBLISHER, FROM JOURNALISTIC MUD-SLINGING TO HEALTH RESORT MUD-BATHING. FITTS FAILED TO REALIZE, HOWEVER, THAT THE NEXT EASY STEP WOULD LEAD TO THE GRAVE...
GRAVE REHEARSAL
THROW HIM INTO THE MUD-GRAVE!
NO! NO! I'M AN IMPORTANT MAN OF CONSEQUENCE! YOU CAN'T DO THIS TO... AA-AAAAAAGHHH!!
"B. S. FITTS, PUBLISHER OF THE DAILY WHISPER, A FOUL, FILTHY, BUT HIGHLY PROFITABLE SCANDAL-SHEET, ADMONISHES A CRINGING EDITOR...
PIG-BRAIN! YOU KNOW MY ORDERS! GIVE 'EM SENSATION! CRAM EVERY SENTENCE WITH LURID DETAILS! GLUT THE PUBLIC WITH ACCOUNTS OF FIENDISH MURDERS, CHEATING WIVES, VICE EXPOSES, ETC... THE SWINE LOVE IT!
AND WHAT HAVE YOU BEEN PRINTING, PIG-BRAIN? —DECENT NEWS STORIES!! WHAT ARE YOU TRYING TO DO, FOOL? RUIN THIS SHEET? YOU'RE FIRED!!
PLEASE, MR. FITTS—YOUR DOCTOR WARNED YOU NOT TO OVER-EXCITE YOURSELF! YOU MUST TRY TO CONTROL YOUR TEMPER!
GET OUT-TTT, YOU SLIMY SNEAK, BEFORE I BREAK YOU IN TWO! OUT-TTT! OH-HH... M-MY SIDE...
SOMEONE GET A DOCTOR! "B. S." HAS HAD AN ATTACK! SOMEONE GET HELP!

WHAT DO YOU MEAN I NEED A LONG REST? ARE YOU TRYING TO SABOTAGE ME, TOO? WHO'S PAYING YOU TO LIE TO ME? I'LL HAVE YOU INVESTIGATED! I HAVE FRIENDS IN WASHINGTON!
UNLESS YOU FOLLOW MY ADVICE, MR. FITTS, YOU'LL DIE... SOON! AND ALL YOUR BLUSTERING WON'T HELP YOU... AFTER YOU'RE DEAD!
AFTER THE MEDICO DEPARTS, FITTS FALLS INTO A DEEP FIT OF DEPRESSION...
THEY'RE ALL AGAINST ME! BUT IT'S TRUE, I NEED A REST. PITKIN! WHY IN BLAZES ARE YOU PUSSY-FOOTING IN? ANSWER ME, MAN!
A PACKAGE FOR YOU, SIR. FROM ABROAD. IT'S FROM THE "GEHARGIT HEALTH RESORT" IN TRANSVANIA. SHALL I OPEN IT FOR YOU, SIR?
MUD? IS SOMEBODY CRAZY? WAIT! THERE'S A NOTE WITH IT. IT SAYS... "IF YOU ARE TROUBLED BY NERVES, RUB THIS ON YOUR FACE, AND RELAX." IT'S SIGNED BY A "MADAME SATIN"!
YIELDING TO ONE OF HIS FREQUENTLY UNPREDICTABLE IMPULSES, FITTS SMEARS THE MUD ON HIS FEATURES. MINUTES LATER, THE BUTLER IS SUMMONED BY A WILD CRY OF PLEASURE...
GOOD HEAVENS, SIR! YOUR FACE! WH-WHAT'S HAPPENED TO Y-YOUR FACE?
STOP GAPING! CHARTER A PRIVATE PLANE FOR ME! I'M FLYING TO TRANSVANIA AT ONCE! I FEEL FINE! SPLENDID! WELL, DON'T JUST STAND THERE! GET MOVING, PITKIN!
YOU WERE EXPECTING ME?
BUT, OF COURSE! WELCOME TO TRANSVANIA, MR. FITTS. I KNEW YOU WOULD BE UNABLE TO RESIST OUR UNUSUAL HEALTH TREATMENTS. IT'S WHAT YOU HAVE ALWAYS BEEN LOOKING FOR... THE ANSWER TO YOUR HEALTH NEEDS!
I SENT NO WIRE! HM-M... THAT'S RATHER PECULIAR!
I HOPE YOUR RESORT WILL MEASURE UP TO MY EXPECTATIONS.
WHAT AN ODD RING! A MINIATURE, LEERING DEATH-SKULL!
YOU WILL NOT BE DISAPPOINTED, SIR. WE HAVE SOME UNIQUE SURPRISES IN STORE FOR YOU, MR. FITTS... SOME UNIQUE SURPRISES, INDEED! VERY UNIQUE!
2

"B.S." SPENDS THE FIRST DAY IN BED...
I DIDN'T FLY ALL THE WAY TO TRANSVANIA FOR THIS! UNLESS I GET SOME ACTION SOON, I'LL CABLE MY ATTORNEYS! IF THEY'RE TRYING TO MAKE A FOOL OF B.S. FITTS, THEY'LL BE VERY SORRY. B.S. FITTS IS NOT TO BE TRIFLED WITH!
BUT...THE NEXT DAY...
STRIP! REMOVE YOUR GARMENTS, MR. FITTS! DON'T DAWDLE, PLEASE! TAKE THEM OFF!!
WHAT? —(HARUMPH!)— NOW WAIT! EXPLAIN FIRST WHAT YOU HAVE IN MIND. I HAVE A RIGHT TO KNOW!
DOWN TO YOUR SHORTS! HEIDT... GOTTFREY... HELP HIM TAKE OFF HIS GARMENTS!
LET GO! I DON'T NEED ANY HELP! I CAN TAKE MY OWN CLOTHES OFF! TAKE YOUR HANDS OFF ME!
WORDLESSLY, HIS ESCORTS LEAD FITTS TO A STRANGE SIGHT IN AN OPEN FIELD...
PEOPLE... STRETCHED OUT IN MUD-HOLES, RESEMBLING GRAVES! SURELY, YOU DON'T EXPECT ME TO...? WAIT! LET'S TALK THIS OVER! LET'S NOT GET RIDUCULOUS!
GET INTO THE HOLE! GET IN, I SAY! OR DO YOU NEED HELP?
NO! I WON'T DO IT! IT... IT ISN'T DIGNIFIED! I WON'T BE BULLIED BY FOREIGNERS! I — I'LL...
THROW HIM IN! PAY NO ATTENTION TO HIS PROTESTS! ONCE HE GETS INSIDE THE HOLE, HE'LL LOVE IT!
THE INDIGNANT PUBLISHER IS FORCED INTO THE SLIPPERY MUCK. SPLASHING ABOUT, HE YELLS ANGRILY...
I'LL CALL THE POLICE! I WON'T STAND FOR THIS! I DEMAND TO SEE THE AMERICAN AMBASSADOR!
I'M MASTER HERE! YOU'LL DO AS I SAY, OR FEEL THE STING OF THE LASH! LIE STILL ON YOUR BACK! DON'T MOVE UNTIL I ORDER YOU TO!
COWED BY THE STRANGE WOMAN'S COMMAND, AND THE FIRE IN HER EYES, FITTS OBEYS, THEN HE RECEIVES A PLEASANT SURPRISE...
I LIIIIKE IT! IT FEELS GOOOOOD! OH, WHAT A WONDERFUL SENSATION! I NEVER DREAMT THAT ROLLING IN STICKY MUD COULD BRING SUCH HEAVENLY ECSTASY!
3

IN THE DAYS THAT FOLLOW, "B. S." WALLOWS HAPPILY IN THE MUD-HOLE LIKE A CONTENTED HOG. STEADILY, HIS ENTHUSIASM FOR THE STRANGE HEALTH TREATMENT RISES..
SO YOU LIKE IT NOW, EH? YOU CAN'T HAVE ENOUGH OF IT? IT MAKES YOU FEEL GOOD ALL OVER? I KNEW YOU WOULD ENJOY IT!
MY BODY IS TINGLING WITH NEW LIFE! I FEEL THIRTY YEARS YOUNGER! I HAVEN'T FELT THIS CALM AND RELAXED FOR YEARS! IT'S A MIRACLE!
MADAME SATIN... YOUR WONDERFUL HEALTH TREATMENTS ARE SUPERB! WHAT IS THE EXPLANATION FOR THIS REMARKABLE PHENOMENON? I MUST KNOW! PLEASE TELL ME!
THIS LAND HAS BELONGED TO MY FAMILY FOR GENERATIONS. WE HAVE ALWAYS KNOWN OF THE MUDS REMARKABLE CURATIVE POWERS. ONCE MY FAMILY WAS WEALTHY AND POWERFUL. THE RICHES ARE GONE, BUT STILL I LIVE OFF THE LAND.
A MARVEL LIKE THIS SHOULD BE SHARED BY ALL HUMANITY! IT'S TOO BIG A THING NOT TO BE PROPERLY EXPLOITED! DO YOU AGREE?
I AGREE. BUT THERE IS THE LITTLE MATTER OF FINANCES. IT TAKES MONEY TO PUBLICIZE AND FURTHER A GREAT CAUSE...
SOME HAVE BEEN KIND ENOUGH TO OFFER LARGE DONATIONS... AND MAKE THE RESORT THE SOLE BENEFICIARY IN EVENT OF THEIR UNTIMELY DEMISE. IT IS A MOST GENEROUS OFFER ON THEIR PART! IF ONLY MORE WOULD GIVE, PERHAPS THE HOPE YOU ENVISION COULD COME TRUE!
AGAIN THE PSYCHOTIC PUBLISHER YIELDS TO AN UNPREDICTABLE IMPULSE...
GIVE ME ONE OF THOSE LEGAL FORMS! WHERE DO I SIGN? QUICK! SHOW ME! WHERE DO I WRITE MY SIGNATURE?
RIGHT THERE! AT THE SPOT MARKED "X"!
BUT LATER THAT NIGHT, IN THE DARKNESS OF HIS GLOOMY ROOM, B. S. REGRETS HIS HASTY DECISION...
BLAST MY INFERNAL ENTHUSIASM! IT CARRIED ME AWAY! I'LL ASK MADAME SATIN TO RETURN THE FORM TO ME TOMORROW. I DON'T KNOW WHAT CAME OVER ME! I MUST LEARN TO EXERCISE MORE CAUTION!
ULP! WHERE D-DID YOU COME FROM SO SUDDENLY? I DIDN'T SEE ANYONE COME IN! DON'T YOU EVER BOTHER TO KNOCK?
WE'VE COME FOR YOU, MR. FITTS. YOU HAVE PROGRESSED TO THE POINT WHERE YOU ARE ENTITLED TO THE "SPECIAL TREATMENT"!
THE SPECIAL TREATMENT IS RESERVED FOR SPECIAL PATIENTS!
4

SOON... FITTS STANDS IN A FIELD, DESERTED EXCEPT FOR MADAME SATIN, HER STARING ASSISTANTS, HIMSELF, AND SOME STRANGE EQUIPMENT...
INTO THE HOLE! GET IN, B.S. FITTS!
BUT... IT'S EMPTY! THERE'S NOTHING IN IT! WHY SHOULD I CRAWL INTO AN EMPTY HOLE? IT DOESN'T MAKE SENSE!
IT WON'T BE EMPTY LONG! POUR IT ON HIM!
THIS ISN'T MUD! IT'S... GOOD GRIEF! IT... IT CAN'T BE! NO! IT COULDN'T POSSIBLY BE...
CEMENT! YOU'RE FILLING THE HOLE W-WITH CEMENT!! UH-HHH!
SILENCE HIM! BASH HIS HEAD! SHUT THAT STUPID, EVER CLACKETING TONGUE!
B.S. FITTS REVIVES TO FIND HIMSELF ENCASED IN A QUICK-HARDENING CEMENT BLOCK THAT IS BEING HOISTED ONTO A TRUCK...
I CAN'T BUDGE! LET ME OUT OF THIS, Y-YOU FIENDS! WHERE ARE YOU TAKING ME?
HA-HA! HE WANTS TO KNOW WHERE HE'S GOING! TELL HIM, MADAME SATIN!
WHERE IT'S COLD-AND LONELY-AND VERY, VERY DEEP!
TO HIS EVER-INCREASING HORROR, FITTS IS DRIVEN, IN HIS HARDENING-PRISON, TO A NEARBY...
CEMETERY! Y-YOU'RE TAKING ME TO A...CEMETERY! WHY? WHY? TELL ME, MADAME SATIN!
I SAID... YOU ARE GOING WHERE IT IS COLD... LONELY... AND DEEP! AS DEEP AS... A GRAVE!
FITTS REFUSES TO BELIEVE THE TERRIBLE TRUTH UNTIL A CRANE BEGINS LOWERING HIM INTO A FRESH-DUG GRAVE...
WHY??? WHY ARE YOU DOING THIS TO ME? WHY???
YOU SIGNED AN IMPORTANT DOCUMENT, REMEMBER? SILLY MAN! YOU CONSIDER YOURSELF A SMART BUSINESS MAN, BUT I HAVE OUTWITTED YOU! HA-HA!
NOW THAT YOU HAVE SUDDENLY DIED OF UNKNOWN CAUSES, YOUR RICHES BELONG TO ME! EVERY CENT OF IT... EVERY WONDERFUL PENNY! AND IT WILL RUN INTO MILLIONS!
BURIED ALIVE!! YAAA-AAA!!
5

"B.S." IS DEAD. NO LONGER WILL HE BULLDOZE WAGE-SLAVES. NO LONGER WILL HE SCREAM ORDERS. IMPORTANT PEOPLE WILL NO LONGER CATER TO HIM. NOW HE HAS ONLY THE WORMS FOR COMPANY...
AND SO PASSES B. S. FITTS, ESQUIRE... THE WORLD WILL BE BETTER OFF WITHOUT THE SWINE! IT WAS A PLEASURE TO MURDER THE VERY IMPORTANT MR. FITTS!
MADAME SATIN RETURNS TO THE SCENE OF HER MACABRE TRIUMPHS...
MANY HAVE DIED IN THE MUD-GRAVE PITS TO SWELL MY COFFERS. BUT NOW THE GRISLY BUSINESS IS AT AN END. FITTS' RICHES WILL ENABLE ME TO RETIRE INTO GRACIOUS RESPECTABILITY...
BUT MADAME SATIN HAS NOT COUNTED ON THE TENACITY, EVEN THOUGH HE IS DEAD, OF THE TERRIBLE-TEMPERED, IMPULSIVE MR. FITTS!
WHO-OOO... ARE... YOU-OO...? WHO-OOO? WHO-OOO?
LIKE YOU-OO ...VICTIMS... OF MADAME SATIN... LIKE YOU-OOO! LIKE YOU!
ARE YOU-OOO MICE, OR ARE YOU-OOO GHOSTS? — REVOLT! — MAKE THAT WITCH PAY FOR HER CRIMES! FOLLOW ME, FELLOW SPECTRES! REVOLT! DOWN WITH MADAME SATIN!
REVOLT!
REVOLT!
OUT OF THE MUD-GRAVES THEY SPILL... PHANTOMS INTENT ON VENGEANCE... LED BY THE ANGRY SPECTRE OF B.S. FITTS.
NO! NOT THE CEMENT-DEATH! NOOO-OOOOOO! PLEASE SPARE ME! IT'S—(SPUTTER)— FILLING MY MOUTH... GAGGING ME! GAAAAA!
THEY FOUND A GREAT STONE BLOCK IN A MUD-HOLE THE NEXT MORNING... AND PROTRUDING FROM IT WAS...
A HAND... WEARING THE DEATH-SKULL RING OF MADAME SATIN! LOOK! THE DEATH-SKULL IS GRINNING!
BUT MOST ASTOUNDING OF ALL... IN THE NEWS ROOM OF THE DAILY WHISPER...
THE FULL HORRIBLE DETAILS OF FITTS' DEATH...! AND THE STORY IS SIGNED BY FITTS HIMSELF! THE PRESS SERVICE DENIES SENDING THE STORY!
TRUST "B. S." TO FILE A SENSATIONAL YARN, EVEN AFTER DEATH!
The End

A Glimpse of the Pit

Horrific 9, January 1954

Horrific was Comic Media's companion to *Weird Terror*; in its thirteen-issue run before changing its title to *Terrific* as a result of the Comics Code, it proved equally as nasty. Artist Pete Morisi, a former cop, is best remembered for his gritty *Johnny Dynamite* strip, also published by Comic Media; his style lent itself to the genre of horror. A friend of Don Heck's, he could use light and dark effects that would have you looking over your shoulder. To some it appears stark, but his style kept him in gainful employment for most of his life. There was an appreciable trend in the horror comics of these years to resort to the gruesome which Pete was never comfortable with; instead he suggested the terror at hand, preferring to leave it to the reader's vivid imagination.

A GLIMPSE OF THE PIT

HERE ONCE AGAIN TO THRILL YOU... TO CHILL YOU... IS THAT MYSTERIOUS NARRATOR OF THE UNKNOWN, THE TELLER!

GREETINGS, LOVERS OF THE OCCULT. I'M SURE YOU'VE MET MY ASSOCIATES HERE... EVEN IF YOU DIDN'T RECOGNIZE THEM AT THE TIME! FROM LEFT TO RIGHT... FREDDY DEMON, GARRY GHOUL, VICTOR VAMPIRE AND WALTER WEREWOLF.

TALES OF HATE by THE TELLER

TALES OF HATE

TALES OF HORROR by THE TELLER

OUR FIRST TALE IS ONE THAT SHOULD BE MARKED, "WARNING! DANGER AHEAD!"... AND UNDERLINED IN RED! IT'S PARTICULARLY APPROPRIATE FOR FREDDIE DEMON HERE TO TELL US. SO, START US OFF, FREDDIE...
YES! OH YES... THIS IS MY MEAT! THIS IS THE TALE OF DORIS DUNCAN, A RICH, SPOILED GIRL. YOU SEE, DORIS' SISTER, ...

...BUT, SUPPOSE WE START AT AN INTERESTING PART OF THE STORY THAT HAPPENED JUST THE OTHER DAY. DORIS WAS ENGAGED A FEW MONTHS AGO TO A YOUNG MAN NAMED HARMON SMITH, BUT SHE SUDDENLY DISAPPEARED. THEN, SEVERAL DAYS AGO....

HARMON SMITH SPOTTED HER IN THE PUBLIC PARK.
NOW, CHILDREN! GENTLY, GENTLY!
DORIS! DORIS DUNCAN! AND OF ALL PLACES...

SHEEP HERDING A BUNCH OF RAGGED KIDS... REALLY! WHY DID YOU RUN OUT ON ME?
I SUPPOSE I DO OWE YOU AN EXPLANATION. SIT DOWN, HARMON. IT'S A LONG STORY!

"OF COURSE YOU KNOW THAT MY OLDER SISTER IRIS AND I WERE BROUGHT UP BY OUR MILLIONAIRE UNCLE, OLD JACOB. WE WERE SPOILED SNOBS, CRUEL AND HEARTLESS...
BUT I DON'T SEE WHAT...?

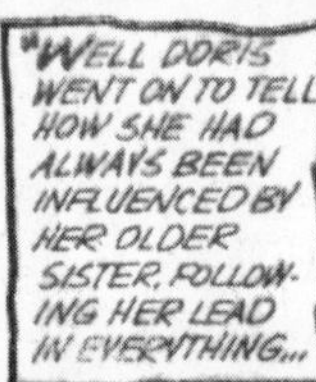
"WELL DORIS WENT ON TO TELL HOW SHE HAD ALWAYS BEEN INFLUENCED BY HER OLDER SISTER, FOLLOWING HER LEAD IN EVERYTHING...

YOU MARRY THAT SMITH BOY, DORIS. HE HAS MILLIONS, AND THAT'S WHAT COUNTS! I KNOW ...HAVEN'T I MARRIED THREE RICH MEN MYSELF!
YES, DORIS. I KNOW YOU'RE RIGHT, BUT...

BUT NOTHING! IT'S MONEY THAT MAKES THE WORLD GO ROUND. REMEMBER THAT!
I... OH, ALRIGHT. I'LL MARRY HIM.

SPEAKING OF MONEY, UNCLE JACOB THERE IS LOADED WITH IT... AND WHEN HE DIES, IT'S ALL OURS! I WISH HE'D DROP DEAD, THE OLD SKINFLINT... AND I THINK I KNOW A WAY TO HURRY HIM ALONG!
IRIS! YOU DON'T MEAN YOU'D...

BUT IRIS DID MEAN IT! AS USUAL, POOR DORIS WENT ALONG. IRIS HAD A PLAN, AND SO LATER THAT NIGHT...
EVERYONE KNOWS HE'S ECCENTRIC, THAT HE COLLECTS OLD TORTURE WEAPONS AND THAT HE EVEN SLEEPS IN A BED WITH A FALLING CANOPY OF SPIKES, JUST TO BE DIFFERENT! ALL WE HAVE TO DO IS PULL THE STEEL PIN THAT KEEPS THE CANOPY UP, AND...
IT WOULD BE MURDER!

IT'S ONLY MURDER IF YOU'RE CAUGHT AT IT! PEOPLE WILL THINK IT WAS AN ACCIDENT... THE PIN SLIPPED OUT. WHO'D SUSPECT US? COME ON... WE'LL DO IT RIGHT NOW!
NO IRIS! PLEASE DON'T MAKE ME GO!

IRIS LED THE WAY INTO THE OLD MAN'S BED-ROOM, AND DORIS WENT ALONG... UP TO A POINT!
BUT HE'S BEEN GOOD TO US, IRIS, AND... NO! NO, I WON'T LET YOU DO IT!
SHUT UP, YOU LITTLE FOOL!

NO, IRIS! COME AWAY FROM THERE!
LET GO OF ME! IF YOU WAKE HIM UP, I'LL KILL YOU TOO!

THERE!
OH, NO! NOOOO!

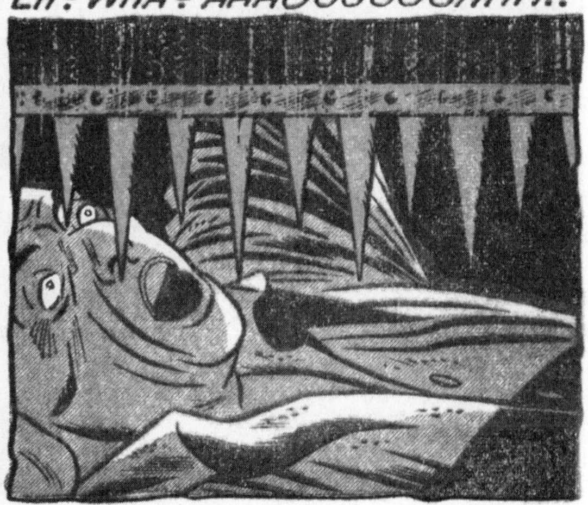
EH? WHA? AAAGGGGGGHHH!!

OOHH! HOW HORRIBLE! HOW CAN I GO ON LIVING, KNOWING OF THIS!?
PERHAPS IT'S BETTER IF YOU DON'T GO ON LIVING, MY SWEET! AFTER ALL, YOU MIGHT TELL SOMEONE. BESIDES I WANT ALL THE MONEY!

IRIS! N-NO PLEASE, NO! DON'T!

SORRY, SISTER DEAR! BUT MY MIND IS MADE UP!

OOOH DORIS, HELP!

IRIS!
EEEEAAAGGH!!

DORIS RACED MADLY DOWNSTAIRS, EXPECTING TO FIND IRIS' SHATTERED BODY ON THE TERRACE BELOW...

BUT SHE WAS WRONG! FOR INSTEAD OF A MANGLED BODY ON THE STONE...

SHE FOUND IRIS, APPARENTLY IN A TRANCE, FOLLOWING A VOICE THAT IRIS ALONE COULD HEAR! FASCINATED, HYPNOTIZED, DORIS FOLLOWED...
I HEAR YOU! I HEAR YOU! YES, I'M COMING!

ACROSS THE FIELDS, THROUGH THE ANCIENT GRAVEYARD, AND INTO THE VERY MOUTH OF A TOMB ITSELF SHE FOLLOWED!

DOWN SLIMY STONE STEPS DORIS FOLLOWED HER SISTER, HELD IN THE GRIP OF A SHUDDERING COMPULSION, UNABLE TO TURN BACK, UNTIL...

SHE'S GONE! AND I'M ALONE! I'M LOST IN THIS HOUSE OF DEATH!

THAT LIGHT... PERHAPS IT'S A WAY OUT! OR...CAN IT BE IRIS? I MUST SEE WHAT....

IRIS!! BUT IT CAN'T BE! SUCH HORRORS LIVE IN DREAMS! AM I GOING MAD?

I DON'T BELIEVE IT! I MUSTN'T LET MYSELF BELIEVE IT! BUT...

YES... YES! I'M COMING!
BUT IT IS IRIS, AND IT IS TRUE!

AND STILL DORIS FOLLOWED, UNTIL AT LAST... SHE SAW...
NO! NO! NOT THERE! I DIDN'T MEAN TO HURT ANYBODY!

NO! PLEASE! EEEE!

I KNOW WHERE 'THERE' IS ...BUT I MUST SEE FOR MYSELF... OOOOHHH! I BURNED MY HAND! BUT I MUST SEE...

AND SO, FOR ONE ETERNAL MOMENT, DORIS STARED DOWN INTO... INTO...

I... HAVE... SEEN... THE VERY... DEPTHS... OF...
DORIS! DORIS DUNCAN! HEAR ME!

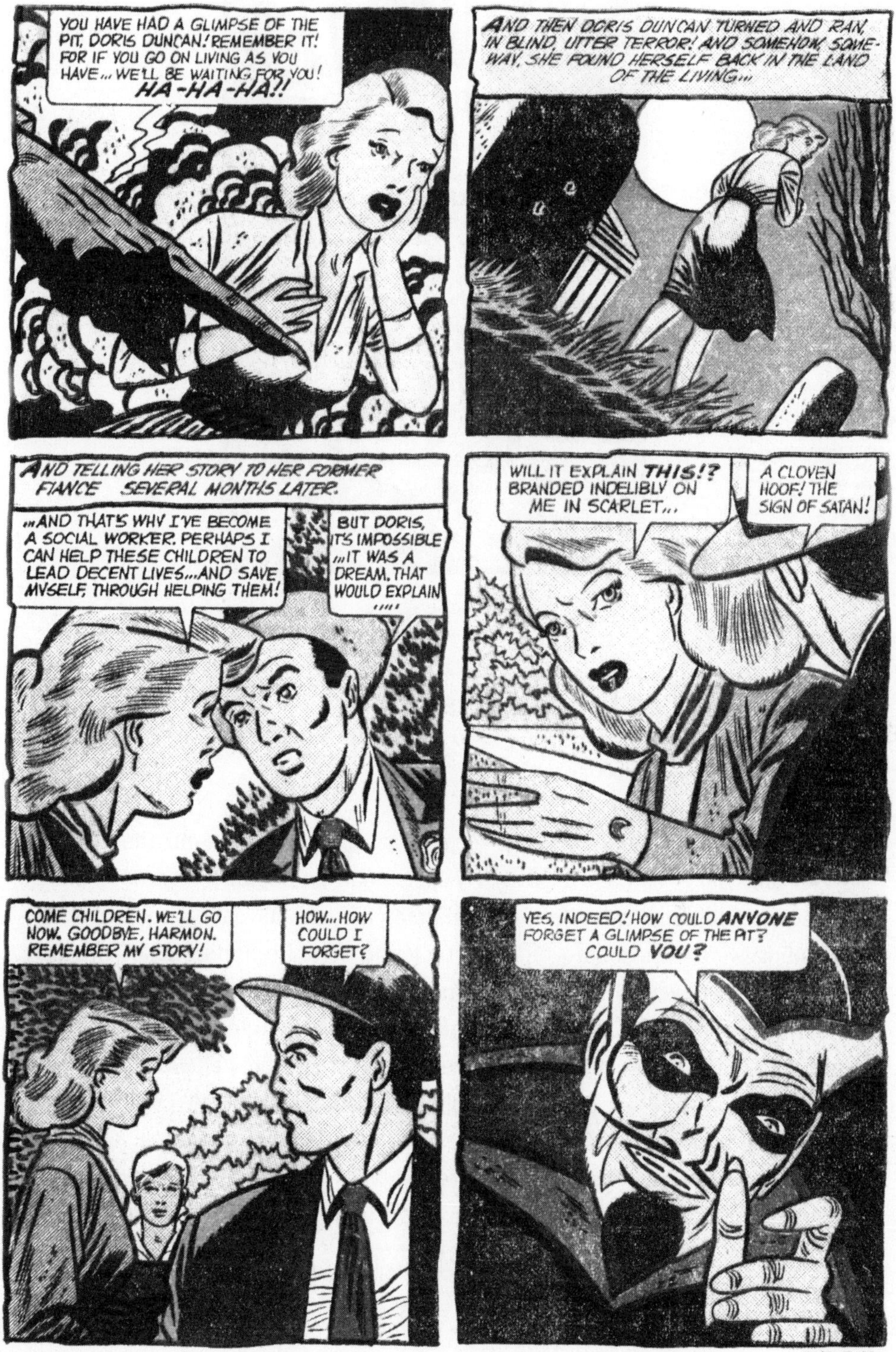

YOU HAVE HAD A GLIMPSE OF THE PIT, DORIS DUNCAN! REMEMBER IT! FOR IF YOU GO ON LIVING AS YOU HAVE... WE'LL BE WAITING FOR YOU! HA-HA-HA!!

AND THEN DORIS DUNCAN TURNED AND RAN, IN BLIND, UTTER TERROR! AND SOMEHOW, SOME-WAY, SHE FOUND HERSELF BACK IN THE LAND OF THE LIVING...

AND TELLING HER STORY TO HER FORMER FIANCE SEVERAL MONTHS LATER.

...AND THAT'S WHY I'VE BECOME A SOCIAL WORKER. PERHAPS I CAN HELP THESE CHILDREN TO LEAD DECENT LIVES...AND SAVE MYSELF, THROUGH HELPING THEM!

BUT DORIS, IT'S IMPOSSIBLE ...IT WAS A DREAM. THAT WOULD EXPLAIN ....

WILL IT EXPLAIN THIS!? BRANDED INDELIBLY ON ME IN SCARLET...

A CLOVEN HOOF! THE SIGN OF SATAN!

COME CHILDREN. WE'LL GO NOW. GOODBYE, HARMON. REMEMBER MY STORY!

HOW...HOW COULD I FORGET?

THE END

The Horror of the Walking Corpse

Dark Mysteries 16, February 1954

Fans of *Dark Mysteries* were in for a treat when this issue hit the stands. Not only did it contain tales by Hy Fleishman and John D'Agostino, there were an additional two offerings containing a dozen surreal pages from A. C. Hollingsworth – seven of which can be found here. Born in 1928, Alvin Carl Hollingsworth was already working in comics when he was only twelve years old, as an assistant at Holyoke Publishing; he later helped out on Catman Comics. Like many of his fellow creators he would provide work for many of the major, and not so major, publishers of the 1940s and 1950s. When this tale appeared in *Dark Mysteries 16*, he was also producing *Kandy*, a strip syndicated by the Associate Press in well over a hundred newspapers. His fine arts degree led to a career in art, producing works whose themes covered contemporary social issues, such as the Civil Rights Movement.

WELCOME GHOULS, TO ANOTHER WELL FERTILIZED DARK MYSTERY OF A GREEDY SISTER PLOTTING FOR AN INHERITANCE– BY LYING, CHEATING, MURDERING! WATCH OUT READERS, FOR HER SOUL IS AS SLIMY AND PUTRID AS THE DECAYING BONES IN THE GRAVE! I KNOW... I AM THE GRAVE KEEPER NOW, HEH! HEH!
The HORROR of the WALKING CORPSE
by A.E. Hollingsworth
NOT LONG AGO, THIS REEKING, DECAYING THING WAS AUSTIN BARLO, A RESPECTED, LOVED MAN. WHEN HE DIED SUDDENLY, NEIGHBORS AND FRIENDS CAME FROM FAR AND WIDE TO MOURN HIM AND BURY HIM...
AUSTEN BARLO
R.I.P.
THE RACKING SOBS OF ANN, THE FARMER'S WIDOW AS SHE HURLED HERSELF ON THE FRESH GRAVE CAUSED TEARS TO FLOW IN MANY EYES..
AUSTEN. I CANNOT LEAVE YOU, EVEN IN DEATH!
AUSTEN BARLO
THIS REEKING, SMELLY CORPSE, RISEN FROM HIS SLIMY GRAVE SEEKING, SEEKING, WAS ONCE AUSTEN BARLO, PROSPEROUS HARD WORKING FARMER, HAPPILY MARRIED TO THE SIMPLE BUT ADORING, ANN. ONLY AFTER DEATH, DID THE EVIL IN THE FAMILY COME FORTH. AND A SUDDEN, STRANGE POWER IN THE EARTH FORCED THE DEAD TO RISE AND SEEK RETRIBUTION!

ANN'S POOR SISTER, PRISCILLA, AND HER HUSBAND, PETER, KEPT CLOSE TO ANN - SO CLOSE, THAT ANN FELT LIKE A PRISONER.
IT'S LUCKY WE LIVE CLOSE BY SO WE CAN BE NEAR YOU IN YOUR SORROW!
TH-THANK YOU, PRISCILLA. BUT PLEASE LEAVE ME ALONE FOR A WHILE!
OF COURSE, AUSTEN WAS NOT ALWAYS A PUTRID DECAYING THING OR A NEWLY DEAD CADAVER. ONCE HE WAS A LOVING, SUCCESSFUL FARMER, ASSISTED BY HIS ADORING ANN.
YOU DON'T HAVE TO HELP ME, ANN, OUT HERE.
I CAN NEVER LEAVE YOU, AUSTEN!

AND THEY HAD A STRANGE FRIEND, JACOBUS, WHO SOLD THEM FERTILIZER AND ALSO ADORED THE FAITHFUL ANN...
YOU SELL US FERTILIZER TO MAKE US RICH AND GIVE US COMPANY TO MAKE US HAPPY!

YAH, YOU ARE MY FRIENDS, I SHALL ALWAYS TRY TO HELP YOU!

BUT NOW, EVERY NIGHT, FOR MANY NIGHTS AFTER THE FUNERAL ANN STOLE AWAY TOWARD THE COLD AND LONELY GRAVE WHERE HER BELOVED AUSTEN LAY AND STAYED UNTIL DAWN..

AUSTEN, AUSTEN, I CAN'T BEAR IT WITHOUT YOU. YOU WERE SO FAITHFUL!

AS ANN'S EYES LIGHTED ON HER OWN NAME MARKED ON THE DOUBLE GRAVE-STONE JUST AS SHE HAD ORDERED, AN EMOTION OF WILD JOY SEIZED HER.

SOMEDAY I WILL LIE NEXT TO YOU FOREVER, MY DARLING!

ONE NIGHT RETURNING HOME FROM THE GRAVE, ANN FOUND PRISCILLA AND PETER WAITING, STRAINED, FIXED SMILES ON THEIR LIPS. THEY HAD LEARNED THE SECRET OF HER NIGHTLY VISITS...

ANN, DEAR, WE'VE COME TO LIVE WITH YOU FOR A WHILE. AND KEEP YOU AWAY FROM THAT GRAVE!
IT'S NOT RIGHT FOR YOU TO VISIT AUSTEN'S GRAVE EVERY NIGHT!
WHAT SHALL I DO? HOW CAN I GET OUT TO BE WITH AUSTEN!

PREVENTED FROM VISITING AUSTEN'S GRAVE, ANN DECIDED ON A NEW, MACABRE PLAN ...

YES! I'LL BRING AUSTEN HERE! BARNEY WILL HELP ME!

THE NEXT DAY, DOWN AT THE BARN, ANN IS PLEADING FRANTICALLY WITH OLD BARNEY, THE HANDYMAN...

BARNEY, YOU MUST HELP ME GET AUSTEN'S BODY, WE WILL BRING HIM TO MY ATTIC. HELP ME AND I'LL PAY YOU WELL!

IT SOUNDS *CRAZY* BUT I'LL DO IT!

UGH!
AND SO THE EMBALMED DECAYING CORPSE OF AUSTEN WAS STEALTHILY BROUGHT TO THE MUSTY OLD ATTIC AND TENDERLY PLACED ON AN OLD SOFA BY ANN AND BARNEY...
NOW, MY BELOVED, I CAN COME TO YOU EVERY NIGHT- UNTIL I JOIN YOU IN ETERNITY!

AND NIGHTLY, ANN VISITED THE DEAD AUSTEN...

FEARFUL SHE WOULD SOON BE CAUGHT WITH AUSTEN'S BODY, ANN BEGAN TO CALL ON MR. WILKENS, THE UNDERTAKER.

AND SO MR. WILKENS, I WANT THE NEW MAUSOLEUM BUILT. WILL YOU TAKE CARE OF THE DETAILS- MAKE IT AS BIG AS MY ESTATE WILL BUY- AND HURRY!
IF YOU INSIST, MRS. BARLO..
REST IN PEACE

ONE DAY, BACK AT ANN'S HOUSE, HER SISTER AND BROTHER-IN-LAW WERE ANGRILY DISCUSSING HER...
SHE STILL SNEAKS OUT WITHOUT OUR KNOWING? WHAT'S SHE UP TO?
I'VE WATCHED THE CEMETERY. SHE DOESN'T GO THERE!
3

ONE THING IS CERTAIN, HUSBAND, SHE CAN'T LAST LONG GOING ON AS SHE IS - AND THEN I INHERIT THE WHOLE FARM!
YOU'RE A SMART GIRL, PRISSY!
A FEW YEARS AGO, PRISCILLA WAS A LITTLE GIRL PLAYING WITH HER SISTER, ANN, TODAY HER GREED-BITTEN SOUL PLAYED WITH EVIL MACHINATIONS...
PETER, I FOUND OUT WHERE ANN WAS TODAY. SHE VISITED THE UNDERTAKER!
D'YA THINK WE SHOULD PAY HIM A CALL TOMORROW, DEAR?

TWO HUMAN SPIDERS SAT IN THE UNDERTAKER'S OFFICE THE NEXT DAY, SEEMINGLY SPINNING THEIR WEB...

YES, PRISCILLA, YOUR SISTER-IN-LAW ORDERED AN ELABORATE MAUSOLEUM FOR HER HUSBAND'S REBURIAL AND PLANS TO ALTER HER WILL SO THAT HER ESTATE WILL COVER THE COSTS!

HER MIND'S A LITTLE UNSETTLED, YOU KNOW!

REST IN PEACE

AT BREAKFAST, THE NEXT MORNING, AFTER ANN'S NIGHTLY VIGIL WITH THE BODY OF AUSTEN - UP IN THE ATTIC, PRISCILLA MAKES A DESPERATE EFFORT TO DISTRACT ANN FROM GOING TO THE LAWYER'S....

ANN, DEAR, I'M WORRIED ABOUT YOU, NO MAN DESERVES SO MUCH DEVOTION AS YOU'RE GIVING AUSTEN'S MEMORY!
YOU'LL NEVER UNDERSTAND THE DEPTH OF OUR LOVE!

THEN THE PLOTTERS HATCHED THEIR EVIL SCHEME...
PETER WAS THE TOWN PHOTOGRAPHER AND KNEW ALL THE TRICKS OF HIS TRADE...

I HAVE A PLAN. ALL THOSE OLD PICNIC PICTURES, I WILL USE THEM TO MAKE INTIMATE PICTURES OF AUSTEN AND YOU AND I'LL ALSO REWRITE SOME LETTERS!

ALL THAT NIGHT, PRISCILLA AND PETER WORKED FEVERISHLY, CUTTING, PASTING AND PHOTOGRAPHING MONTAGES AND REPASTING PARTS OF LETTERS AND PRISSY PLAYED HER HAND...

WH- WHAT'S THIS? **NO!** YOU AND AUSTEN! I DON'T BELIEVE IT! AND IN THIS LETTER HE SAYS HE LOVES YOU!

I HAD TO CONFESS, ANN- TO SAVE YOU FROM WASTING YOUR LOVE ON A DEAD MAN WHO BETRAYED YOU!

RAGE AND FURY FILLED THE SEETHING MIND OF THE SHOCKED ANN AS SHE SAW THE FAKE ROMANTIC POSES BETWEEN HER SISTER AND HER ADORED HUSBAND...

I'M SORRY, ANN, BUT AUSTEN AND I LOVED EACH OTHER!
AND I PLANNED TO KILL MYSELF TO BE WITH HIM. I EVEN WROTE A SUICIDE NOTE! HOW HE FOOLED ME!
4

ALL THE GRIEF AND HEART-ACHE IN ANN TURNED TO WILD HATRED AND FURY THAT NIGHT.

YOU MONSTER! MAKING LOVE TO MY OWN SISTER! PRETENDING TO ADORE ME! I WILL GET RID OF YOU FOREVER!

WITH SUPERHUMAN STRENGTH, ANN AND BARNEY DRAGGED THE CORPSE OF HER HUSBAND FROM THE ATTIC, ACROSS THE FIELDS, UNDER A WILLOW TREE WHERE SHE HAD DUG A GRAVE....

THERE! YOU CAN ROT HERE! THE GRAVEYARD IS TOO GOOD FOR YOU!

I HATE YOU! I HATE YOU!

SOON PRISCILLA WAS READY WITH PART TWO OF HER HASTY PLAN. IN ANN'S BEDROOM, PRISCILLA PUT SLEEPING PILLS IN HER NIGHTLY GLASS OF MILK...

THIS WILL KNOCK YOU OUT, MY PRETTY SISTER!

WITH COLD CALCULATION, PRISCILLA WENT ABOUT HER MURDEROUS TASK AS HER SISTER SLEPT IN A DRUGGED SLEEP...

A PERFECT SUICIDE! THE GRIEF-STRICKEN WIFE! THIS GAS WILL KILL YOU!

PRISCILLA'S PLANS WORKED TO PERFECTION. WHEN ANN'S NOTE WAS FOUND HER DEATH WAS CALLED SUICIDE -OF COURSE AUSTEN'S BODY WAS FOUND MISSING

WHAT A TERRIBLE TRAGEDY! BUT AUSTEN'S GRAVE IS EMPTY! WHERE'S HIS BODY?

NOW PETER AND PRISCILLA OWNED THE FARM AND WORKED HARD TO INCREASE THE PROFITS...

IT'S GOOD TO OWN THE PLACE AT LAST, PETER!

WE'LL BE RICH, BEFORE I GET THROUGH WITH IT!

AS THEY GLOATED OVER THEIR NEW PROPERTY, PETER AND PRISCILLA WERE STARTLED BY THE APPEARANCE OF THE QUEER LITTLE MAN, JACOBUS...

REMEMBER, I ALWAYS SOLD AUSTEN FERTILIZER? I HAVE A NEW BRAND, IT WILL MAKE YOU RICH! YOU MUST PUT IT UNDER THE OLD WILLOW TREE AND YOU CAN HAVE IT FREE!
GIVE IT TO US, WE PROMISE!
5

JACOBUS WAS CONVINCING, THEY TOOK THE FERTILIZER, AND PROCEEDED TO SOW THE FARM WITH IT...

EAGERLY THE TWO SOWED THE MIRACLE FERTILIZER - AND AS THEY PROMISED JACOBUS.. UNDER THE WILLOW TREE...
THE FERTILIZER WILL HAVE TO BE GOOD TO MAKE THINGS GROW OVER THIS AREA!

TO THE DELIGHT OF THE AMBITIOUS PRISCILLA AND PETER, THE MIRACLE FERTILIZER DID ITS WORK - WITH AMAZING RESULTS...
LOOK! I'VE NEVER SEEN SUCH GROWTH - SUCH FERTILITY!
PETER, WE'RE RICH!

THE FERTILIZER WAS INDEED PERFORMING MIRACLES BUT IT ALSO FERTILIZED AUSTEN'S CORPSE! AT THE EDGE OF THE FARM, THE SHALLOW GRAVE WAS OPENING...

WHAT POWER WAS BEING WORKED ON THE EARTH THAT THRUST FORTH, EVEN THE DEAD?

ON CREAKING JOINTS, THE FERTILIZED SKELETON OF AUSTEN, THE AXE SPLITTING HIS CRANIUM, GREW STRONG.. IT ROSE FROM THE GRAVE AND GAZED TOWARD THE FARM WHERE PETER AND PRISCILLA NOW LIVED...

PLODDING SLOWLY BUT INEXORABLY, THE BONY FIGURE TOOK A STRAIGHT PATH TOWARD THE HOUSE...

PLODDINGLY, THE REEKING THING ENTERED THE HOUSE...

WAKED FROM A PEACEFUL SLEEP FILLED WITH DREAMS OF WEALTH AND POWER, PRISCILLA AND PETER LAY FROZEN IN HORROR, PARALYZED... AS THEY SAW AUSTEN'S SKELETON BESIDE THEM...
G-GO AWAY... YOU'RE DEAD!
UGH... WH-WHAT DO-YOU - WANT?

WHAT DID AUSTEN'S SKELETON WANT? YOU HAVE YOUR ANSWER, PETER AND PRISCILLA!

BUT NOW, WHERE ARE YOU GOING, AUSTEN? HAVEN'T YOU FINISHED YOUR MISSION?

IS IT ANN YOU'RE SEEKING, AUSTEN? SHE LIES LONELY, MURDERED, IN HER GRAVE, BESIDE YOUR EMPTY ONE...
BAY
CEM

A WEIRD SOUND OF CLANKING BONES, SUDDENLY ECHOED THROUGH THE CEMETERY AND BROUGHT THE WATCHMEN, WONDERING, FRIGHTENED...
WHAT WAS THAT? MAYBE THE GHOULS!

THE MEN HURRIED IN THE DIRECTION OF THE EERIE SOUND...
IT CAME FROM THERE...

AUSTEN'S WALK WAS ENDED. AT LAST HE CAME TO REST OVER HIS WIFE'S GRAVE...
IT'S AUSTEN BARLO'S REMAINS! BUT WHY, HOW? LET'S RE-BURY IT NEXT TO HIS WIFE, QUICK!
ANN BARLO
THE END

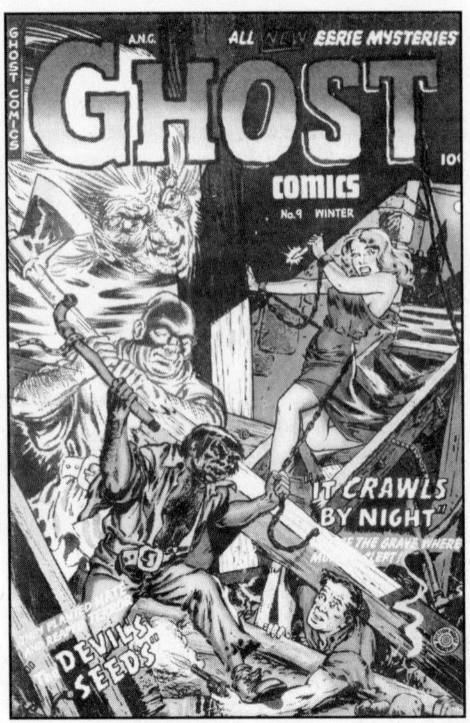

The Thing That Walked at Night

Ghost Comics 9, Winter 1953

There is something crisp about the work of Bill Benulis and Jack Abel. Their collaboration always seemed ideally suited to science fiction; alas, those tales of alien worlds, rocket ships and robotic subversion did not enjoy such great popularity. Here is a chance to see them at work within the tenebrous embrace of horror. This offering from Fiction House reveals a clever pacing, one that takes this strip beyond the boundaries of juvenile entertainment.

The THING THAT WALKED AT NIGHT
OUT OF THE DEAD BLACK NIGHT IT CAME... A BUBBLING SCREAM FROM LIPS THAT WERE NOT HUMAN! AND THE DULL ECHO OF IT HUNG HEAVILY ON THE CLOSE AIR IN FRED ACKERS' BEDROOM, SENDING CHILLS OF FEAR RACING THROUGH HIM AND HIS SLEEP-DAZED WIFE... THEN, THEY WERE SHADOWS, CROUCHED IN THE HALLWAY, LOOKING FOR... THE THING THAT WALKED AT NIGHT!
Benulis Abel
THERE WAS SILENCE NOW, BUT THE DREAD WAS THERE IN THEIR POUNDING HEARTS...
IT CAME FROM OUTSIDE, ALICE! AND IT WAS HER VOICE...
IMPOSSIBLE, FRED! THE DOOR'S LOCKED AND THE WINDOWS ARE BARRED!
THERE WAS NOT A SOUND FROM WITHIN THE ROOM, AS THEY OPENED THE DOOR...
WHY, SHE'S NOT HERE! NO ONE'S HERE! BUT HOW DID SHE...
THE WINDOW... GREAT SCOTT! LOOK AT IT...
THE HEAVY DUTY METAL BARS BENT LIKE STRAW TOLD FRED ACKERS AND HIS WIFE A MUTE TALE...
SUCH A FRAGILE LITTLE THING... HOW COULD THIS HAPPEN, FRED?
I DON'T KNOW! THERE WAS SOMETHING ODD ABOUT HER FROM THE BEGINNING... REMEMBER?

FRED ACKERS' THOUGHTS CARRIED HIM BACK FIVE YEARS; BACK TO THAT DAY BOTH HE AND HIS WIFE HAD GONE TO THE ORPHANAGE. THE INTERVIEW WITH THE SUPERINTENDANT HAD BEEN VERY PLEASANT...

...FOR HE SEEMED TO UNDERSTAND THEIR PROBLEM CLEARLY...

MANY MARRIED COUPLES WHO CANNOT HAVE CHILDREN OF THEIR OWN COME HERE. ADOPTION IS BECOMING A COMMON CUSTOM AND, I THINK, A MOST WISE ONE.

THEY'D LOOKED AT DOZENS OF CHILDREN, BUT ONLY ONE HAD MADE AN IMPRESSION ON ALICE...

NAME'S JOAN. PARENTS DIED DURING WORLD WAR II. SHE'S AN ATTRACTIVE CHILD, ALMOST BRILLIANT AT TIMES...HOWEVER, THERE IS ONE THING I OUGHT TO TELL YOU...

I DON'T THINK IT MATTERS, SIR; SEEMS LIKE MY WIFE'S ALREADY MADE UP HER MIND.

IT WAS LITTLE JOAN THEY'D TAKEN HOME WITH THEM...

SHE'S SUCH A DEAR, FRED! I-I'M JUST AWFULLY GRATEFUL TO YOU!
IT'S THANKS ENOUGH, DARLING, THAT YOU LOVE HER AND ARE HAPPY!

ALMOST FOUR YEARS HAD PASSED, THEN ONE NIGHT A LATE PHONE CALL...

EVERYTHING'S JUST FINE, DAN...SURE, PROWLER? AROUND YOUR PLACE? WELL, I NEVER... HEADED HERE? HA, YOU MUST BE MISTAKEN, OR MEBBE SOMETHING YOU ATE...OF COURSE, I'M SURE...

REPORTS PILED IN OF A "THING" THAT PROWLED AT NIGHT; A HAGGISH SHAPE THAT PURSUED SMALL ANIMALS...

EVEN WHEN THE FINGER POINTED AT JOAN, FRED ACKERS WOULD NOT PART WITH HER...

YOU'LL BE SAFE HERE NOW, JOAN BABY! THE BARS AND THE DOOR WILL PROTECT YOU FROM, FROM...
HE MEANS IT WILL KEEP YOU FROM ROAMING THE NIGHT, DEAR!

AND SHE HAD BEEN KEPT SAFE, UNTIL TONIGHT! FRED AND ALICE WAITED LONG, TORTUROUS HOURS...

OH DEAR HEAVEN, I HOPE NOTHING'S HAPPENED, I...
HUSH! SOMETHING MOVING OUTSIDE THE WINDOW...

SLOWLY, SOFTLY AND WITH LABORED BREATHING, A MISSHAPEN THING CLIMBED TOWARD THE ROOM...

ALTHOUGH THEY HAD KNOWN, NEVER HAD EITHER OF THEM SEEN THE GIRL IN THE MIDST OF ONE OF HER SEIZURES, BUT NOW ....
OH FRED...NO! I-I FEEL FA-A-AINT... OOOH!
G-GOOD HEAVENS! IT CAN'T BE!

THIS WAS THE CHILD THEY HAD TAKEN INTO THEIR HOME! THIS WAS THE THING THAT WALKED AT NIGHT...
RAAAAAAAAAA

A FEW MINUTES LATER THE DOORBELL WAS JANGLING HARSH AND LOUD...
RRIIIIIIIIIINGGG
QUICK, ALICE! PULL YOURSELF TOGETHER! GET THE CHI...THE... HER TO BED AS FAST AS YOU CAN. YOU'RE NOT AFRAID?
NO, FRED-- NOT AFRAID. YOU ANSWER THE DOOR!

A BABBLE OF ANGRY VOICES GREETED HIM WHEN HE OPENED THE DOOR...

WHY, BILL, JOE, JIM... WHAT'S UP?

TIME FOR A SHOWDOWN, FRED! THAT HAG OR THING OR WHATEVER IT IS HAS BEEN PROWLING AGAIN. LOOK HERE...

THE BOX LID WAS LIFTED TO REVEAL THE TWISTED MANGLED BODIES OF DOGS AND CATS, LYING QUIETLY DEAD...

YOU'RE MISTAKEN...ALL OF YOU! NOW GET OFF MY PROPERTY BEFORE I CALL THE POLICE! GET OFF!
THE TRACKS LEAD HERE, FRED, WE'LL GO NOW, BUT THE NEXT TIME, FRED, THE NEXT TIME...
3

AT FIRST, FRED AND ALICE TRIED TO SHUT THEIR EYES AND EARS TO THE TERRIBLE TRUTH. BUT AS TIME WENT ON, EVEN THEY WERE FORCED TO SEE THINGS AS THEY WERE...

AND ONE NIGHT, AS THE WIND WENT WHISTLING THROUGH THE TREES...

I'M PRETTY SURE I SAW SOMETHING LEAVE FRED ACKERS' PLACE!

SHHH! LOOK THERE, FELLAS... SOMEONE COMING!

IN THE MOONLIGHT, THEY SAW HER RUNNING DOWN A FRIGHTENED DOG...

BUT AS SHE STARTED TO PASS THE MEN, A LASSO HISSED TOWARD HER...

GOT THE DEVIL! NOW, CLOSE IN AROUND HER...
RAAAAAAAAAAAA

LIKE A BEAST SHE WHIRLED AND THEY SAW HER FACE FULL IN THE MOON-LIGHT...

FROM ANOTHER POSITION, FRED ACKERS WATCHED--STUNNED...

SHE'S GOT DAN STROUT. SHE'LL-- SHE'LL KILL HIM, SURE! GOTTA STOP HER...
URRRAAAA.....

JOAN! JOAN! RUN, THEY'RE COMING. THEY'LL GET YOU. RUN HOME, QUICKLY. GO NOW!

SOMEHOW HIS VOICE PENETRATED HER DULL BRAIN AND SHE'D RUN OFF TOWARD HOME--BUT FRED'S MIND WAS AWHIRL...

IT STARTED WITH ANIMALS. NOW HUMANS. NEXT THING'LL BE M-MURDER...NO, I CAN'T ALLOW THAT. I CAN'T...

AT HOME, BEFORE THE FIRE, THE VAGUE THOUGHTS BEGAN TO TAKE SHAPE IN FRED'S MIND...

IT WAS THE NEXT MORNING THAT HE SPOKE TO ALICE...

YOU LOOK WORRIED, FRED. IT'S JOAN, I KNOW...BUT WHAT CAN WE DO?
I'VE MADE THE DECISION, DEAR... THE ONLY DECISION THAT CAN BE. SHE'S GOT TO DIE BEFORE SHE KILLS SOMEONE!

FRED COULD ALMOST FEEL THE ANGUISH ALICE FELT AT THAT MOMENT...

NO, FRED! THERE MUST BE ANOTHER WAY. WE-WE'LL MOVE AWAY FROM HERE, WE'LL...

YOU DIDN'T SEE HER LAST NIGHT, ALICE. I'VE THOUGHT IT ALL OUT...THIS IS THE ONLY WAY. DON'T YOU SEE, I LOVE HER TOO MUCH TO WANT ANYTHING TO HAPPEN TO HER!
YOU MEAN THOSE MEN WOULD K-KILL HER? OH, NO!

ALICE FINALLY AGREED AND THEY TOSSED A COIN TO SEE WHO WOULD DO IT...

I UNDERSTAND NOW, FRED, THERE...
WHY, YOU'VE CALLED IT. IT'S HEADS. Y-YOU'VE ELECTED YOURSELF TO DO THE JOB...

FRED DIDN'T SEEM TO NOTICE THAT HIS WIFE QUICKLY PALMED THE **DOUBLE-HEADED** COIN SHE HAD TOSSED...

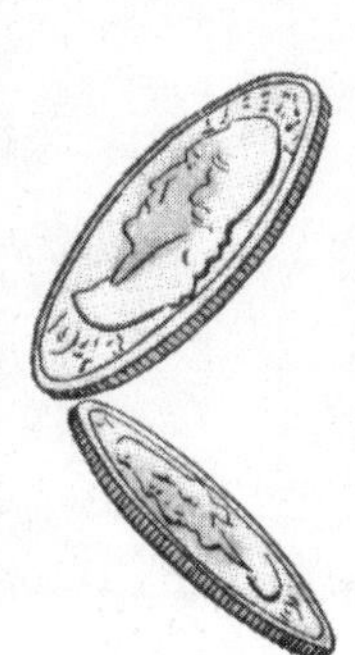

SO NOW THE PLAN WAS SET. FRED HANDED HER A HARD, COLD METAL OBJECT...

BE CAREFUL, IT'S LOADED. TOMORROW... OUT IN THE COUNTRY SOMEWHERE... WE'LL PRETEND IT'S A PICNIC...

NEXT MORNING, FRED DROVE THEM FAR OUT INTO THE COUNTRY...

BEAUTIFUL DAY, ISN'T IT?
WONDERFUL. I-I WISH IT COULD LAST FOREVER...JUST THIS ONE DAY, AND...

FRED KNEW ALICE WAS SOFTENING, IN A MOMENT HE'D BE SOFTENING HIMSELF...

NOW, ALICE--NOW, TAKE HER INTO THOSE TREES THERE AND DO IT!
Y-YES FRED!

FRED WATCHED THEM GET UP, WATCHED ALICE LEAD THE CHILD OFF ABOUT FIVE YARDS...

COME ON, JOAN--YOU AND I WILL PICK SOME OF THOSE WILD FLOWERS OVER THERE!

HE SAW THEM STOP, AND HE SAW ALICE TURNING TOWARD HIM--SLOWLY...

ALICE! WHAT ARE YOU STOPPING FOR? GO ON, GO ON...HEY WHAT'RE YOU DOING...

HE HEARD THE SHARP REPORT, SAW THE GUN-SMOKE, FELT THE IMPACT OF SOMETHING HITTING HIS CHEST...

ALICE, NO...NO... I...OOOH!
BLAM
BLAM

FRED, FRED...I'M SORRY. THERE WAS NO OTHER WAY AT ALL. AND IF YOU'D KNOWN THE TRUTH--EVEN YOU WOULD HAVE AGREED...

HE NEVER KNEW AND I COULD NEVER TELL HIM THAT YOU ARE MY REAL DAUGHTER, JOAN...THAT YOU WERE BORN AS THE ATOM BOMB FELL WHILE I WAS A PRISONER OF WAR AT HIROSHIMA! SHE REALLY ISN'T DANGEROUS, FRED!

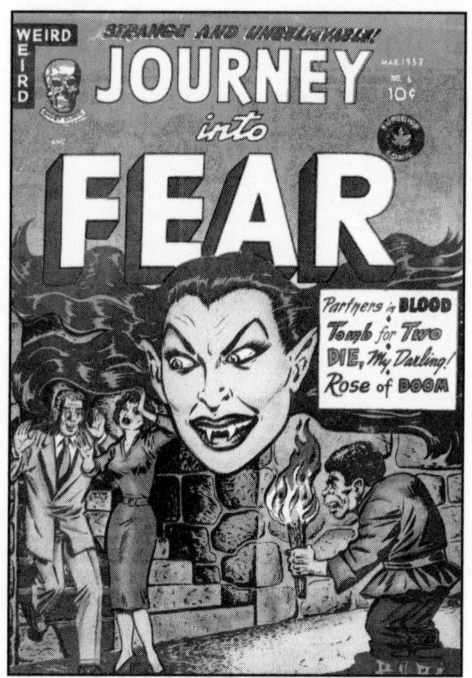

Partners in Blood

Journey into Fear 6, May 1952

Canada's Superior Comics had a dependence on Jerry Iger's team of artists. In this instance the artwork is far from being prosaic. Although it follows the distinctive style associated with the studio, there are traces of the sumptuous aspects found in the work of Matt Baker, Jack Kamen and Al Feldstein. The nature of the story also begs a few questions in that there is a discernible air of eroticism at play. Superior Comics were no strangers to eroticism, as the covers to titles such as *Brenda Starr* will attest.

Partners in BLOOD
For centuries it brooded by the turgid Rhine, a crumbling pile of lost hopes and bloody memories! At night a woman screamed there—and fearful villagers shunned it as they would the devil! Vampir Schloss—they called it! Castle of Vampires...
One dank night in November, a car leaves Cologne and heads south along the Rhine...
This is a dangerous thing, Herr Martin! Visiting Vampir Schloss!
But so exciting!
A scientist cannot be a coward! Drive on.
Hours later...
There, Herr Martin! Vampir Schloss! Please let us turn back!
Uncle! It—it is forbidding!
All the better, Rose. No one will bother us.

THE ROAD TWISTS SUDDENLY AND...
HIMMEL! SOMEONE IN TROUBLE.
A WOMAN ALL ALONE.
STOP, HANS! MAYBE WE CAN BE OF ASSISTANCE.
WILL YOU GIVE ME A LIFT PLEASE! MY CAR HAS SMASHED A WHEEL.
OF COURSE! BUT WE'RE ONLY GOING TO— TO THE CASTLE YONDER. IF YOU DON'T MIND...

NO—I AM NOT SUPERSTITIOUS. AND I KNOW ALL THE STORIES ABOUT THE VAMPIR SCHLOSS!
GOOD! BUT ALLOW ME— I AM PROFESSOR MARTIN. THIS IS MY NIECE, ROSE. WE ARE GOING TO LIVE AT THE CASTLE.

HERE WE ARE! NOW IF THE MAN I HIRED HASN'T RUN AWAY...
UNCLE HAD A TERRIBLE TIME FINDING A SERVANT. FINALLY HE GOT A DWARF.

GREETINGS, HERR MARTIN! EVERYTHING IS READY.
THERE YOU ARE, TOR! FINE! BETTER GET OUR LUGGAGE INSIDE!

LATER...
I AM THE BARONESS VON ERICH. DOES THE NAME MEAN ANYTHING TO YOU, PROFESSOR MARTIN?
VON ERICH! THAT'S THE FAMILY THAT USED TO LIVE IN THIS CASTLE! FOR CENTURIES!
OH—A REAL BARONESS!

YES — THE SAME FAMILY. I AM THE LAST. NOW I LIVE IN A LITTLE COTTAGE NOT FAR AWAY. I SELDOM COME HERE! BUT IF YOU WILL LET ME STAY UNTIL MY CAR CAN BE REPAIRED...
OF COURSE, BARONESS.
SOON...
GOODNIGHT..TOR WILL SHOW YOU THE BEDROOMS. SEE YOU TOMORROW.
GOODNIGHT, UNCLE.
YOU ARE KIND, PROFESSOR MARTIN.
OHH — ISN'T IT SPOOKY? BUT UNCLE IS DETERMINED TO KNOW IF VAMPIRES REALLY EXIST!
VAMPIRES! THOSE OLD STORIES! HAH-HAH — BUT I WON'T LET ANYTHING HAPPEN TO YOU, MY DEAR.
YOU ARE LOVELY, MY DEAR! SUCH A SOFT, WHITE COMPLEXION...
T-THANK YOU, BARONESS! GOODNIGHT!
HER HANDS— SO COLD!
SECONDS LATER...
THIS WAY, BARONESS! DOWN AND DOWN! THE COFFINS HAVE NOT BEEN DISTURBED. YOU WILL SLEEP WELL!
FOOL! BUT I FORGIVE YOU. AND I SHALL NOT SLEEP TONIGHT. THERE IS WORK TO DO.
GOODNIGHT, BARONESS. DO NOT FRIGHTEN THE LITTLE ONE.
I WILL NOT FRIGHTEN HER! SHE IS TOO SWEET— TOO TENDER.
3

WHILE BELOW, PROFESSOR MARTIN IS EXULTING...
I WAS RIGHT TO COME HERE! THIS OLD BOOK—THERE WAS A VAMPIRE IN THE VON ERICH FAMILY! A WOMAN WHO DIED IN 1543 AND CAME BACK AS A VAMPIRE! WHAT A PAPER THIS WILL MAKE FOR THE PSYCHIC SOCIETY!
A BAT! A REGULAR GIANT!
C—CAN'T SEEM TO CATCH IT! OUT OF B-BREATH! BUT I SUPPOSE IT'S HARMLESS!
SQUEEEEE—EEE—
YOU'LL NEVER KILL THAT BAT, OLD FOOL.
WHILE UPSTAIRS...
BRRRR—I CAN'T SEEM TO GET WARM! BUT I MUST OPEN A WINDOW! HOPE UNCLE DOESN'T WORK TOO LATE.
I WONDER IF THERE REALLY ARE VAMPIRES! UNCLE SEEMS TO THINK SO. WELL—MAYBE WE'LL KNOW SOON.
4

VAMPIRES! HAH-HAH- YOU'LL KNOW SOON, MY DEAR. JUST AS YOU SAY.
SLEEP WELL, MY LOVELY! SOON YOU SHALL BE AS I AM.
AHA- SO YOUNG AND SOFT...
SUDDENLY A RAT SQUEALS IN TERROR AND FALLS FROM ITS LEDGE IN THE WALL...
A-A RAT! HELP- UNCLE- AAAAAAAAAAAA...
CURSE THAT RAT! BUT THERE WILL BE OTHER TIMES... TOMORROW NIGHT!
5

NEXT MORNING...
BUT I CAN'T STAY HERE, UNCLE! I WON'T! NOT AFTER LAST NIGHT!
BUT ROSE, MY WORK...
WHAT'S ALL THIS ABOUT LEAVING?
PROFESSOR MARTIN TOLD THE BARONESS WHAT HAPPENED DURING THE NIGHT...
THERE, MY DEAR. I'LL FIX IT. YOU CAN STAY AT MY COTTAGE.
FINE! AND I CAN WORK HERE IN PEACE.
WELL— ALL RIGHT.
HER HANDS AGAIN! LIKE ICE.

AND SOON...
THIS IS ALL THAT IS LEFT OF THE VON ERICH FORTUNE, ROSE. BUT I AM CONTENT HERE.
BUT IT'S LOVELY. SO DIFFERENT FROM THE CASTLE.
YOU CAN REST SAFELY HERE! NO RATS, I ASSURE YOU.
UGH—DON'T REMIND ME! IT WAS HORRIBLE.

THAT NIGHT...
NOW! NOTHING WILL STOP ME THIS TIME! I AM SO THIRSTY! SO THIRSTY...
SOMETHING AWAKENS ROSE...
OHH—SUCH A FUNNY DREAM! MY THROAT! A LITTLE SORE.
DO NOT BE AFRAID, GIRL! YOU MUST OBEY! YOU ARE ONE OF US NOW. DO YOU UNDERSTAND?
ONE OF Y-YOU! YES—I UNDERSTAND. I AM NOT AFRAID OF YOU.
GOOD! YOU ARE A VAMPIRE NOW, ROSE! YOU WILL BE IMMORTAL.
YES. I OBEY. I AM A VAMPIRE NOW.
7

AT THAT MOMENT, IN THE CASTLE...
N-NO! IT CAN'T BE! STILL, PUT HER IN MODERN CLOTHES AND IT'S THE BARONESS! AND ROSE IS WITH HER! I'VE GOT TO BE SURE!
I SEE YOU HAVE FOUND HER, PROFESSOR MARTIN. MY POOR ANCESTOR! THEY CALLED HER A VAMPIRE!
BARONESS! Y-YES, I WAS JUST THINKING HOW MUCH ALIKE YOU ARE.
POOR WOMAN! THEY BURNED HER, YOU KNOW.
I MUST BE CRAZY, BUT THERE'S ONE SURE TEST FOR VAMPIRES. THIS MIRROR WILL SHOW!
SUDDENLY...
YOU! THERE IS NO IMAGE! YOU ARE THE VAMPIRE!
NO—GET IT AWAY FROM ME! I HATE MIRRORS, YOU FOOL!
HAH-HAH—SO YOU KNOW! MUCH GOOD IT WILL DO. I HAVE YOUR NIECE! FOOL-FOOL! SHE IS MINE.. MINE!
NO—YOU LIE! YOU FIEND! WHERE IS ROSE? WHAT HAVE YOU DONE?
MAD WITH RAGE AND GRIEF, THE PROFESSOR LEAPS AT THE VAMPIRE...
YOU FORGET THAT I KNOW VAMPIRES AND HOW TO KILL THEM. AND I CAME PREPARED!
NO-NOT THE STAKE! GET AWAY FROM ME!
8

AFTER A CHASE, THE PROFESSOR CATCHES THE VAMPIRE ON THE ANCIENT BATTLEMENTS...
NOW — THIS STAKE THROUGH YOUR EVIL HEART! ONCE MORE — AND AGAIN AND AGAIN...
AAAAAAAAAAA..
BUT AS HE TURNS FROM HIS GRISLY TASK...
ROSE! WHAT ARE YOU DOING, ROSE?
YOU KILLED HER! MURDERED MY FRIEND! I WANTED TO BE WITH HER! NOW I KILL YOU!
NO — I'M YOUR UNCLE— AHHHHHHHHH...
I HATE YOU! DIE — DIE! I AM A VAMPIRE NOW.
GOOD! YOU HAVE SLAIN HIM... NOW WE ARE FREE- JUST WE TWO! WE WILL LIVE IN THE CASTLE FOREVER— TOGETHER!
YES, TOR! JUST THE TWO OF US. TAKE ME AWAY QUICKLY!
OH— WE'LL FALL! BE CAREFUL, TOR.
FALL! HO-HO- I NEVER SLIP— AGGGGGG...
EEEEEEE!
AND SO THE VAMPIR SCHLOSS STILL STANDS AND BROODS. THERE ARE BATS, AND RATS AND OTHER THINGS TOO. THE VILLAGERS STILL FEAR IT AND AVOID IT, AND AT NIGHT THEY CAN HEAR SCREAMS THAT FREEZE THE BLOOD AND STOP THE HEART. THE PSYCHIC SOCIETY IS LOOKING FOR ANOTHER MAN TO TAKE THE PLACE OF PROFESSOR MARTIN. PERHAPS YOU ARE UN-EMPLOYED...
The End

Dead Man's Revenge

Shocking Mystery Cases 50, September 1952

It was 1952, boom time for the horror comic. *Shocking Mystery Cases* seemingly graced the news-stands as a newcomer, but had actually appeared as the crime title *Thrilling Crime Cases* for a couple of years. In the 50th issue, publisher L. B. Cole was lured by the ever-burgeoning horror phenomenon. This tale, exquisitely rendered by Jay Disbrow, is essentially a crime caper. Both the cover and the story within, however, contain an element of H. P. Lovecraft's "Herbert West – Reanimator" along with the more familiar creation of Mary Wollstonecraft Shelley, "Frankenstein"; although it should be remembered she was still Mary Godwin at this time in her life.

Star Comics was the creation of L. B. Cole and his friend Jerry Kramer. With only five staff they released a variety of comic books until their demise in the face of the ravages of the Comics Code. L. B. Cole's hallucinogenic covers would have had no place in the controlled world of the Code.

DEAD MAN'S REVENGE
by JAY DISBROW
BANG! BANG!
WARNING:- DO NOT TAMPER WITH THE FORCES OF NATURE! DEATH AND DISASTER MAY FOLLOW WHEN ONE DELVES INTO THE MYSTERIES OF THE UNKNOWN AND FERRETS OUT THE HIDDEN SECRETS OF LIFE.
THIS IS THE STORY OF A SCIENTIST WHO REFUSED TO HEED THIS WARNING: HIS ONE DESIRE WAS TO CREATE HUMAN LIFE IN HIS LABORATORY, AND HE SUCCEEDED IN DOING SO; BUT THE CONSEQUENCES THAT FOLLOWED WERE CATASTROPHIC.
IN A DINGY THIRD AVENUE TAVERN, ON NEW YORK CITY'S EAST SIDE---
YOU'RE PROFESSOR REARDON, THE FAMOUS SCIENTIST, AREN'T YOU? WHAT ARE YOU DOING IN A CRUMMY JOINT LIKE THIS? I THOUGHT YOU NEVER LEFT YOUR UPTOWN BROWNSTONE.
WHA--- OH, IT'S MR. NICK RAMONO, THE INFAMOUS KING OF THE UNDERWORLD!--- WHY AM I HERE?--- BECAUSE I'M A FAILURE! I FAILED TO COMPLETE THE GREATEST UNDERTAKING IN THE HISTORY OF MAN!
YEAH, I HEARD THAT YOU WERE STYMIED ON ONE OF YOUR EXPERIMENTS. HOW ABOUT TELLING ME ALL ABOUT IT? WHAT'S HOLDING YOU UP?
A BRAIN--- A HUMAN BRAIN!--- YOU ARE AN UNDERSTANDING MAN, SO I WILL TELL YOU ABOUT IT.
FOR YEARS MY ONE AMBITION WAS TO CREATE HUMAN LIFE, AND TOWARD THIS END I LABORED DAY AND NIGHT IN MY LABORATORY. BUT I NEEDED HUMAN TISSUE. THE ONLY WAY I COULD GET IT, WAS TO STEAL IT FROM A GRAVE YARD, AND THIS I DID, WITH THE AID OF MY YOUNG ASSISTANT, PETER DIKE.
1

"AND SO WE UNEARTHED GRAVE AFTER GRAVE, SELECTING ONLY THOSE PARTS OF EACH CORPSE THAT WERE BEST PRESERVED, FROM WHICH WE HOPED TO CONSTRUCT A COMPLETE BODY. MIND YOU NOW, I AM NO LURID THRILL SEEKER, NOR AM I A COMMON THIEF; BUT NOTHING MUST INTERFERE WITH THE COURSE OF TRUE SCIENCE, AND IN THIS CASE, THE ENDS JUSTIFIED THE MEANS!"

"WE TOOK THE BODIES BACK TO MY LABORATORY, AND THROUGH A PROCESS OF GRAFTING AND DELICATE INTERFUSION, WE SLOWLY BEGAN THE CONSTRUCTION OF A 'MAN-MADE-MAN.' THE HEAD WAS HUGE AND EXTREMELY GROTESQUE, THE ARMS WERE LONG AND UNGAINLY, BUT IT WAS THE BEST THAT WE HAD TO CHOOSE FROM.
READY WITH THE ELECTRO-THERAPY REJUVENATOR PROFESSOR.
TURN IT ON, PETER!

"NEXT CAME THE PROBLEM OF SUPPLYING BLOOD TO THE CREATURE, AND WE OVERCAME THIS DIFFICULTY BY BOTH DONATING A PINT OF BLOOD ONCE EVERY TWO WEEKS. WE MADE UP THE DEFICIENCY BY CONSUMING LARGE AMOUNTS OF LIVER AND VITAMIN B COMPLEXES. SOON WE HAD THE FOURTEEN PINTS WE NEEDED."
THE SUBJECT IS READY FOR TRANSFUSION, SIR!
ATTACH THE INJECTTERY HOSE!

"FINALLY, ALL WAS COMPLETED, ALL SAVE ONE THING, THE MOST IMPORTANT THING--"
WE CAN GO NO FURTHER PETER! --WE MUST HAVE A BRAIN; THE BRAIN OF A MAN DEAD NOT MORE THAN SIX HOURS. ACCORDING TO MY HYPOTHESIS, THE TISSUE OF A BRAIN WHICH HAS CEASED FUNCTIONING FOR A PERIOD LONGER THAN SIX HOURS CAN NOT BE REACTIVATED!
AND THAT'S THE STORY, MR. NICK RAMONO, NOW YOU KNOW WHY THE WORLD'S GREATEST SCIENTIST BECAME A DRUNK-SODDEN FOOL! BECAUSE HE FAILED!
YOU'RE TAKIN' THIS TOO HARD, FRIEND-- I CAN GET A BRAIN FOR YOU, YEAH, ONE MADE TO ORDER!

IF THIS IS YOUR IDEA OF A JOKE, SIR, I FAIL TO SEE THE HUMOR OF IT! I MAY BE INEBRIATED, BUT I'M NOT STUPID!
IT'S NO JOKE, POP. I SAID I CAN GET YOU A BRAIN, AND I MEANT IT! GIVE ME TWENTY FOUR HOURS AND I'LL CALL YOU AND TELL YOU WHERE TO COME FOR IT. BUT DON'T MENTION IT TO ANYBODY OR THE DEAL'S OFF!

AS THE RACKET BOSS LEAVES THE TAVERN, HIS MIND IS CONSUMED WITH AN EVIL PLAN.
YEAH, I'LL GIVE YOU A BRAIN, PROFESSOR--- THE BRAIN OF RUSS MORETTY! FOR MONTHS I BEEN TRYIN' TO THINK OF A UNIQUE WAY TO RUB HIM OUT; AND THIS IS PERFECT! HIS BODY WILL BE DEAD, BUT HIS BRAIN WILL LIVE ON IN THAT UGLY CARCASS! AH, HOW I HATE THAT GUY!
2

WHEN I THINK OF THAT CHEAP HOOD AND HIS TWO-BIT MOB, PUSHIN' OVER BANKS, MUSCLING IN ON MY TERRITORY, I COULD BLOW MY TOP!
AND HE'S BUMPED OFF SO MANY OF MY BOYS I LOST COUNT, BUT NOW HIS LUCK IS GOIN' TO RUN OUT!
BRACK!
ARRIVING AT HIS APARTMENT, RAMONO MAKES A HURRIED TELEPHONE CALL---
HELLO, ZIGGY. I WANT YOU TO SET-UP A MEET FOR ME WITH MORETTY --- YEAH, TELL HIM THERE'S NO POINT IN US TRYIN' TO CUT EACH OTHERS THROAT. THERE'S ROOM ENOUGH IN THE RACKETS FOR BOTH OF US. I'D LIKE TO DISCUSS A PARTNERSHIP WITH HIM.--YEAH, TELL HIM TO MEET ME ON THE DOCKS AT TWELVE TONIGHT.---OKAY ZIGGY, THANKS!
AT TWELVE THAT NIGHT, MORETTY ARRIVES ON THE DOCKS TO KEEP THE NOCTURNAL RENDEZVOUS.
WHERE IS THAT CRUMB, RAMONO! HE HASN'T SHOWN UP! IT COULD BE A TRAP. WHA---?
I'M HERE, BEHIND YOU, MORETTY!
TAKE IT, RAT!
AGH!
A SHORT TIME LATER--
I'VE GOT THE BRAIN I PROMISED YOU PROFESSOR! A "FRIEND" OF MINE PASSED AWAY SUDDENLY AND HE WILLED HIS REMAINS TO SCIENCE.
KNOWING THE KIND OF MAN YOU ARE, RAMONO, I'M SURE THERE'S SOMETHING CROOKED; EVEN MURDEROUS INVOLVED, BUT I'VE GONE TOO FAR TO TURN BACK NOW! I CAN'T AFFORD THE LUXURY OF SCRUPLES! TAKE ME TO HIM.
WITH DEFT HANDS THE PROFESSOR REMOVES THE BRAIN FROM THE DECEASED MOBSTER AND THEN PROCEEDS TO TRANSFER IT INTO THE CRANIUM OF THE HORRIFIC THING WHICH HE CREATED.
THE BODY OF RUSS MORETTY IS RETRIEVED, AND A FEW MOMENTS LATER PROFESSOR REARDON WHEELS IT INTO THE LABORATORY.
WELL, YOU GOT YOUR BOY NOW, POP, SO I'LL BE ON MY WAY, BUT I'LL KEEP IN TOUCH, TO SEE HOW YOU MAKE OUT!
VERY WELL, MR. RAMONO.
TIGHTEN THE SUTURES, PETER!
3

MEANWHILE, AT POLICE HEADQUARTERS, KEN ROSS, A BRILLIANT YOUNG DETECTIVE IS ENGROSSED IN SERIOUS CONVERSATION WITH THE DESK-SERGEANT.
WHAT MAKES YOU THINK RUSS MORETTY HAS BEEN KNOCKED OFF? NO REPORT OF IT HAS COME IN TO US.
AN INFORMANT WITH UNDERWORLD CONNECTIONS TOLD ME! HE ALSO CLAIMS THAT ZIGGY GATSON SET UP A MEETING BETWEEN NICK RAMONO AND MORETTY, SO RAMONO IS OUR NO. 1 SUSPECT!

AT THIS PRECISE MOMENT, IN REARDON'S LABORATORY, THE SURGICAL OPERATION HAS BEEN COMPLETED AND THE POWERFUL ELECTRONIC GENERATORS ARE TURNED ON. THE HEAT BECOMES INTENSE AS THE RAYS RUN THE FULL SPECTRUM OF COLOR.
IT'S WORKING, PROFESSOR! HE'S COMING TO LIFE!
YES, BUT THE ELECTRODES ARE STIMULATING THE PITUITARY GLANDS-- HE'S GROWING!

THE TITANIC CREATURE SLOWLY REGAINS CONSCIOUSNESS, AND A LOOK OF ANGER OVERSPREADS HIS DISFIGURED COUNTENANCE AS HE OBSERVES HIS CONDITION.
WHA---WHAT HAPPENED TO ME! ----I'M BIG AND UGLY!--- WHERE AM I?----- NOW I REMEMBER! RAMONO SHOT ME! THE SWINE! I'LL SETTLE WITH HIM!

BUT YOU ARE RESPONSIBLE FOR TURNING ME INTO THIS UGLY FREAK! FOR THAT YOU DIE!
STOP, YOU FOOL! DON'T KILL ME! I GAVE YOU LIFE! YOU OWE YOUR SOUL TO ME!

THE HUGE MONSTER FLINGS REARDON ASIDE AND ATTEMPTS TO ESCAPE FROM THE CONFINES OF THE LABORATORY. BUT HE IS UNACCUSTOMED TO THE LARGE, GROSS LIMBS, WHICH HAVE LONG BEEN LIFELESS AND CONSEQUENTLY HE BLUNDERS INTO THE SCIENTIFIC APPARATUS AND PARAPHERNALIA. THE POWERFUL CHEMICALS IGNITE AND BURST INTO FLAME. ENRAGED BY THIS ANNOYANCE, THE THING REDOUBLES ITS EFFORT TO FREE ITSELF FROM THE SITE OF ITS REGENERATION.

TEARING A METALLIC FIXTURE FROM ITS SOCKET, THE TITAN WIELDS IT AS A BLUDGEON, CUTTING A BROAD SWATH THROUGH THE DELICATE INSTRUMENTS, WHILE THE HUNGRY FLAMES LEAP HIGHER AND HIGHER ABOUT HIM.
GOT TO GET OUT! GOT TO GET RAMONO!
THE CREATURE AT LAST EXTRICATES ITSELF FROM THE LABORATORY, AND AS HE LUMBERS INTO THE STREET, A DAZED FIGURE RISES FROM THE DEBRIS.
HE MUST BE STOPPED!--I'VE GOT TO DESTROY THE THING I HELPED CREATE, BEFORE HE KILLS SOMEONE ELSE!---THE ELECTRONIC-RETRACTOR WILL NEUTRALIZE HIS ENERGY AND RENDER HIM INANIMATE!-- MUST TAKE IT ALONG!
A SHORT TIME LATER, AT POLICE HEADQUARTERS---
THERE'S A FIRE RAGING OUT OF CONTROL ON 97TH. STREET, KEN, PROF. REARDON'S PLACE! A BYSTANDER SAYS HE SAW A BIG GUY RUNNING FROM THE HOUSE! IT MAY BE A CASE OF ARSON!
I HAVE A HUNCH THIS TIES IN WITH THE RAMONO AFFAIR! HE WAS SEEN ENTERING REARDON'S HOME RECIENTLY! I'LL GET RIGHT ON IT!
A FEW MOMENTS LATER----
IT'S AN INFERNO! IF ANYONE WAS IN THERE HE MUST HAVE PERISHED!--WHICH ONE OF YOU SAW THE MAN THAT CAME OUT?
IT WAS ME, I SAW HIM!
HE WAS A GREAT BIG GUY, AT LEAST SEVEN FEET TALL! HE HAD THE UGLIEST FACE I EVER SAW, JUST LIKE THE CHARACTERS IN THEM HORROR MOVIES! HE KEPT MUTTERING TO HIMSELF, "GOT TO GET RAMONO!"
HE MUST HAVE MENT NICK RAMONO, THE RACKET BOSS!
KEN ROSS HAILS A CAB, AND IS SOON SPEEDING THROUGH THE CITY STREETS ON A DESPERATE MISSION.
RAMONO NEVER ATTEMPTED TO GO INTO HIDING, BECAUSE WE'VE BEEN UNABLE TO PIN A RAP ON HIM, SO I KNOW WHERE HE LIVES, BUT IT'S QUITE POSSIBLE THAT THIS "GIANT" ALSO KNOWS WHERE TO FIND HIM! IT'S A RACE AGAINST TIME NOW; TO SEE WHICH ONE OF US GETS TO HIM FIRST!
HURRY DRIVER!
BUT THE YOUNG DETECTIVE HAS ALREADY LOST THE RACE, FOR AT THAT MOMENT, IN RAMONO'S HOME---
NOW I HAVE YOU RAMONO!
WHAT THE!
5

DIE!--WHY DON'T YOU DIE?--- NO-- STAY BACK, DON'T COME NEAR ME!
YOU CAN NOT KILL THAT WHICH HAS ALREADY BEEN DEAD!
BANG! BANG!
BANG
THE CRINGING GANGSTER MAKES ONE DESPERATE ATTEMPT TO ESCAPE, BUT THE MONSTER GRASPS HIM AND MERCI-LESSLY BLUDGEONS HIM WITH THE METAL ROD.
AND SO I TAKE MY REVENGE!
AAAGH!
THE CREATURE DROPS THE LIFELESS NICK RAMONO, AND TURNS SUDDENLY AS PETER DIKE STAGGERS INTO THE ROOM.
YOU--- I THOUGHT YOU DIED IN THE BURNING LABORATORY WITH THE OTHER SCIENTIST!
I LIVED LONG ENOUGH TO FOLLOW YOU HERE, FOR THE PURPOSE OF DESTROYING YOU, YOU DEVIL'S-SPAWN!
THE MONSTER LUNGES AT THE YOUTH, BUT WITH THE SWIFTNESS OF THOUGHT, DIKE TURNS ON THE ELECTRONIC-RETRACTOR. THERE IS A SUDDEN BLINDING FLASH OF LIGHT. THE THING PAUSES, TRANSFIXED, AS ALL THE ENERGY IS DRAWN FROM HIS EMACIATED BODY. THEN WITH A TERRIFYING SCREAM, HE COLLAPSES TO THE FLOOR, DEAD!
AIEECH!
BUT THE RETRACTOR IS UNINSULATED, AND BEFORE THE YOUNG SCIENTIST CONSIDERS THIS FACT, THOUSANDS OF VOLTS OF COSMIC ENERGY PASSES THROUGH HIS BODY, ELECTROCUTING HIM.
A FEW MINUTES LATER KEN ROSS ARRIVES AT RAMONO'S APARTMENT.
I'M TOO LATE! THE GIANT GOT TO HIM FIRST! BUT HE'S DEAD TOO! AND I WONDER WHO THIS OTHER CHAP IS?
THE NEXT DAY, AT POLICE HEADQUARTERS---
HERE'S THE CORONER'S REPORT, KEN! PREPARE YOURSELF; IT'S A PUZZLER! "NICK RAMONO: CAUSE OF DEATH, CONCUSSION OF THE SKULL, INFLICTED BY A BLUNT INSTRUMENT! PETER DIKE: CAUSE OF DEATH, ELECTROCUTION! PROFESSOR REARDON: CAUSE OF DEATH, CREMATION! UNIDENTIFIED GIANT: CAUSE OF DEATH, UNKNOWN! ---- AUTOPSY INVESTIGATION REVEALED THAT SAID GIANT POSSESSED THE DENTURES OF ALBERT ST. JOHN, WHO DIED NOV. 3RD., 1950. THE TORSO WAS THAT OF HENRY JONES, WHO DIED APRIL 21ST., 1951. RIGHT AND LEFT ARMS IDENTIFED AS THOSE OF CHARLES CONTI, WHO DIED JUNE 10TH, 1951. LEFT LEG WAS THAT OF JON WEYMORE, WHO DIED AUGUST 12TH., 1951. RIGHT LEG WAS THAT OF WILLIAM JACKSON, WHO DIED FEB. 7TH, 1952!"----- THAT'S IT, KEN, WHAT DO YOU THINK OF IT?
IT'S INCREDIBLE! I DON'T KNOW WHAT TO THINK!-- THERE'S NO MENTION OF MORETTY, SO HIS DISAPPEARANCE WILL FOREVER REMAIN A SECRET.-- BUT, YOU KNOW, MORETTY WAS SMART; IF HE HAD TEAMED UP WITH PROF. REARDON, HE MIGHT HAVE BEEN THE "BRAINS" BEHIND SOME PRETTY CLEVER EXPERIMENTS!
END.

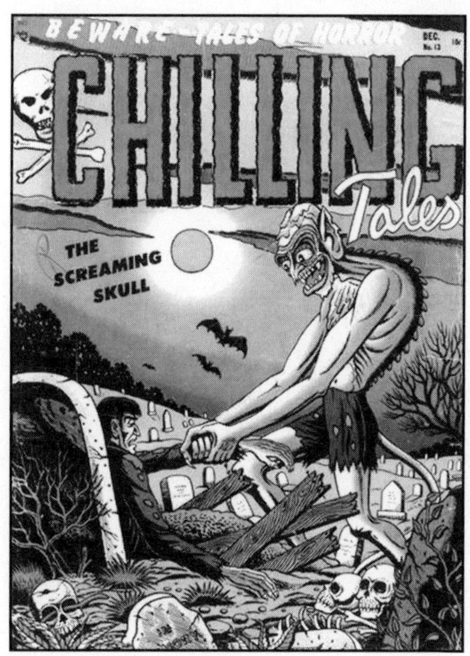

The Hand of Glory

Chilling Tales 13, December 1952

Artist Matt Fox has acquired a cult following over the last three decades. This devoted assembly have but one complaint about his work in comics: there was never enough. During the late 1940s he produced eleven highly stylized covers for *Weird Tales* plus a plethora of interior illustrations for this and several other fantasy and horror related pulps; within a matter of years he was also contributing to comics, predominantly Atlas. For Youthful's *Chilling Tales* he produced this one story plus three extraordinary covers, each of which seemed borne from the very pits of hell. There is an air of disquiet to his vision, yet it charms through a surreptitious blending of the primitive with the mockingly insane. His characters border on the lunatic, seemingly at home in his landscapes, concealing a darkness corruptive of the soul. His work has been confused with that of Basil Wolverton and exhibits elements of both Al Feldstein and Terrance Lindall, neither of whom have any cognisance of his work. This tale has previously been reprinted in Renegade's experimental 3-D *Danse Macabre* in 1988.

THE HAND OF GLORY
A DREADFUL RELIC OF THE DEAD, "THE HAND OF GLORY," TORN FROM THE ARM OF AN EXECUTED CRIMINAL AS HE SWUNG FROM THE GIBBET CHAINS, HELD A WAXEN TAPER MADE WITH THE FAT OF A HUMAN HEART. ITS EERIE LIGHT, WHICH PROTECTED THE EVIL-DOER FROM ALL HARM, SHONE STRAIGHT FROM THE DEPTHS OF HELL....
M. FOX
1

A STORMY NIGHT IN YORKSHIRE IN THE FALL OF 1824 AS TWO MUFFLED FIGURES GALLOP TOWARD A DESERTED CROSSROADS...
HAVE WE FAR TO GO? THERE'S A STORM BREWING.
IT IS ONLY A LITTLE WAY NOW. OLD JEM WILL BE GLAD TO SEE US.
CRAACK!
SEE THERE HE SWINGS. I TOLD YE HE WOULDN'T DISAPPOINT US.
LET'S GET ON WITH IT. I DON'T LIKE IT HERE.
DISMOUNTING, ONE OF THE MEN CLIMBS THE CREAKING GIBBET...
I'LL FEEL A LOT BETTER WHEN WE'RE DONE. THE DEAD DON'T LIKE TO BE DISTURBED.
BAH! OLD JEM MUST BE LONELY SWINGING UP THERE. AFTER ALL, WE'RE OLD FRIENDS.
AH, JEM, IT LOOKS LIKE YOU'RE GOING TO DO US MORE GOOD DEAD THAN ALIVE...
REACHING THE BODY, THE MAN GHOULISHLY SEVERS THE CORPSE'S RIGHT HAND...
YE'LL NEVER MISS IT, JEM, AND THERE'LL BE LESS OF YE TO BURN IN HADES...
ALL RIGHT, TOM, LET'S GO!
AYE! I CAN FEEL THE DEVIL BREATHING ON MY NECK...GET UP, THERE!
WITH THEIR GRISLY TROPHY SAFE, THE TWO GALLOP OFF AS IF ALL THE HOUNDS OF HELL WERE AFTER THEM....
CRAAASH!
2

RETURNING TO THEIR HIDEOUT, THE TWO WORK FAR INTO THE NIGHT CONCOCTING A GRUESOME AND MYSTIC MIXTURE.
IT'S DONE, TOM! GET THE MOLD, QUICK!
AYE, 'TIS THE MASTER OF DARKNESS' OWN BREW.

ARE YOU SURE IT WILL WORK?
AS SURE AS I AM THAT YOU ARE BY MY SIDE, TOM. YOU'LL SEE!

WHEN THE AWFUL TALLOW HAS COOLED...
FROM THIS TIME ON WE ARE SAFE. WHOEVER BE ASLEEP WHEN THE CANDLE IS LIT WILL STAY ASLEEP...
...AND THOSE WHO BE AWAKE FALL INTO A TRANCE. BUT WHAT IF IT SHOULD GO OUT?

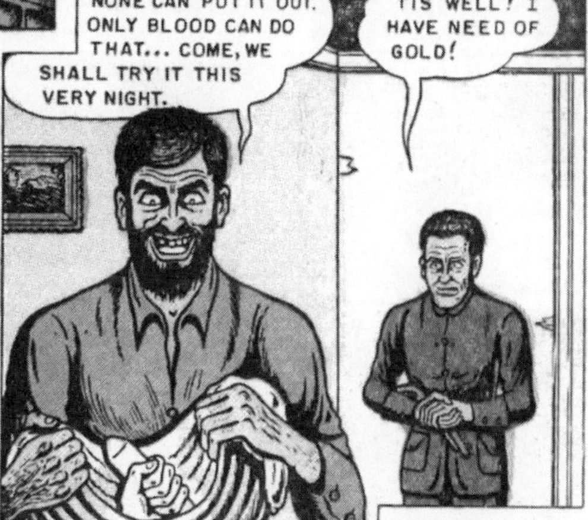
NONE CAN PUT IT OUT. ONLY BLOOD CAN DO THAT... COME, WE SHALL TRY IT THIS VERY NIGHT.
'TIS WELL! I HAVE NEED OF GOLD!

MANY WERE THE EVIL DEEDS COMMITTED THROUGH THE USE OF THE HORRIBLE HAND UNTIL AT LAST...
HE'S RIDING INTO THE FOREST! SHOOT HIM DOWN!
STOP, YE THIEVIN' BLACKGUARD!

NO USE FOLLOWING HIM. WE'LL NEVER FIND HIM IN THERE.
BLASTED HIGHWAYMAN! HE'S GOT CLEAN AWAY... WELL, HE'LL HANG, SOME DAY.
3

BUT IT WAS NOT TO BE! IN A TINY COTTAGE NOT FAR AWAY THE HIGHWAYMAN IS DYING FROM A BULLET...
THEY MAY HAVE GOT ME... BUT... THEY'LL... NEVER GET... THE "HAND OF GLORY."

ALL RIGHT, JEM... I'M COMING TO SEE YOU AGAIN... THIS... TIME... FOR... GOOD... UNHH!

ONE HUNDRED AND TWENTY FIVE YEARS LATER AS TWO HOBOS SEEK SHELTER IN AN ABANDONED COTTAGE IN YORKSHIRE...
THERE'S A PLACE, BILL. LET'S GET IN THERE!
RIGHT! WE'LL DROWN IF WE STAY OUT HERE.

IT'S AN ABANDONED SHACK. WE CAN SLEEP HERE.
LET'S GET A FIRE GOING. I'M SOAKED.

LATER...
IT'S GOOD TO BE WARM AGAIN, EH?
YEAH, IT... HEYY!

HEY, BILL, LOOK! BURIED TREASURE!
GORBLIMEY, WE'RE RICH!
4

WHEN THE BOX IS OPENED...
WHAT KIND OF TREASURE IS THIS? SOMEBODY'S BEEN GRAVE ROBBIN'! JUST OUR LUCK!
WE ARE IN LUCK! THIS IS THE HAND OF GLORY! OUR FORTUNE IS MADE!

USING THEIR GRUESOME FIND, THE PAIR COMMIT THEFT AFTER THEFT! SOME MONTHS LATER...
AH, THIS IS THE LIFE. WE'RE ALMOST RICH ENOUGH TO RETIRE.
WE WILL BE AFTER OUR NEXT JOB. LOOK AT THIS!

WHAT IS IT?
AN ARTICLE ABOUT THADEUS FLINT, THE GEM COLLECTOR. HE KEEPS A MILLION POUNDS WORTH OF JEWELRY IN HIS HOUSE... WE'VE A DATE WITH HIM TOMORROW NIGHT.

THE FOLLOWING NIGHT AT THE FLINT MANSION...
WE'RE IN. I THOUGHT THE PLACE WAS WELL GUARDED!
SO DID I. I'LL GET THE HAND READY.

HURRY, BILL! I DON'T LIKE THIS. IT'S TOO QUIET...
WHAT DID YOU EXPECT IN THE MIDDLE OF THE NIGHT... A RECEPTION?

AS BILL LIGHTS THE GRISLY TAPER...
RAISE YOUR HANDS!
A GUARD!
HAND OF GLORY SHED THY LIGHT!
LET THOSE WHO REST MORE DEEPLY SLEEP!
LET THOSE AWAKE THEIR VIGILS KEEP!
5

I SAID, RAISE YOUR..... UHH!
HE WON'T BOTHER US ANY MORE AND NEITHER WILL ANY ONE ELSE IN THE HOUSE.
WHEW! THAT WAS CLOSE.

PROTECTED BY THE HAND OF EVIL THE TWO CALMLY BLOW OPEN THE SAFE . . .
THAT DOES IT!
COME ON, LET'S GET THE LOOT!
T. FLINT

OWW! I CUT MY HAND!
HERE, YOU HOLD THE HAND! I'LL GET THE JEWELS!

AS THE INJURED ROBBER REACHES FOR THE HAND HIS BLOOD FALLS ON THE FLAME...
BLASTED DOOR! THAT EDGE IS SHARP AS A RAZOR.
LOOK OUT, YOU'RE BLEEDING ON THE CANDLE!
T.FLINT

LOOK!
THE ...THE LIGHT IS TURNING GREEN!
T.FLINT

AAAH! IT'S MOVING!
THE HAND! IT LET GO OF THE CANDLE!

AS THE STRANGE, EERIE GLOW GROWS... THE TWO THIEVES FRANTICALLY GRAB THE JEWELS FROM THE SAFE...
GRAB WHAT YOU CAN AND LET'S GET OUT OF HERE!
DON'T WORRY, YOU COULDN'T KEEP ME HERE WITH WILD HORSES!
BUT AS THEY TURN TO FLEE...
I CAN'T MOVE!
I... WANT... MY... HAND...
GET ME OUT OF HERE!
HELP!
AAAGHH!
UUUGH!
AND SO THEY WERE FOUND THE NEXT MORNING. EACH OF THEM HAD THEIR RIGHT HAND MISSING. OLD JEM HAD RECLAIMED HIS HAND... BUT WHAT HAD HAPPENED TO THEIRS?
THE END-

The Man Who Would Be Fate

Hand of Fate 21, August 1954

In the last eighteen months of life as a publisher of horror comics, Ace Magazines showcased Lou Cameron at his finest. This issue of *Hand of Fate* is no exception, revealing Lou at the pinnacle of his imaginative vigour. Anyone acquainted with DC's *Spectre* in the halcyon period that lasted from the end of the 1960s through until the early 1970s may find some of the images in these pages vaguely familiar.

THE MAN WHO WOULD BE FATE
SO YOU WOULD LIKE TO BE AS POWERFUL AS FATE? YOU SHALL HAVE YOUR WISH, ROGER DUNNING. I HEREBY ABDICATE AS FATE---AND YOU WILL TAKE MY PLACE AS THE MASTER OF ALL DESTINY.
HA HA! I'VE ACHIEVED MY LIFELONG DREAM! I AM FATE, RULER OF THE UNIVERSE!
MANY MEN HAVE HAD DREAMS OF LIMITLESS POWER, OF BEING SUPREME RULER OVER THE LIVES AND DESTINIES OF COUNTLESS HUMAN BEINGS. BUT WHILE MOST MEN REALIZE THE IMPOSSIBILITY OF FULFILLING THOSE DREAMS, ROGER DUNNING TRIED TO MAKE THEM COME TRUE ... AND THOUGHT THAT HE COULD USURP THE AWFUL POWERS OF FATE.
LET US PICK UP THE TANGLED THREAD OF ROGER DUNNING'S LIFE BEFORE HIS DREAM LAY WITHIN HIS GRASP, IN INDIA, LAND OF MYSTERY...
SEIZE THE INFIDEL! HE HAS STOLEN THE SACRED BOOK OF THE OCCULT!
THEY'LL NEVER CATCH ME NOW! I'LL LOSE ANY PERSUERS IN THE CROWDS NEAR THE BAZAAR!
SOON AFTERWARDS, ABOARD A STATES-BOUND SHIP...
I THOUGHT THIS BOOK OF OCCULT WOULD TEACH ME HOW TO GAIN POWER OVER OTHERS ... BUT ALL I'VE BEEN ABLE TO UNDERSTAND IS HOW TO RAISE THE SPIRITS OF THE BEYOND. WELL, I'LL SUMMON THE SPIRITS AND SEE WHAT THEY LOOK LIKE!

IT WOULD HAVE BEEN USELESS TO TRY TO WARN ROGER DUNNING OF THE PERILS INVOLVED IN TAMPERING WITH THE UNKNOWN! NOTHING WOULD HAVE HALTED HIS WILD QUEST FOR POWER AT THIS TIME...
THOSE SPIRITS SURE ARE WEIRD-LOOKING CREEPS! I COULD MAKE A FORTUNE AS A MAGICIAN JUST SUMMONING THEM UP IN FRONT OF AUDIENCES! AND AFTER THAT— WHO KNOWS WHERE IT WILL LEAD ME?
BACK IN THE STATES, ROGER DEMONSTRATED HIS MAGIC TO THE TOP IMPRESARIO OF THE ENTERTAINMENT WORLD . . .
WELL, WHAT BOOKINGS CAN YOU GET ME ON THE BASIS OF THIS ACT?
WITH MAGIC LIKE THAT, YOU CAN START AT THE VERY TOP!
THE LEADING STATESMEN OF THE WORLD ARE HOLDING AN INTERNATIONAL CONFERENCE NEXT WEEK...AND I'VE BEEN ASKED TO FURNISH SOME ENTERTAINMENT FOR THE DIPLOMATS AFTER THEIR ARDUOUS MEETINGS!
AND YOU, MR. DUNNING, WILL BE THE FEATURE OF THAT ENTERTAINMENT!
MAYBE I CAN USE THE SPIRITS TO INTIMIDATE THOSE STATESMEN INTO DOING MY BIDDING... AND THEN WORLD POWER WILL BE MINE!
WHEN THE WORLD'S MOST POWERFUL STATESMEN AND DIPLOMATS HAD GATHERED...
BEHOLD...WHILE I SUMMON UP THE DREAD SPIRITS OF THE BEYOND!
BEWARE, ROGER DUNNING --- DO NOT GO THROUGH WITH YOUR PLAN!
WHA...?
YOU WERE NOT MEANT TO UTILIZE STOLEN POWERS YOU CANNOT CONTROL! YOU HAVE BEEN WARNED!
SACRÉ BLEU! THAT APPARITION MATERIALIZED OUT OF NOWHERE --- THIS IS INDEED GREAT MAGIC!
2

I DON'T KNOW WHO THAT CHARACTER BEHIND ME IS ... BUT I'LL PLAY ALONG WITH THE AUDIENCE'S IDEA THAT HE'S PART OF THE SHOW!
HA HA! I HOPE YOU ENJOYED THAT LITTLE DIVERSION ... AND NOW I'LL PROCEED WITH SUMMONING THE SPIRITS OF THE BEYOND!

BUT WHEN THE SPIRITS HAD BEEN RAISED...
SOMETHING'S WRONG! I—I CAN'T SEEM TO CONTROL THE SPIRITS THE WAY I DID IN MY PRACTICE SESSIONS! THEY DON'T OBEY MY THOUGHT COMMANDS!

OF COURSE NOT! IN THE PRESENCE OF SO MANY PEOPLE, WITH SO MANY INTERFERING BRAIN WAVES AROUND, YOUR MENTAL ENERGY ISN'T ENOUGH TO CONTROL THE SPIRITS!
THE SPIRITS ARE GOING ON A RAMPAGE! THEY'RE ATTACKING THE AUDIENCE!

THAT IS TO BE EXPECTED! THE SPIRITS ARE ABSORBING THE SECRET, HATRED-FILLED THOUGHTS OF THE LEADERS OF THE TOTALITARIAN COUNTRIES! AND THEY RESPOND TO THOSE AGGRESSIVE THOUGHTS BY ATTACKING THE STATESMEN OF THE DEMOCRACIES!
GUARDS--- HELP!

AS THE AMERICAN SECRET SERVICE MEN BLAST INTO ACTION...
OUR BULLETS GO RIGHT THROUGH THOSE DEMONS! WE'RE HELPLESS!
HEAR ME, O SPIRITS OF THE BEYOND! RETURN TO THE REALM OF THE NETHERWORLD!
BAM

THEY'RE GONE... VANISHED!
13

YOU HAVE SEEN HOW DANGEROUS IT IS TO TAMPER WITH THE FORCES OF THE BEYOND, ROGER DUNNING! I WARN YOU --- DO NOT SUMMON THOSE SPIRITS AGAIN!
WHO IN BLAZES ARE YOU TO GIVE ME ORDERS LIKE THAT?
YES, WHO ARE YOU? YOU OWE US AN EXPLANATION!
I SHALL TELL ALL OF YOU WHO I AM... BY GIVING EACH OF YOU A GLIMPSE INTO YOUR FUTURE!
INTO EACH ONE'S BRAIN FLASHED A VISION OF THE FUTURE... BUT ONLY THE LEADERS OF THE DICTATORSHIP COUNTRIES SHRANK FROM THE SIGHT OF THE HORROR AND DEATH THAT WAS TO COME TO THEM!
WHILE ROGER DUNNING RECEIVED ANOTHER KIND OF VISION... A GLIMPSE OF HIS FUTURE THAT SATISFIED HIS WILDEST, POWER-MAD DREAMS!
I AM FATE, RULER OF THE UNIVERSE!
AS THE VISIONS FADED...
BY JOVE, YOU MUST BE FATE HIMSELF!
NOM DE NOM... YOU ARE LE DESTIN!
I KNOW YOU NOW... KISMET!
YES, I AM KNOWN BY ALL THOSE NAMES! NOW THAT YOU HAVE SEEN ME, YOU SHOULD REALIZE THAT ALL OF YOU ARE RESPONSIBLE TO A GREATER POWER THAN YOURSELVES! YOUR EVERY THOUGHT AND DEED IS RECORDED IN THE BOOK OF FATE... AND HE WHO SEEKS EVIL POWER WILL COME TO AN EVIL END!
HEED THAT WARNING, ROGER DUNNING! IF YOU FORCE THE HAND OF FATE AGAIN, YOUR DOOM IS SEALED!
HE—HE'S BECOMING TRANSPARENT... DISAPPEARING!
4

WELL, YOU'RE NOT GOING TO PULL A DISAPPEARING ACT LIKE FATE!
YEAH, YOU'RE UNDER ARREST FOR HAVING ENDANGERED THE LIVES OF EVERYONE IN THIS ROOM!
LATER, IN ROGER DUNNING'S PRISON CELL...
I CAN'T FORGET THAT VISION OF MY FUTURE--- I WAS FATE! BUT WHY SHOULD I WAIT TO FULFILL MY DREAM OF LIMITLESS POWER...WHY SHOULDN'T I START CONTROLLING THE WORLD NOW?
I'M ALONE HERE, SO THERE WON'T BE ANY INTERFERING BRAIN WAVES FROM OTHERS IF I SUMMON THE SPIRITS OF THE BEYOND! I'LL BE ABLE TO CONTROL THEM... AND I'LL MAKE THEM BREAK THROUGH THESE PRISON WALLS AND SET ME FREE!
SOON...
HA! THESE SPIRITS WILL BE USEFUL IN HELPING ME BREAK INTO A COSTUME SHOP... AND IN CARRYING OUT THE REST OF MY PLAN!
IN THE DARK HOURS BEFORE DAWN, NO ONE WAS ABROAD IN THE STREETS TO NOTICE THE SOUNDLESS CRUMBLING OF MASONRY IN ONE OF THE EMBASSY BUILDINGS. . .
WAKE UP, GENERALISSIMO!
EH? AM I SEEING THINGS ---OR IS IT REALLY FATE?
OF COURSE I AM FATE...DO YOU NOT REMEMBER ME FROM THIS EVENING? I HAVE COME TO TELL YOU THAT UNLESS YOU TAKE ALL MY FUTURE ORDERS AND PUT MY POLICIES INTO EFFECT WHEN YOU RETURN TO YOUR COUNTRY, YOU WILL DIE A HORRIBLE DEATH AT THE HANDS OF THESE SPIRITS FROM THE BEYOND!
IF YOU REFUSE, NOT ONLY WILL YOU DIE...BUT I WILL ALSO TORTURE TO DEATH ALL OF YOUR KINFOLK, ONE BY ONE!
I—I WILL OBEY YOU! WHO AM I TO DEFY THE MIGHTY POWER OF FATE?

HOURS LATER, AS DAWN TINGES THE SKY. . .
AH, THAT WAS THE LAST ONE! I'VE VISITED THE LEADERS OF ALL THE MAJOR POWERS IN THE WORLD, AND THEY'VE AGREED TO FOLLOW MY ORDERS! NOW I JUST HAVE TO DEVISE POLICIES THAT WILL MAKE ME RULER OF THE WORLD!
FOOLISH MORTAL, DO YOU THINK YOU ARE WORTHY OF SUCH POWER?
WHA..? YOU!
YES, I! DID YOU THINK A COSTUME ROBE AND A MASK WERE ALL YOU NEEDED TO TAKE MY PLACE?
THEN I HEREBY ABDICATE AS FATE---AND YOU WILL TAKE MY PLACE AS MASTER OF THE DESTINIES OF ALL LIVING HUMANS... AND OF THE PAST DESTINIES OF ALL THE COUNTLESS BILLIONS OF HUMANS WHO EVER LIVED!
YES... YES!
THEY'RE GONE, BLAST YOU! BUT I'M STILL NOT AFRAID OF YOU--- BECAUSE YOU YOURSELF SHOWED ME A VISION OF MY FUTURE IN WHICH I TOOK YOUR PLACE AS FATE!
WOULD YOU LIKE TO BECOME FATE NOW, ROGER DUNNING?
I'LL FIX YOU! SPIRITS OF THE BEYOND--- DESTROY FATE!
I COUNTERMAND YOUR ORDER! RETURN FROM WHENCE YE CAME, SPIRITS OF THE BEYOND!
AND...
HA HA! I AM FATE... RULER OF THE UNIVERSE AND MASTER OF ALL DESTINY!
YES, YOU ARE FATE... FOR AS LONG AS YOU CAN BEAR IT! THIS IS THE VISION OF YOUR FUTURE THAT I SHOWED YOU... YOUR VISION HAS COME TRUE AS OF THIS MOMENT! BUT, FOOLISH MORTAL, I DID NOT SHOW YOU WHAT WOULD HAPPEN TO YOU AFTER THIS MOMENT!
6

YES, ROGER DUNNING, KNOW WHAT IT MEANS TO CONTROL THE STRINGS OF DESTINY FOR COUNTLESS BILLIONS OF THE LIVING AND THE DEAD! FIND OUT IF YOUR MORTAL BRAIN CAN COPE WITH THE INFINITE KNOWLEDGE NECESSARY TO DETERMINE THOSE INNUMERABLE DESTINIES!
YII! MY MIND CAN'T HOLD ALL THAT KNOWLEDGE...MY HEAD'S BURSTING WITH IT! THE PAIN... THE PAIN...!
FORGET YOUR AGONY, ROGER DUNNING... BE CAREFUL NOT TO LET THE STRINGS OF DESTINY BECOME LOOSE! DON'T FORGET THAT THOSE STRINGS ALSO EXTEND TO THE WORLD OF THE DEAD, WHERE DWELL COUNTLESS SPIRITS WHO HAVE A GRUDGE AGAINST FATE!
LOOK! THERE IS A SLACK IN THE CONTROLLING LINES OF OUR AFTERLIVES!
NOM DU CHIEN... YOU ARE RIGHT! FATE HAS LOST CONTROL OF US! NOW IS THE TIME FOR REVENGE AGAINST FATE!
LOOK OUT, ROGER DUNNING! THERE ARE SO MANY OF YOUR ENEMIES---THOSE WHO BURN WITH ETERNAL HATRED BECAUSE FATE CUT THEM OFF IN THE PRIME OF THEIR LIVES...AND THOSE WHO THIRST FOR VENGEANCE BECAUSE DESTINY DID NOT ALLOW THEM TO FULFILL THEIR WORLDLY AMBITIONS!
NO...NO! I'M NOT REALLY FATE...I WASN'T RESPONSIBLE FOR YOUR DEATHS!
REVENGE! DEATH TO FATE!
TOO LATE, ROGER DUNNING...THEY DON'T BELIEVE YOU! BUT YOU'RE RIGHT ABOUT ONE THING---YOU'RE NO LONGER FATE, BUT A MORTAL WHO SOUGHT IMMORTAL POWER... AND WHO MET HIS DOOM!
BUT NOW THE REAL FATE RESUMES CONTROL OVER THE DESTINIES OF THE LIVING AND THE DEAD ...TILL THE END OF TIME! IN THE AEONS TO COME, THERE WILL BE MANY MORE EVIL MEN WHO WILL TRY TO BECOME MASTERS OVER THE DESTINIES OF OTHERS.. BUT LIKE ROGER DUNNING, THEY TOO WILL BE STRUCK DOWN BY THE HAND OF FATE!

The Terror Returns

1960s and 1970s

The Comics Code may have laid the vampires and werewolves to rest, but it did not diminish interest in any of those comic books with a supernatural persuasion. Atlas, the precursor to Marvel, continued to expand their line of weird titles, now devoid of the once customary blood and guts; DC and the American Comics Group also continued to thrive. In the place of the gore of the early Fifties came radioactive monsters and mutant minds bent on global domination. While they may not have shocked in the same way as their predecessors, there was a genuine enthusiasm for these imaginative creations.

In the end, it wasn't one of the regular four-colour comics that rekindled the craze for blood-curdling terror but it came from an equally spine-tingling source. Set loose on an unsuspecting America in 1958, James Warren and Forrest J. Ackerman's *Famous Monsters of Filmland* finally filled the demand growing since the introduction of the Comics Code for unbridled terror. A host of monster magazines soon followed, one of which was Warren's own *Monster World*, which dared to print a couple of horror stories in their first two issues in the latter months of 1964. Neither of these had the approval of the Code.

Now there was no stopping Warren, who realized the black-and-white magazine format was beyond the auspices of the crippling Code. With fervour still burning for magazine-style horror he released the black--and-white *Creepy* – and the world of comic book terror was never quite the same. At the outset *Creepy* was designed as an attempt to carry on the tradition established more than a decade before by EC, albeit in more gothic surroundings. For the first few years, luminaries once in the employ of EC were regular contributors to the pages of Creepy and its gruesome companion *Eerie*. Reed Crandall, Frank Frazetta, George Evans, Al Williamson and

Angelo Torres all returned to terrorize readers just as they had years before. When the Warren line seemed to be struggling, they engaged the sexy vampire theme in the enticing shape of Vampirella in 1969, and for the next fourteen years they did much to push the accepted boundaries of the comic book medium.

As with Bill Gaines' EC, Jim Warren also had his imitators. Initially it came from Eerie Publishing, a company that thrived on exploitation draped in a gory carnal lure never before seen in a comic book. First there came *Weird* in 1966, a tawdry version of Warren's polished product. A largely unknown collection of artists redrew stories originally seen in the 1950s, relying on an abundance of licentious imagery and butchery; this bloodlust only heightened the ardour to hunt them out on the news-stands. Before the end of the decade Eerie Publications were in a position to unveil several new titles: *Horror Tales*, *Tales from the Tomb*, *Tales of Voodoo*, *Terror Tales* and *Witches' Tales*, each as defiling as the one before it. Stanley P. Morse also returned with *Shock, Stark Terror* and *Ghoul Tales*. Just as he had during the early 1950s, Morse quickly ascended the bandwagon, this time offering only black-and-white reprints of the tales he had sold fifteen years before.

Another pretender to the throne of comic book horror challenged Jim Warren at a time when his own company was in a dire straits. Richard C. Sproul was a shameless imitator of anything he considered successful in the world of magazine publishing. His new horror magazine *Web of Horror* seemed destined for unprecedented success, with an assemblage of young talent including editor Terry Bisson along with Jeff Jones, Bernie Wrightson, Mike Kaluta, Frank Brunner, Ralph Reese and Bruce Jones. But *Web of Horror* is the tale of the one that got away: its fourth issue never saw publication. With the departure of editor Terry Bisson, Bernie Wrightson and Jeff Jones had assumed editorial control. These aspiring creators were in a position to call upon the likes of Roy Krenkel, Frank Frazetta and Al Williamson, giving them the chance to rival Jim Warren's faltering magazines. Yet it wasn't to be; Sproul vanished with the artwork to what many feel would have been an awe-inspiring issue.

The revival in the fortunes of the horror comic hadn't gone unnoticed by the two largest comic book publishers of the day, Marvel and DC, as well as the ever-resourceful Charlton Comics. Four-colour comic book horror had managed to survive the ravages of the Code with Dell and Gold Key's lukewarm titles *Ghost Stories, Ripley's Believe It Or Not True Ghost Stories, Dark Shadows, Boris Karloff's Tales of Mystery* and a host of horror film adaptations. While it is easy to malign these companies, it is worth remembering Dell were responsible for the giant-sized edition of *Tales from the Tomb* and the first issue of *Ghost Stories*, written by John Stanley, both of which shocked their readers and unfortunately their parents. The ensuing run of *Ghost Stories* was as a result very much toned down.

Early in 1968 DC transformed their long-running titles *House of Mystery* and *House of Secrets* to the mystery format. Sex and gore were not for sale here; with a range of formidable creators they were able to offer something immeasurably more palatable. Former EC artist Joe Orlando was brought in as editor; his reputation alone allowed him to acquire the support of Neal Adams, Bernie Wrightson, Mike Kaluta and later Alex Nino and Alfredo Alcala. Their selection of mystery titles would survive into the early 1980s, with their most acclaimed work appearing largely in the five or six years after their return to the dark side. These anthology titles proved a great success, but they were overshadowed by the creation of Len Wein and Bernie Wrightson in the pages of *House of Secrets 92*, Swampthing, who went on to acquire his own muck-infested title.

Marvel were a year later in daring to tread again the darkened pathway of horror. *Chamber of Chills* and *Tower of Shadows*, while exemplary titles, were regrettably short-lived when compared to their relentless counterparts at DC. However in the latter months of 1971, following pressure from the publishers desperate to compete with the growing popularity of the black-and-white horror magazine market, the stipulations of the Comics Code witnessed a degree of moderation. With the stake removed from its heart, the horror comic was able to set free the lycanthrope and vampire. Marvel's *Tomb of Dracula* brought together Marv Wolfman, Gene Colan and Tom Palmer to produce one of the finest horror comics ever to see print. *Werewolf Night* rendered by Mike Ploog followed, and shortly after *Manthing*, *Morbius* and *Frankenstein*, along with copious reprint titles, some of which included pre-Code terror. With the success of their four-colour comics, Marvel then swamped the news-stands with their own line of black-and-white horror magazines: *Dracula Lives*, *Tales of the Zombie*, *Haunt of Horror*, *Monsters Unleashed*, *Monsters of the Movies* and *Vampire Tales*.

Charlton Comics were never the largest of comic book publishers, but had remained in business for almost three decades. They were producing their own brand of strange tales throughout the Sixties. By the time the stranglehold of the Comics Code lifted, they had several formidable creators at their behest including Joe Gill, Joe Staton, Sanho Kim, Steve Ditko and Tom Sutton. Their titles were often overlooked when placed next to the abundance of Marvel and DC titles, but for those who ventured to seek out *Ghostly Haunts*, *Ghostly Tales*, *Ghost Manor*, *Haunted*, *The Many Ghosts of Dr Graves*, *Scary Tales* and *Monster Hunters* they contained many treasures.

At the very beginning of the 1970s a new publisher appeared on the scene, Skywald. They presented Jim Warren with potentially his greatest threat. Their early efforts bordered on being poor copies of *Creepy* and *Eerie*, although they could boast some beautiful covers from the likes of Boris Vallejo along with the occasional interior shocker. But this pitiful effort was thrown aside when Alan Hewetson, a former contributor to Jim Warren's magazines and one-time assistant to Stan Lee at Marvel, assumed the mantle as editor to Skywald's crop of titles. His creative drive gave birth to a maniacal offspring, the *Skywald Horrormood*, an unsettlingly surreal collection of macabre psychosis. With Alan at the helm, any staid constraint was replaced by stark terror now cast in its most acute form.

Early issues played host to the esteemed talent of Bruce Jones, Tom Sutton, Bernie Wrightson, Mike Kaluta and Bill Everett, but subsequently artists such as Maelo Cintron, Pablo Marcos, Jesus Suso, and Ricardo Villamonte came to the fore to craft the kaleidoscopic terror embraced by the *Horrormood*. The unearthly creations of H. P. Lovecraft crawled from the bowels of the earth to spread their rancorous disease over our fragile plane of existence, as Alan Hewetson's foul collective of creators dared to probe the very essence of horror.

Then, by the early months of 1975, the horrors started to fade. Although the news-stands had been overrun by these comic book terrors and competition was still fierce, the rising cost of printing, paper and distribution put paid to their diabolical machinations. Some have also suggested a change in the political climate of the US due to the resignation of Richard Nixon, had an effect on the country's psyche, meaning that the horrors of the comic book could no longer engender a mass appeal. Either way, for the remainder of the decade only Jim Warren's menagerie, Marvel's *Tomb of Dracula* and DC's occasionally inspired mystery titles survived. The horror comic, however, was far from dead and buried.

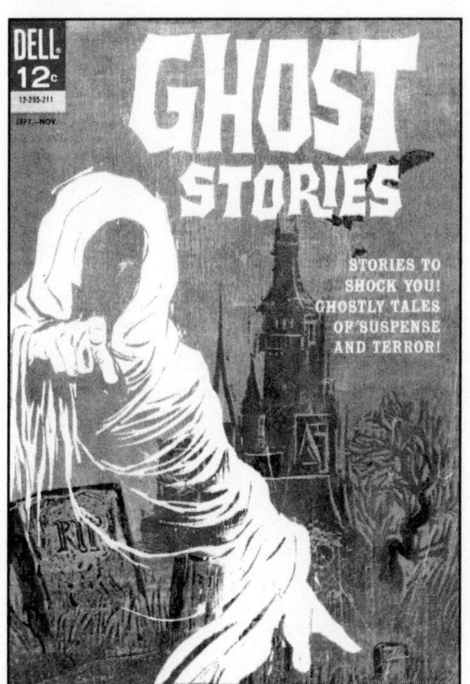

The Monster of Dread End

Ghost Stories 1, September 1962

Dell Comics were one of the few companies to remain self-regulating following the introduction of the Comics Code and due to the wholesome content never required a seal of approval. The first issue of *Ghost Stories* was appreciably different to anything they had published before, principally because of the writing of one John Stanley. His name was associated with the long-running *Little Lulu* but this debut for *Ghost Stories* and the giant-sized issue *Tales from the Tomb*, which appeared a month later, revealed a different side to his composition. For the time, the artwork exhibits an unusually dark quality, although it might come as a surprise to learn John didn't care much for the final result.

In these pages the atmosphere remains taut throughout, never once allowing you to be distracted from the terror within. John didn't have to resort to the gore so relished by his predecessors, but his ability to craft such a forbidding tale proved his undoing. There were many complaints from the parents of the children reading this tale and others that appeared in this issue and the ensuing *Tales from the Tomb*. He never worked on the title again.

THE MONSTER OF DREAD END...

LONG EMPTY OF HUMAN LIFE, THE DARK, DECAYING TENEMENTS OF **DREAD END** STARE SILENTLY ACROSS AT EACH OTHER AS THOUGH STILL FROZEN IN HORROR AT THE MEMORY OF THE FRIGHTFUL SCENES THEY ALONE HAD ONCE BEEN WITNESS TO...

KEEP OUT

TIME WAS... WHEN DREAD END, THEN KNOWN AS HAWTHORN PLACE, WAS A BUSY, NOISY, HAPPY STREET THAT ECHOED TO THE SOUND OF CHILDRENS' LAUGHTER...

...THEN EARLY ONE MORNING THE FIRST... ONE... WAS FOUND...
WH-WHAT'S THAT-?

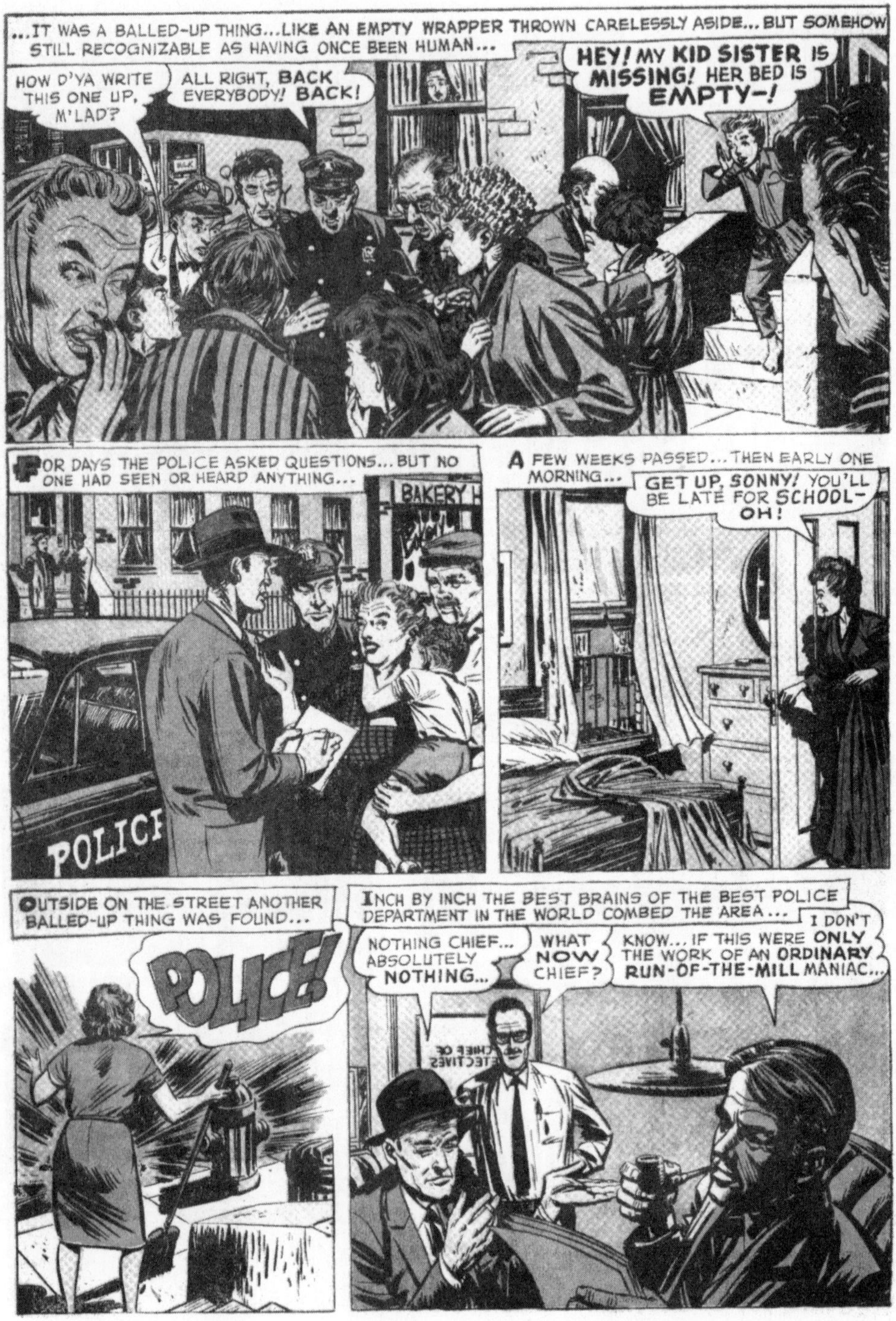

...IT WAS A BALLED-UP THING...LIKE AN EMPTY WRAPPER THROWN CARELESSLY ASIDE... BUT SOMEHOW STILL RECOGNIZABLE AS HAVING ONCE BEEN HUMAN...
HOW D'YA WRITE THIS ONE UP, M'LAD?
ALL RIGHT, BACK EVERYBODY! BACK!
HEY! MY KID SISTER IS MISSING! HER BED IS EMPTY-!

FOR DAYS THE POLICE ASKED QUESTIONS... BUT NO ONE HAD SEEN OR HEARD ANYTHING...
BAKERY
POLICE

A FEW WEEKS PASSED... THEN EARLY ONE MORNING...
GET UP, SONNY! YOU'LL BE LATE FOR SCHOOL- OH!

WHEN, A WEEK LATER, IT HAPPENED AGAIN, THE PANIC-STRICKEN INHABITANTS OF HAWTHORN PLACE BEGAN TO FLEE, SOME EVEN LEAVING THEIR FURNITURE BEHIND..
I DON'T CARE IF WE HAVE NOWHERE TO GO--AS LONG AS WE GET AWAY FROM HERE...
HURRY!
MOVNG

THE FEW WHO REMAINED, BOARDED UP THEIR WINDOWS AND DOUBLE LOCKED THEIR DOORS...
THAT OUGHT TO DO IT...

BUT AGAIN THE TERROR STRUCK!
THE TWINS ARE GONE!!

COMPLETELY BAFFLED, THE AUTHORITIES COULD ONLY EVACUATE THE REMAINING TENANTS, AND DECLARE THE STREET OUT OF BOUNDS TO ALL...
KEEP OUT

AS THE YEARS WENT BY, FEARFUL RESIDENTS OF NEIGHBORING BLOCKS GRADUALLY MOVED AWAY, UNTIL FINALLY, DREAD END WAS SURROUNDED ON ALL SIDES BY OTHER SILENT, EMPTY BLOCKS...
TAVERN

AFTER DARK, NO ONE EVER DARED VENTURE INTO EVEN THE OUTER FRINGES OF THIS NO-MAN'S-LAND, LET ALONE THE VERY CENTER OF IT... UNTIL...TONIGHT...

THOUGH ONLY SEVEN WHEN HIS LITTLE SISTER BECAME THE FIRST VICTIM OF THE DREAD END MONSTER, JIMMY WHITE RESOLVED THAT IF THE POLICE DIDN'T FIND HER KILLER, SOME DAY HE WOULD...

AS JIMMY GREW OLDER, HE BECAME MORE AND MORE OBSESSED WITH THE IDEA THAT THE KILLER STILL LURKED SOMEWHERE ON THAT SINISTER BLOCK...

NOW, AT THE AGE OF 15, JIMMY FEELS HE IS OLD ENOUGH TO FERRET THE MONSTER OUT...

CROUCHED IN THE SHADOWS OF AN ALLEY NEXT TO THE HOUSE HE HAD ONCE LIVED IN, JIMMY BEGINS HIS LONELY AND FEARFUL VIGIL...
I WISH I COULD BE SURE SOMEBODY WILL HEAR THIS POLICE WHISTLE...

THE HOURS DRAG BY, BUT NO SOUND DISTURBS THE UNEARTHLY QUIET OF THE DEAD, DESERTED STREET...

WHEN A FAR-AWAY CHURCH BELL TOLLS THE HOUR OF FIVE, JIMMY STANDS UP TO STRETCH...
DAWN IN A LITTLE WHILE... I'D BETTER BE GOING... MAYBE NEXT TIME...

JIMMY STOPS IN MIDSTRETCH...

...THEN QUICKLY CROUCHES BACK INTO THE SHADOWS...

HIS WHISTLE FORGOTTEN, JIMMY STARES, UNABLE TO BELIEVE HIS EYES!!!

SLOWLY, A GIANT, CLAW-LIKE HAND, FOLLOWED BY A THICK, SINUOUS, LIZARD-LIKE ARM SLITHERS OUT OF THE MANHOLE...
SLOWLY... LIKE A BLIND BOA CONSTRICTOR SEARCHING FOR SOMETHING, THE HAND GROPES ITS WAY ACROSS THE STREET... AND UP THE SIDE OF A WALL... GROPING... GROPING... SEARCHING... SEARCHING...

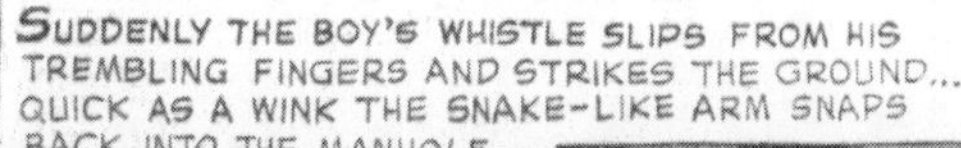
SUDDENLY THE BOY'S WHISTLE SLIPS FROM HIS TREMBLING FINGERS AND STRIKES THE GROUND... QUICK AS A WINK THE SNAKE-LIKE ARM SNAPS BACK INTO THE MANHOLE...

IT'S GONE! NOW'S MY CHANCE TO RUN--

BUT... IT MOVES SO FAST... IT COULD SHOOT OUT AND GRAB ME BEFORE I COULD...

TOO LATE... IT'S COMING... OUT AGAIN...

THIS TIME... TOWARD ME...

SLOWLY THE HAND GROPES TOWARD THE PETRIFIED BOY...IT STOPS...TO EXPLORE A GARBAGE CAN...

FINDING NOTHING, IT CRUSHES THE CAN AS THOUGH IT WERE TISSUE...
CRUNCH!

THEN, TO JIMMY'S RELIEF, IT TURNS AND GROPES ITS WAY OUT OF SIGHT...

JIMMY WATCHES THE REPULSIVE ARM CONTINUE TO FLOW OUT OF THE MANHOLE... IT SEEMS ENDLESS... BUT THE MORE THAT COMES OUT, THE FARTHER AWAY THE HAND IS GETTING...

THEN A SIXTH SENSE WARNS JIMMY—

BUT TOO LATE--THE MONSTER HAS FOUND HIM!

LIKE A RATTLER THE CLAW STRIKES-- AND CLOSES ON THIN AIR...

FOR A WHILE JIMMY SOMEHOW MANAGES TO DUCK AND DODGE THE LIGHTNING--LIKE THRUSTS OF THE TERRIBLE CLAW... BUT THE END IS INEVITABLE...

...CERTAIN OF ITS' PREY, THE CLAW HOVERS...

SUDDENLY A SHATTERING SERIES OF EXPLOSIONS TEAR THE NIGHT APART!..
BOOM! BAM! POW
BAM! BAM!
BAM! BAM! BAM!
KAK-KAK-KAK KAK-KAK-KAK-KAK-KAK-KAK-KAK-KAK-KAK-KAK-KAK-KAK-KAK-KAK-KAK-KAK-
POW POW POW

THEN SILENCE AGAIN...JIMMY OPENS HIS EYES... AND STARES DOWN AT THE GREAT LIMP CLAW...
ARE YOU ALL RIGHT, BOY?
SORRY WE HAD TO LET IT GO SO FAR, BUT WE WANTED AS MUCH OF IT OUT IN THE OPEN AS POSSIBLE, TO MAKE SURE!
YOU WERE HERE ALL THE TIME..?
WE'VE BEEN HERE FOR YEARS, SON!
AND IT MIGHT HAVE BEEN YEARS LONGER IF YOU HADN'T SHOWN UP!
LOOK... THOSE LARGE PORE-LIKE OPENINGS IN THE PALM... IT'S FED BY ABSORPTION... AFTER CRUSHING IT'S VICTIM...
DID YOU KNOW-- IT WAS THERE, TOO?
YES... WE'D SEEN IT A FEW TIMES, BUT IT NEVER CAME OUT FAR ENOUGH... ITS' SENSE OF DANGER WAS SO ACUTE AND ITS' SPEED SO LIGHTNING-LIKE WE DIDN'T WANT TO RISK ONLY WOUNDING IT, AND LETTING IT GET AWAY...
THE END

Santa's Claws

Web of Horror 3, April 1970

A collection of horror stories wouldn't be complete without a tale ushered in from Christmas past. This issue of *Web of Horror* was scheduled to have appeared as the Yuletide festivities reached their climax, and what an issue it proved to be. Still in his early twenties, Frank Brunner was the creative mind behind this tale. It was the start of a career that left an indelible impression on the world of comic books. Frank went on to work at Marvel, where he gave the character of Doctor Strange – first created by Steve Ditko – an entirely new dimension, one that reflected the creative excitement in this period of comic publishing. Marvel Premiere proved the perfect showcase for Frank's artistry, though his work would also be seen in many of Marvel's horror comics and magazines of the time. His use of shade and the eroticism of his women kept him away from the superheroes. Later he worked on Michael Moorcock's *Elric*, then returned to comics to work on First Comics' *Warp*. During the 1980s he was to enter a satisfying career in television and movie animation. These pages mark the beginning of his time in comics. *Web of Horror* allowed him to write, pencil and ink, something Marvel didn't give him the chance to do.

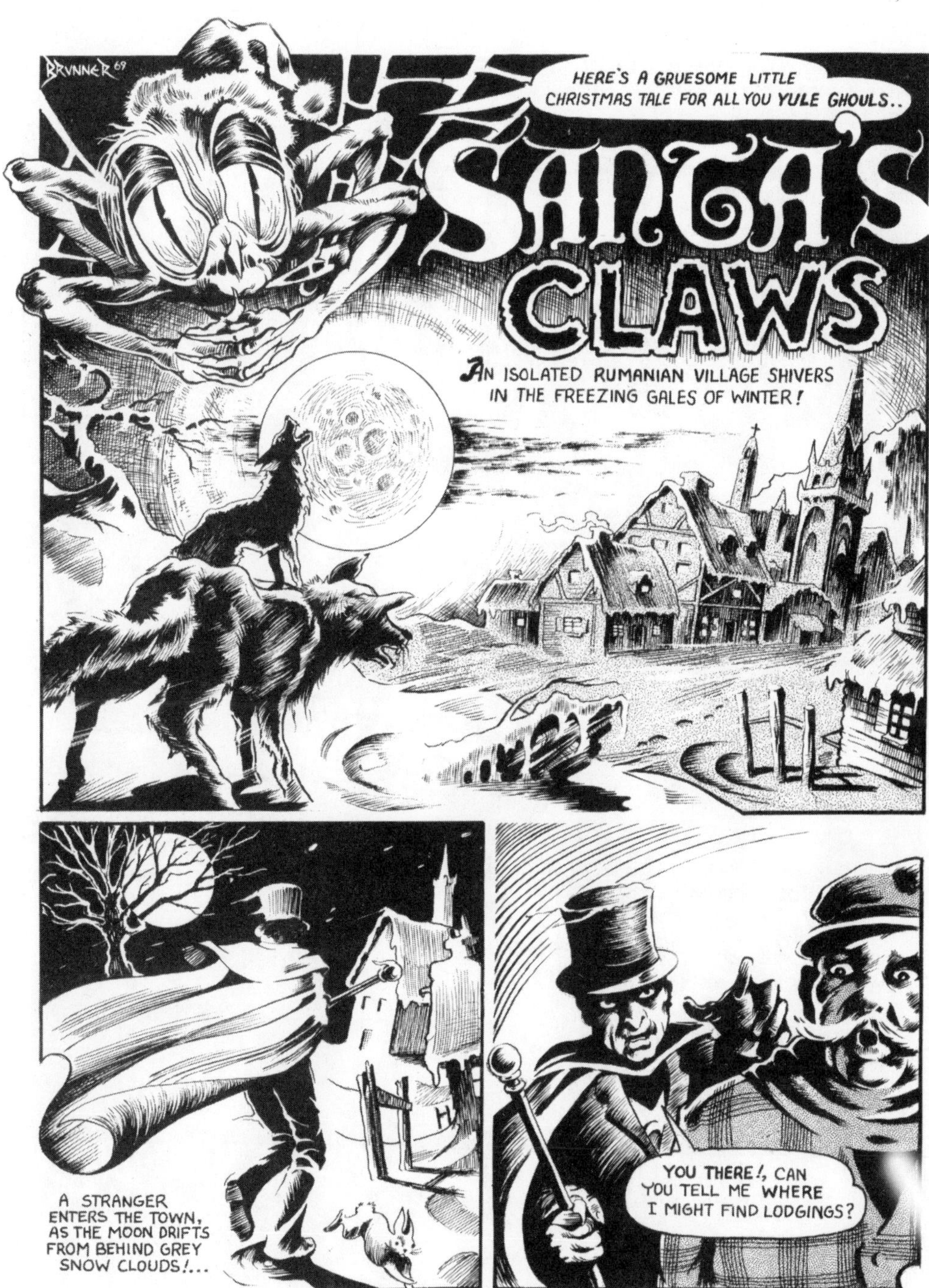

FRANK BRUNNER

THE PEASANT TURNS, STARTLED BY THE COMMANDING TONE OF THE STRANGER!
WHAT DO YOU WANT ??
A PLACE TO SHELTER MYSELF!!
YOU COULD TRY OVER AT THE INN!.. BUT IT IS LATE !!
TURNING QUICKLY, THE MAN HEADS FOR THE INN!, WITHOUT SO MUCH AS A "THANK YOU!"
BAM! BAM!
ALRIGHT ALRIGHT, I'M COMING, WHO IS IT ??
I AM A STRANGER IN TOWN, AND I NEED A PLACE TO STAY!
INN
WHY IT'S NEARLY FOUR IN THE MORNING!..
I DON'T CARE YOU FOOL!, JUST LET ME IN QUICKLY!
IT'LL BE..ER..FIVE MARKS A NIGHT.. IN ADVANCE!
VERY GOOD!.. MY LUGGAGE WILL BE HERE SHORTLY!
THE VERY NEXT NIGHT!..

TWO WEEKS PASS.... TWO WEEKS OF **HORROR** THAT SHOCK THE SLEEPY VILLAGE !!..
IT'S NOT GOOD, THESE UNSOLVED MURDERS! THE PEOPLE ARE STAY--ING IN DOORS AND I AM UNABLE TO FIND THE KILLER!
YES, BÜRGERMEISTER, I'M AFRAID IT'S GOING SPOIL THE HOLIDAYS TOO!
I'LL HAVE TO QUESTION EVERYONE, I CAN'T AFFORD TO TAKE CHANCES....
YOU'RE RIGHT, OF COURSE, BUT PERHAPS YOU SHOULD QUESTION JUST ONE PERSON!
WHO DO YOU MEAN?
I MEAN THAT STRANGER WHO ARRIVED TWO WEEKS AGO!, HE HASN'T BEEN SEEN YET....IN THE DAYLIGHT!
YES I'D LIKE TO QUESTION THIS.. ...THIS COUNT.. "ALFONSE"!
.. OH HE'S NEVER AWAKE AT THIS TIME OF DAY!.., HE'S AN INSOMNIAC, YOU KNOW... WRITES AND READS AT NIGHT!
.. I DON'T CARE!, I WANT TO SEE HIM **RIGHT NOW**!!
ALRIGHT, COME THIS WAY!
20

THE INNKEEPER KNOCKS, BUT GETTING NO REPLY, HE USES HIS PASS-KEY AND BOTH ARE STARTLED BY WHAT THEY FIND !!...
NOTHING!!... THERE IS NO ONE HERE, IS THIS SOME SORT OF JOKE!??
NO NO!... HE IS SUPPOSED TO BE HERE!
WELL, I'LL CATCH HIM YET!.... YOU LET ME KNOW IF HE TRIES TO LEAVE..... OR ENTER!
YES, YES SIR!
LATER, DEEP UNDER THE INN!!...
DON'T WORRY, COUNT, I SENT HIM AWAY, HE WON'T BOTHER YOU ANY-MORE! NOR WILL HE FIND YOUR RESTING PLACE DOWN HERE!
SOON NO ONE IS VENTURING OUT IN-TO THE STREET AT NIGHT! AND THE COUNT'S HUNGER FOR BLOOD GROWS!.......
THE TOWN IS WISE!! THEY WON'T GO OUT AND I HAVE NO WAY OF ENTERING THEIR HOMES! BUT I MUST HAVE WHAT I NEED!!

CHRISTMAS ARRIVES AND DESPITE THE CURFEW AND THE TOWN'S FEAR, THE FESTIVITIES PROCEED!
MEANWHILE, BELOW THE TAVERN, COUNT ALFONSE IS GETTING MORE AND MORE DESPERATE!!...
MASTER, I CAN-NOT CONTINUE TO LURE PEOPLE TO THE INN ANYMORE!..
YOU FOOL! I MAY YET HAVE TO RESORT TO...YOU!!
....OH NO...NO MASTER!..PLEASE! BESIDES THEY'D MISS ME AND BECOME SUSPICIOUS WITH CHRISTMAS HERE AND...
CHRISTMAS, MASTER!, YOU KNOW, SANTA-CLAUS AND....
WHAT ??..WHAT DID YOU SAY??....
SHUT UP!! I THINK IM GETTING A PLAN!!
CHRISTMAS EVE, AND THE TOWNSPEOPLE GET TO BED EARLY IN THE EXPECTATION OF A JOYFUL CHRISTMAS MORNING....

...BUT A FEW LITTLE PEOPLE CAN'T WAIT, AND HOPE TO SEE A CERTAIN VISITOR!

SUDDENLY ALL THEIR DREAMS BECOME REALITY, AS TWO FAMILIAR BOOTS APPEAR!

HO
HO
HO
...AND WHAT ARE YOU THREE LITTLE ONES DOING UP SO LATE ??

JUST THEN ANOTHER FIGURE APPEARS FROM THE FIREPLACE !, THE SURPRISED "COUNT ALFONSE" TURNS....
WHAT?
ARRRGH!

NEXT MORNING, TWO PARENTS ARE SHOCKED TO SEE THEIR CHILDREN FAST ASLEEP ON THE FLOOR!...
...BUT NO EXPLANATION COULD BE GOTTEN FROM THE CHILDREN, JUST A STRANGE GIFT IN ONE OF THE STOCKINGS !!...
..AND TO ALL, A GOOD NIGHT!
FINIS

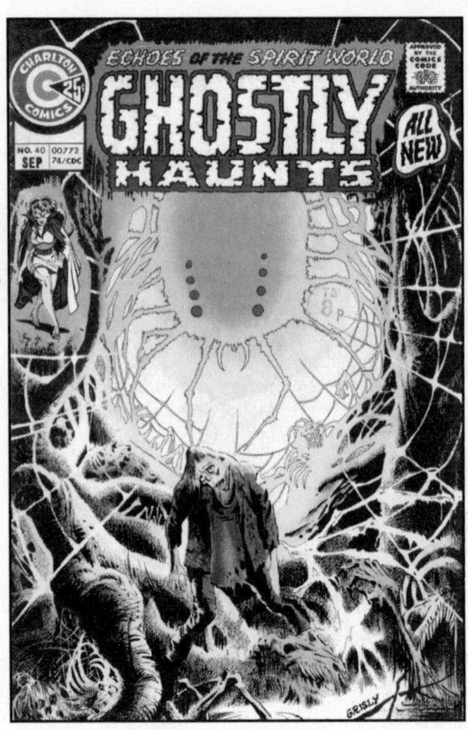

The Game Keeper

Ghostly Haunts 40, September 1974

During the 1970s, Charlton Comics managed to pull together an interesting team of creators. Unfortunately their comics paled when placed next to the giants of Marvel and DC; they always had. For those prepared to try something different, they wouldn't always be entirely disappointed, certainly not if Tom Sutton had been let loose at the drawing board. There are several of Tom's contributions to Charlton's years of terror in this section. The 40th issue of *Ghostly Haunts* is a delight in that it features a particularly fine tale lurking behind one of his eerie cover creations. It wasn't unusual for him to receive a call from one of the company's editors asking for a story almost at the drop of a hat. Tom relished the challenge and the freedom he was given; it gave rise to some of the most perturbing yet sublime tales from the period.

RUN, AVIS DROOD! RUN AS FAST AS YOUR LOVELY LEGS CAN CARRY YOU, FOR THE FULL MOON BURGEONS BEYOND DROOD CASTLE AND THE GAME IS AFOOT! DARE TO HOPE, AVIS DROOD! HOPE THAT YOUR FLYING FEET CAN OUTRACE YOUR POUNDING HEART THOUGH THAT HEART BE BOUND TO...

THE GAME KEEPER

THESE MONSTROUS BEASTS, ALL SO FAMILIAR TO JAN, SO LOVING TO HIM, ARE OUT TO KILL ME!

AND JAN, MY STRANGE HUSBAND IS OUT HERE SOMEPLACE WITH HER!

ART-SCRIPT...TOM SUTTON

THE GAME, THE GIANT FANGED BATS, THE MONSTROUS LUMBERING APE-THING, THE SLAVERING WOLVES, THE GIANT SLITHERING SERPENT, WERE THEY WATCHING THAT BRIGHT SUNNY DAY NOT LONG AGO WHEN JAN VAN DROOD FIRST BROUGHT YOU HERE AS HIS BRIDE?

D-6211

HOW EXCITING JAN VAN DROOD WAS, HOW DIFFERENT FROM OTHER MEN!
THERE, AVIS! DROOD CASTLE!
JAN! IT'S LIKE SOMETHING OUT OF A FAIRY TALE!
MORE LIKE A GOTHIC ROMANCE. THIS HAS BEEN THE ANCESTRAL HOME OF THE DROODS FOR EIGHT CENTURIES!

IMAGINE! MISTRESS OF DROOD CASTLE!
THERE IS BUT ONE MISTRESS HERE AND SHE IS NEITHER YOUNG NOR BEAUTIFUL!
SALIC! WATCH YOUR TONGUE LEST YOU LOSE IT! FETCH UP THE LUGGAGE!

PAY NO MIND TO SALIC. HIS SENILE BRAIN IS AS MOSSED AND CRUMBLING AS THE STONES OF DROOD CASTLE!

THAT STRANGE REMARK BY THE OTHERWISE INOFFENSIVE OLD SERVANT HAUNTED YOUR DAYS AT THE CASTLE, DIDN'T IT, AVIS?
WWHEE-OOOO!
AWHOOOOO
GRROWWLL!!
AND THE NIGHTS, THE NIGHTS BROUGHT THINGS STRANGER YET!

THOSE ANIMALS! WHAT MAKES THEM CALL LIKE THAT!?
THEY CALL TO ONE ANOTHER... TO THEIR MATES!
HOW SWEET! EVEN THE BEASTS OF THE GLADE ARE IN LOVE HERE IN THESE TIMELESS CARPATHIAN MOUNTAINS!
LOVE? OH, LORD! AVIS, IF YOU ONLY KNEW!
2

HEAR ME, YOUNG WIFE, AND MARK MY WORDS WELL. YOUR VERY LIFE MY DEPEND ON YOUR UNQUESTIONING OBEDIENCE!
YOU MUST NEVER LEAVE THE CASTLE AFTER DARK!

BUT YOU OFTEN WALK THE WILD MOUNTAIN PASSES LONG AFTER THE RISING OF THE MOON. HOW IS IT ANY LESS DANGEROUS FOR YOU, JAN?
I AM A DROOD! I WAS BROUGHT UP HERE...HAVE ALWAYS BEEN HERE. THEY... THEY ARE FAMILIAR WITH ME!

SSKKREE
CHIT-CHIT-CHIT.
SALIC! WOULD YOU HAVE ME END YOUR WRETCHED EXISTENCE THIS INSTANT!?
IT IS SHE, MASTER!

HEAVENS! WHAT IN THE WORLD COULD HAVE MADE THAT SOUND?
ENOUGH! I,-I MUST GO NOW!

THAT WAS WHEN YOU FIRST BEGAN THINKING ABOUT HER, WASN'T IT, AVIS? SUSPICION AND, YES... JEALOUSY ATE AWAY AT YOUR HEART, DROVE YOU TO PRY OPEN A MONSTROUS SECRET!
SALIC, WHY IS THAT DOOR ALWAYS LOCKED?
IT IS THE MASTER'S WISH, MISS. MASTER DROOD HAS THE ONLY KEY!
3

THE NEXT MORNING AS JAN SLEPT, EXHAUSTED FROM HIS NOCTURNAL WANDERINGS YOU TOOK THE BIG IRON KEY-RING FROM HIS BELT.

SOMEHOW YOU KNEW THE ANSWER TO JAN'S MYSTERIOUS SECRET LIFE LOOMED DARKLY BEHIND THAT LOCKED DOOR!
THIS LOCK HASN'T BEEN TURNED IN YEARS!

THE FEEBLE DAYLIGHT ADMITTED BY RENTS IN THE HEAVY ROTTING DRAPERY REVEALED A MUSTY ANTIQUE GALLERY OF...
PAINTINGS! A PICTORIAL CHRONOLOGICAL HISTORY OF THE ANCIENT DROOD FAMILY!

AND EACH OF THE DROODS, FROM THE DARK AND FORBODING WARRIOR KING ERIK DOWN TO JAN VAN DROOD. EACH OF THEM WERE DEPICTED IN THE COMPANY OF GREAT AND SAVAGE BEASTS!
INDEED, THE RACE OF DROOD SEEMED TO SHARE SOME MYSTERIOUS SECRET WITH THESE UNCANNY ANIMALS!
DO YOU LIKE THE PAINTINGS, MISS AVIS? YOU ARE THE FIRST OUTSIDER WHO HAS EVER SEEN THEM.
4

I AM NO OUTSIDER, SALIC! I AM THE WIFE OF JAN VAN DROOD!
I AM MISTRESS HERE!

WILL YOU EVER FORGET THE WAY SALIC LAUGHED AT THAT? THE WIZENED LITTLE HUSK OF A MAN TURNED TOWARD THE FOREST BEYOND THE WINDOWS AND CACKLED INSANELY AT YOUR PRESUMPTION!

HIS QUAKING, MADLY RANTING LAUGHTER ECHOED DOWN THE GRIM STONE HALLS AS YOU RAN FROM THAT GHASTLY GALLERY.

THAT NIGHT, WHEN JAN STRODE OFF INTO THE WOODS YOU WERE BUT A SHADOWS-LENGTH BEHIND HIM.

BUT THE WOODS BECAME VERY DENSE!
I'VE LOST HIM. WAIT... THAT MUST BE HIM AHEAD!
5

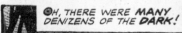

DELIBERATELY, THE BIG CATS DROVE HER DOWN A WELL WORN TRAIL.

EACH TIME SHE BLINDLY FLOUNDERED OFF THE PATH ANOTHER CREATURE WAITED TO DRIVE HER BACK ON THE WAY THEY HAD OBVIOUSLY CHOSEN FOR HER.

OH, THERE WERE MANY DENIZENS OF THE DARK!
CREATURES BIG AND SMALL AS IF WITH A SINGLE PURPOSE, FAMILIAR BEASTS AND SOME THINGS THAT SIMPLY COULD NOT BE!

AFTER AN INTERMINAL AGONY OF LASHING BRANCHES, TRIPPING VINES AND KNIFING THORNS THE CRASHING AND GUTTERAL GROWLING STOPPED.
THEY JOINED IN PURSUING YOU, AS IF BY A CUNNING, AN INTELLIGENCE BEYOND THE KEN OF MERE ANIMALS!
...JAN!
THEY HAD YOU WHERE THEY WANTED YOU... THE ANIMALS HAD BROUGHT YOU TO...
6

DON'T COME ANOTHER STEP AVIS! WHY COULDN'T YOU HAVE OBEYED ME?
I SAW THE PAINTINGS, JAN.
THEN YOU KNOW...THE CURSE OF THE DROODS! OUR LINE DEPARTED FROM THE MAINSTREAM OF HUMAN DEVELOPMENT...WE NEVER BECAME ENTIRELY HUMAN!
ON THE NIGHTS OF THE MOON WE REVERT TO OUR ANIMAL SELVES! ...A RACE OF WERE-CREATURES!
AND HER? THE TRUE MISTRESS OF DROOD CASTLE, SALIC SPOKE OF? WHAT OF HER?
STOP! KEEP AWAY! SHE IS ANGRY!
NOTHING CAN HELP ME NOW, AVIS!
YOU CAME ALL THIS WAY TO SEE HER, DON'T LOOK AWAY NOW! AVIS!
ISN'T SHE MAGNIFICENT? NOW YOU KNOW HOW FUTILE IT WOULD BE TO COMPETE IN HER WORLD...
YARRRRAAARRRGH!
NOW YOU KNOW HOW INADEQUATE YOUR LOVE IS COMPARED TO HER TIMELESS PASSION.
A SEETHING RELENTLESS LUST COMSUMATING ITSELF IN... DEATH!
END

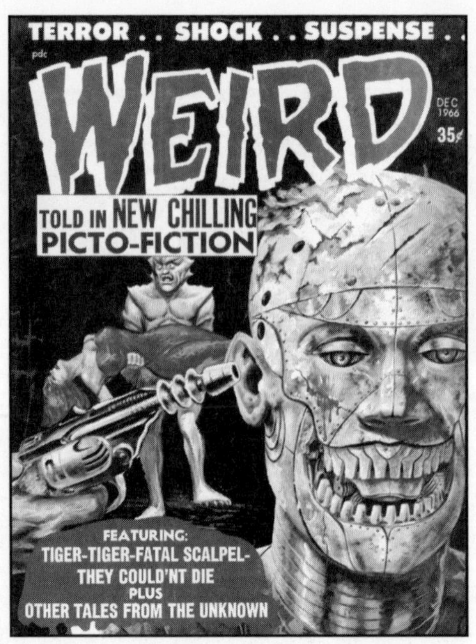

Fatal Scalpel

Weird Vol. 2 No. 1, December 1966

If exploitative horror is your poison then look no further! Eerie Publications excelled at horror of the sleaziest kind. Their tales are often retellings of stories from the Farrell Comics of the 1950s: *Voodoo*, *Strange Fantasy*, *Fantastic Fears* and *Haunted Thrills*. Robert W. Farrell had owned both companies so had access to an abundance of artwork, all of it already paid for. The art in this tale is still very reminiscent of the Iger Studios mentioned in Part I. *Weird* was probably the earliest imitator of the groundbreaking Warren black-and-white magazines. The covers, while significantly more gaudy, had a similar attraction; and the interiors were full of black-and-white horror, although it has to be said there was a huge difference in quality. *Creepy* had the sardonic wit of Uncle Creepy to rely upon when introducing these stories; *Weird* had Morris the Caretaker of Weird in their employ as host up until 1968.

FATAL SCALPEL
RELENTLESS HATRED BROODED LIKE A POISONOUS SPIDER IN THE BRAIN OF DR. ALEX HARDING! THEN ONE NIGHT HIS REASON SNAPPED AND HIS VENOM FASHIONED A TERRIBLE WEAPON IN THE JEALOUS BLADE...
A FAMOUS PLASTIC SURGEON, ALEX HARDING, MAKES A NEW FACE FOR SOME UNFORTUNATE...
SUTURES! QUICKLY!
YES, DR. HARDING!
MARVELOUS JOB, DOCTOR!
YOU'RE A GENIUS, HARDING! NO OTHER MAN COULD HAVE DONE WHAT YOU DID TODAY!
THANKS, MIKE!
37

BUT LATER, DOCTOR HARDING'S ACTIONS ARE STRANGE...
I HOPE ROGERS HAS SOMETHING FOR ME TODAY! I'M GOING CRAZY! I'VE GOT TO KNOW!
HE PROMISED IT TODAY!
BERNIE ROGERS
PRIVATE INVESTIGATIONS
AND...
H-HELLO, ROGERS! DID Y-YOU GET IT?
HI, DOC! YEAH! I GOT WHAT YOU WANTED!
YOUR WIFE IS CHEATING ON YOU, ALL RIGHT! SHE'S BEEN SEEING A MAN NAMED VINCENT ROMEZ, A LATIN AMERICAN! BUT HE LEFT TOWN YESTERDAY!
SO IT'S TRUE! CATHERINE LOVES SOME-ONE ELSE!
I-I CAN HARDLY BELIEVE IT! SHE'S MUCH YOUNGER, OF COURSE, BUT I THOUGHT SHE LOVED ME!
DON'T TAKE IT SO HARD, DOC! MIGHT HAPPEN TO ANYONE! ANYWAY, THE GUY IS GONE NOW-- I SAW HIM BOARD A PLANE!
YOU'RE SURE HE'S GONE THEN MAYBE SHE'LL FORGET HIM! YES-- SHE WILL! AND I'LL PRETEND THAT I DON'T KNOW-- THAT IT NEVER HAPPENED!
38

WHEN HARDING LEAVES...
WHAT A CHUMP! I BETTER CALL CATHERINE AND TELL HER WHAT A DUMMY SHE MARRIED!
HI, BABY! I JUST TALKED TO YOUR HUSBAND! I GAVE HIM MY-- HAH-HAH-- REPORT!
DARLING! WHAT DID HE SAY? DID HE BELIEVE IT?
HE WENT FOR IT HOOK, LINE AND SINKER! HE THINKS YOU'VE BEEN SEEING A GUY NAMED VINCENT ROMEZ, WHO JUST LEFT TOWN! SO HE AIN'T GONNA SAY ANYTHING TO YOU! PRETTY SMART, EH?
YOU'RE A CLEVER DARLING! PUTTING HIM ONTO A FALSE TRAIL! SEE YOU SOON!
SO, AN HOUR LATER...
HELLO, DARLING! HAVE A NICE DAY?
NOT WITHOUT YOU, ALEX! I MISSED YOU!
LOVELY! I'LL FORGIVE HER THIS TIME!
FOOL! I HATE HIM! IF ONLY HE WOULD DIE AND LEAVE ME HIS MONEY!
WHILE EVEN THEN FATE IS STIRRING THE INGREDIENTS INTO THE POT-- FEAR... HATE... REVENGE... HORROR...
YEP, I'M PRETTY CLEVER! GUESS I'LL JUST *HIC* HAVE ONE FOR THE ROAD! AND TO DOC HARDING'S BEAUTIFUL WIFE! WHAT A CHUMP HE IS...
39

MINUTES LATER...
THAT FOOL! GONNA CRASH!
GAAAA!
AND...
HE'S ALIVE!
YEAH -- BUT LOOK AT HIS FACE! UGH! CUT TO PIECES! MAKES ME SORT OF SICK!
NEXT MORNING WHEN DOCTOR HARDING REACHES THE HOSPITAL...
AN EMERGENCY CASE, DOCTOR! AUTO CRASH! HIS NAME IS BERNIE ROGERS!
ROGERS! BUT I...
DOCTOR HARDING
MINUTES LATER...
HE'S STILL UNDER MORPHINE, DOCTOR! TALKS A LOT!
I SEE! I WON'T NEED YOU FOR A WHILE, NURSE!
40
THE SHOCKING TRUTH COMES HOME TO HARDING...
HAH-HAH! I LOVE YOU, CATHERINE! BUT WHAT A DUMMY YOU MARRIED! HO-HO! HE BELIEVED THAT YARN ABOUT YOUR LATIN LOVER! WHILE ALL THE TIME IT'S YOU AND ME! HA-HA!
SO THAT'S IT! THIS MAN AND MY WIFE! I WAS A FOOL!

SOMETHING CRACKS IN HARDING'S BRAIN! HE GOES INSANE IN HIS DESIRE FOR REVENGE...
I WAS A FOOL! BUT NO LONGER! CHEAT ME, WILL THEY? MAKE A FOOL OF ME! WE'LL SEE WHO HAS THE LAST LAUGH!
HAH-HAH! IT'S NOT OFTEN THAT A MAN HAS SUCH AN OPPORTUNITY FOR REVENGE! AND WHAT A REVENGE!
AFTER THE OPERATION...
WHY, DOCTOR HARDING! TAKING YOUR TOOLS HOME?
YES! I'VE GOT A LITTLE-- HAH-HAH-- HOME WORK TO DO TONIGHT!
YES, A LITTLE HOME WORK! WITH MY DARLING CATHERINE, WHO LOVES ME SO! HAH-HAH!
GOOD! NOBODY AROUND! NO ONE TO INTERRUPT ME! I'LL GET STARTED AT ONCE!
CATHERINE HARDING KNOWS INSTINCTIVELY THAT SOMETHING HAS GONE HORRIBLY WRONG...
ALEX! W-WHAT ARE YOU DOING HOME NOW?
IF YOU'RE DRESSING FOR BERNIE ROGERS, MY DEAR, YOU'D BETTER NOT! HE WON'T BE COMING TODAY!
41

B-BERNIE? ARE YOU CRAZY, ALEX? I DON'T KNOW WHAT YOU MEAN!
I MEAN THAT I'M NO LONGER A FOOL! YOUR LOVER IS IN THE HOSPITAL!
BERNIE! THE HOSPITAL! WHAT HAVE YOU DONE?
YOU'LL SEE, CATHERINE! BECAUSE I'M GOING TO DO THE SAME THING TO YOU! NOW!
A LITTLE ETHER SO YOU WON'T FEEL PAIN! UNTIL - HAH-HAH -- LATER!
NO! GAAA--
THE DOCTOR ARRANGES A CRUDE OPERATING TABLE IN THE KITCHEN...
ABOUT READY! IN A MINUTE NOW, I'LL START MAKING YOUR NEW FACE, MY DEAR!
YOU DIDN'T WANT ME, DEAR CATHERINE! YOU WANTED HIM! SO YOU'RE GOING TO HAVE YOUR WISH! YOU TWO WILL NEVER LEAVE EACH OTHER WHEN I'M FINISHED!
HALF AN HOUR LATER...
DONE! NOBODY CAN EVER UNDO THIS WORK OF MINE! I'VE GOT ONE LAST THING TO DO!
42

AFTER A CALL TO THE POLICE...
ALMOST THROUGH NOW! ONE MORE THING!
AND WHEN THE PUZZLED COPS ARRIVE...
HE MUST HAVE BEEN NUTS! HE DID THIS TO HER FACE-- THEN LEFT HER ALL HIS MONEY!
IF SHE MARRIES THIS BERNIE ROGERS GUY!
YEAH! FIGURE THAT! THOSE TWO GOTTA GET MARRIED, OR NO DOUGH! AND HE ALSO OPERATED ON THE ROGERS GUY THIS MORNING! BEATS ME!
TODAY, IN THE DESOLATE MOUNTAINS, THERE IS AN OLD HOUSE WHERE LIVE A STRANGE MARRIED COUPLE! NO ONE EVER SEES THEIR FACES...
ANOTHER DAY GONE, BERNIE!
YES, CATHERINE!
AND THIS IS DOCTOR HARDING'S REVENGE!
THE END
43

The Weirdest Character I've Ever Known

Ghostly Haunts 38, May 1974

Here is a marvellous play upon caricature in a tale where the cackling of the dark humour once endorsed by EC will continue to ring in your ears even as you turn the final page. For enthusiasts of Tom Sutton's work this issue of *Ghostly Haunts* is another gem, with a darkly comedic cover by him that leads directly into an irrepressible tale conceived by Charlton stalwart Joe Gill. On too many occasions one of his eerie images would adorn the cover with the interior pages devoid of his compelling accomplishments.

JASON BLIGGS (HIS PEN NAME) WROTE HORROR STORIES... HIS CRITICS SAID MR. BLIGGS LIVED IN A WORLD ALL HIS OWN... AND IF THEY COULD'VE VISITED HIM IN THE WEIRD OLD HOUSE HE'D FINALLY FOUND, THEY WOULD'VE BEEN TERRIFIED TO DISCOVER EXACTLY WHAT SORT OF WORLD IT WAS!
THE WEIRDEST CHARACTER I'VE EVER KNOWN!
GEO WILDMAN EDITOR
JOE GILL WRITER
D-5762
IN A MOMENT, ALBERT... AS SOON AS I FINISH MY LATEST "CREATION PAPER" HEH HEH!
NECRONOMICON
AGATHA IS MY LATEST CHARACTER... SHE'S VOLUPTUOUS, EVIL TO THE CORE, WITH EYES IN WHICH GLITTER THE FIRES OF HELL, AND THE APPETITES OF A VAMPIRE!
LET US SEE IF I HAVE CREATED WELL!
YES... I'VE DONE IT AGAIN ...YOU, AGATHA, SHALL BE THE CHIEF CHARACTER IN MY NEXT STORY!
1

I HAVEN'T DECIDED YET ...AND SAVE YOUR SMILES FOR SOMEONE ELSE...I CREATED YOU ...I KNOW THE EVIL THAT LIES IN YOUR HEART!
HOW SWEET, JASON... WILL THE STORY HAVE A HAPPY ENDING ?

AN UNLIKELY STORY, ISN'T IT? HOW COULD A WRITER, EVEN ONE OF JASON BLIGGS' HORRIFIC TALENTS, WRITE CHARACTERS INTO ACTUAL LIFE? ACCORDING TO POLICE ACCOUNTS AND AN OLD JOURNAL, IT ACTUALLY HAPPENED.. YOU CAN BELIEVE IT OR NOT!
ALBERT, WHEN I SAY BRING ME BRANDY, BRING ME THE USUAL SORT...DON'T CONCOCT SOMETHING SPECIAL JUST TO SHOW OFF!

THIS ROOM IS GETTING RATHER CROWDED...THE REPTILEAN MAN I CREATED THREE NOVELS BACK TAKES UP TOO MUCH ROOM...
BLIGGS

IT'S EASY TO RID MYSELF OF MY UNWANTED GUESTS...ALL THAT'S NEEDED IS TO BURN THEIR "CREATION PAPERS" ...LIKE SO...

AS THE PAPER JASON TOSSED IN THE FIREPLACE BLAZED UP, A STRANGE THING HAPPENED TO THE REPTILEAN MAN...HE VANISHED!
IT ALWAYS AMAZES ME... HOW EASILY I RID MYSELF OF THEM!
2

RRIINGG
THERE GOES MR. SMILES, NOW I ... WHO CAN THAT BE?
YOU'RE MR. JASON BLIGGS, I BELIEVE ... I'M MABEL FERMOY. I'M WRITING AN ARTICLE FOR A WOMAN'S MAGAZINE... IT'S ABOUT HORROR STORIES... I'VE INTERVIEWED SEVERAL OTHER WRITERS AND I WANT TO DISCUSS YOUR WORK TOO! MAY I COME IN?
ACTUALLY, MISS FERMOY, I'M BUSY AT THE MOMENT! I DON'T ENTERTAIN CASUAL VISITORS!
YOU DON'T HAVE TO ENTERTAIN ME, MR. BLIGGS.
NO, ALBERT... YOU CAN'T DO THINGS LIKE THAT ANY MORE!
ALBERT WHO...OH... ALBERT WAS ONE OF YOUR MOST REPULSIVE VILLAINS ...ACTUALLY, HE WAS A ZOMBIE WASN'T HE?
SH-SHE DOESN'T LIKE ME, MASTER.
YOU MUST BE CAREFUL WHAT YOU SAY HERE! ALBERT IS VERY SENSITIVE!
SMASH!
3

WHAT ABOUT YOUR OTHER CHARACTERS, MR. BLIGGS? THE REPTILE MAN, FOR INSTANCE...
GONE... HE WAS A DULL CLOD!

WHAT ABOUT YOUR CREEPY MR. SMILES? HE WAS SUCH A TREACHEROUS SORT...
HE CONSUMED TWO BOTTLES OF MY FAVORITE BRANDY... SMOKED ALL OF MY CIGARS...

I'VE JUST BEEN REVIEWING SOME OF MY CREATIONS ... ONE MUST HOUSE-CLEAN NOW AND THEN OR THE PLACE GETS ALL CLUTTERED!

EEEEEEEEEE!!!!!
WHAT'S THAT, MR. BLIGGS?
THAT? OH...THAT MUST BE CYRIL...

THEY HEARD HEAVY STEPS ON THE STAIRS, THEN CLUMPING NOISES IN THE HALL AND...
HE SEEMS TO BE IN PAIN, JASON!
OH, DEAR... I SHOULD NEVER BE INTERRUPTED WHEN I'M DOING MY HOUSECLEANING!
4

AS THE GIANT NEARED JASON BLIGGS, HE HURRIEDLY THRUST THE ENTIRE PAPER INTO THE FLAMES...
HE DISAPPEARED!

I WITNESSED THAT, SIR! YOU ARE A MURDERER!
NONSENSE, GIRL! HOW CAN I MURDER SOMEONE WHO HAS NEVER EXISTED OUTSIDE MY IMAGINATION!

BUT HE DID EXIST... I SAW HIM... I HEARD HIM... AND I SAW YOU MAKE HIM DISAPPEAR!
YOU LITTLE FOOL... HE WAS A CHARACTER FROM MY THIRD NOVEL, THE GIANT WALKED BY NIGHT... I CREATED HIM!

SUDDENLY, SHE SNATCHED THE PAPERS FROM HIM AND RAN...
HOW MANY OTHERS ARE YOU GOING TO DESTROY YOU MANIAC? I'M GOING TO SEARCH THIS HOUSE AND SAVE THEM WHILE I CAN!
WAIT, MISS FERMOY! DON'T GO BEYOND THAT DOOR!

JASON BLIGGS IS A MURDERER! I MUST SAVE HIS VICTIMS...

A GIANT BAT! MAYBE IT'S A...

...VAMPIRE... FROM KILLER'S MOON... I REMEMBER IT NOW!
AND THE WOLF-MAN... HE'S THE BAD GUY IN HOWL AT THY KILLER!

AAARRRGGHH!
AWAY, BEAST... BACK TO YOUR KENNEL! I, THE VAMPIRE, WILL FEAST TONIGHT!
SHE'S MINE YOU MONGRELS ...ALL MINE!

MR. BLIGGS WAS RIGHT... HE SHOULD DESTROY HIS WORK AFTER A BOOK IS FINISHED!
6

I MUST REACH HIM... THESE PAPERS MUST BE BURNED!
YOU SEE, MISS FERMON? I WAS RIGHT! NOW, IF YOU'LL GIVE ME THOSE PAPERS, I...
THERE'S NO TIME...
THE PAPERS WERE DRY AND THE FIRE HOT... THEY ALL BURST INTO FLAMES... BEFORE JASON BLIGGS COULD BRING THEM OUT!
THERE, MR. BLI... MR. BLIGGS!
HE'S GONE TOO!
I NEVER DREAMED HE WASN'T FOR REAL ... I WONDER WHO CREATED JASON BLIGGS IN THE FIRST PLACE?
IN THE OLD HOUSE, HAUNTED FOR THESE MANY YEARS... A SHADOWY FIGURE SAT AT A DESK AND...
LET'S SEE... WHAT SHALL I BE THIS TIME... AN ACTOR? NO... A GREAT ARTIST, PERHAPS? NO... I'LL BE A COMIC BOOK ILLUSTRATOR ... IT DOESN'T TAKE MUCH TALENT!
The End

Now… Another Maniac!

Psycho 18, May 1974

The layouts of this tale were uncompromising in their darkness. The lush toning usually associated with the design of Maelo Cintron was not in evidence here; the story simply didn't demand it.

Bronx artist Maelo will be remembered for his *Human Gargoyles*, one of Skywald's most celebrated ongoing series and one destined to return in the not too distant future. The work he produced on the original series was beautiful; however it proved very time-consuming and for the aspiring young artist, not particularly lucrative. The closure of the Skywald offices in 1975 saw him move into the world of illustration and book covers. His paintings for the covers of the *Star Trek* books of the 1990s are collector's items in themselves.

NOW...
ANOTHER MANIAC!
WRITTEN BY HOWIE ANDERSON
ILLUSTRATED BY MAELO CINTRON

...DAWN... NOBODY UP YET...DON'T SEE A SOUL...
KRASH!
GOD-DAMNIT! SOME KID'S BIKE ...PROB'LY WOKE UP THE WHOLE DAMN NEIGHBOR-HOOD...
NOTHING MUST GO WRONG.
...THE MOST IMPORTANT DAY OF MY LIFE...
...TODAY I GOTTA KILL A MAN!!

I PLANNED THIS SO LONG... DON'T KNOW NOW IF...IF I GOT THE GUTS!
...GETTIN' REAL LIGHT...DAWN... GOTTA GET MOVIN' ...KEEP TO MY SCHEDULE!
KNICK
KLIK

...HUH?
...LOU...
WHAT...
BE QUIET...
SHUT-UP...

NOW LOOK
LOU, I...
SHUT-UP!

TURN HERE ONTO ROUTE 8... TAKE THE FIRST DIRT ROAD ON YOUR LEFT... DRIVE TO THE END...

ALL RIGHT, STOP HERE AND GET OUT...
NOW LOOK LOU... WE BEEN PARTNERS A LONG TIME...WE CAN CLEAR THIS UP EASY...
...IT'S TOO LATE...
DIG...
WHAT?
DIG A HOLE!
...PASS THE SHOVEL UP... GIVE IT TO ME...
PLEASE LOU... PLEASE...I'M SORRY I DID IT...I CAN UNDO IT...PLEASE... LOU...PLEASE...
JUST GIVE ME THE SHOVEL...
BRAAANNNG!

THANK GOD...IT'S FINISHED!
THANK GOD IT'S FINISHED...I NEVER THOUGHT I COULD GO THROUGH WITH IT...
21
MY GOD...MY GOD... WHAT WENT WRONG? EVERYTHING WAS PERFECT... WHAT WENT WRONG?
MR. LOU WATERS?
YES!
YOU RUN OVER A BICYCLE IN YOUR DRIVEWAY THIS MORNING?
OH, GOD... ...HA HA HA... THAT'S ALL IT IS...THE BIKE... THE KID'S BIKE...
YES...I DID...AHH WHOEVER OWNS IT...I'LL BE GLAD TO PAY FOR IT... I...AH...DON'T KNOW WHAT IT WAS DOING IN MY DRIVEWAY!
...IT WAS YOUR PAPER-DELIVERY BOY'S BIKE...HE WAS DELIVERING YOUR MORNING PAPER...
OH?
I DON'T KNOW WHERE YOU WERE GOING AT THAT HOUR OF THE MORNING, MR. WATERS... BUT THE BOY IS DEAD...
...DEAD?
HE WAS ON THE BIKE WHEN YOU RAN OVER IT...

Through a Glass Darkly

Ghostly Tales 113, February 1975

Tom Sutton's seniors at Charlton once again granted him a free rein. This time he toyed with their notoriously lax approach to the job of editing their comics. "Through a Glass Darkly" is unique in the annals of four-colour comic book publishing in that it was presented in black and white with an exceptional use of grey tone. His instructions were explicit, and thankfully followed to the letter, that there was to be no use of colour. In contrast the cover was a hallucinogenic dreamscape, tempting the would-be reader to plunge into azure worlds unknown. The influence of H. P. Lovecraft, the baroque prince, is also in evidence in these pages.

CURIOSITY SHOP
CURIOSITY DROVE ME HENCE, FROM ONE OBSCURE SHOP TO ANOTHER, DELVING EVER DEEPER THE DARK SECRETS!
EVEN WHEN I FINALLY SAW IT... HELD IT IN MY HAND, I HARDLY DARED BELIEVE IT TRULY EXISTED!!
I CARRIED OFF A DREAM CLOSED IN A BRAZEN BOX.
SO, THIS INSATIABLE THIRST TO KNOW THE UNKNOWABLE HAS LED ME TO THIS!
...MORE YEARS TRACKING DOWN EVIDENCE OF AN ELDER RACE POSSESSING A KNOWLEDGE OF CELESTIAL SECRETS LOST FROM A TIME BEYOND MEMORY...
SECRETS SEEN...
THROUGH A GLASS DARKLY
WRITTEN AND DRAWN BY
YEARS OF TEDIOUS STUDY FROM MY FIRST HINT OF THE THING IN THE FRAGMENTED ROE PAPYRUS...
...THEN IN THE MANUSCRIPT OF THE MAD MONK AZZEXES AN ACTUAL DESCRIPTION OF THE BOX ...AND THE INSCRIPTION!
"I HAVE SEEN THE DARK UNIVERSE YAWNING WHERE THE BLACK PLANETS ROLL WITHOUT AIM...WHERE THEY ROLL IN THEIR HORROR UNHEEDED, WITHOUT KNOWLEDGE OR LUSTER OR NAME!"
FINALLY IT IS MINE! THE LENSE OF NEMESIS!
1

THE LENSE OF NEMESIS... NO MERE POLISHED GLASS THIS! RATHER AS REVEALED IN THE BOOK OF EIBON, A FANTASTIC PERFECT CRYSTAL BROUGHT TO EARTH BY THE ELDERS.
THE MERE POSSESSION OF THE THING WAS ENOUGH TO MAKE A MAN MAD WITH POWER!
I MUST MOUNT IT IN THE TELESCOPE AT ONCE!
AMAZING! SUCH A WORK OF LENSE MAKING I HAVE NEVER SEEN!
MY HANDS TREMBLED TOUCHING THAT WHICH THE ELDERS HAD HELD.
FEVERISHLY I SOUGHT INFORMATION ON SETTING MY LENSE...
THE PNAKOTIC ASTRONOMERS INDICATE NO SPECIAL ARRANGEMENT
I SET THE LENSE ARBITRARILY IN THE EYEPIECE OF MY INSTRUMENT AND...
By the BEARD of KADATH!
INSTANTLY I WAS SWEPT INTO THE MIDST OF THE COSMOS!
BLAZING SUNS AND MYRIAD MILLIONS OF DARK WORLDS SWIRLED ABOUT ME!
2

I WAS NO LONGER PEERING THROUGH A TELESCOPE AT THE MYSTERIOUS NIGHT SKY...
I HAD BEEN HURLED INTO THE STAR FIELDS THEMSELVES...
AND THERE WERE OTHER THINGS AMONG THE NIGHT WORLDS! THINGS NO ASTRONOMER EVER DREAMED OF!
I WAS CARRIED BACK TO REALITY ON THE ECHO OF MY SCREAM.
SO SHAKEN WAS I BY WHAT I'D SEEN, THAT I FELL AWAY FROM THE TELESCOPE AND...
N-NO! IT'S NOT POSSIBLE...
UNGH!
...TRIPPED!
UMPH!
...AND FALLING GRASPED THE TELESCOPE FOR SUPPORT.
FOOL THAT I AM I NEARLY DESTROYED THE LENSE! BUT WAIT...!
GREAT GODS!
PLOP!
3

BY THE SERPENT-BEARDED BYATIS!
NO WONDER THE LENSE POSITION IN THE TELESCOPE MADE NO DIFFERENCE!
WHAT I SAW... THE COSMOS IS WITHIN THE LENSE!
THE ENORMITY OF THIS NEW REVELATION SO OVERWHELMED ME I COULD BUT GAZE FEARFULLY INTO THE FAMILIAR NIGHT SKY AND WONDER...
IS IT THEN, NOT POSSIBLE THAT THE LENSE OF NEMESIS CONTAINS A DUPLICATE UNIVERSE?!
IS IT ONE AND THE SAME?
IS IT NOT WRITTEN THERE BE WORLDS WITHIN WORLDS?
WAS THIS WHAT THE ELDERS HINTED AT? I HAD TO KNOW!
THE ANCIENT VOLUMES WERE DUMB ON THE SUBJECT.
I WOULD HAVE TO FIND OUT FOR MYSELF!
4

I WAS LOATHE TO PASS THROUGH THE LENSE A SECOND TIME.
I WAS SEEING WHAT NO MAN COULD EXPERIENCE AND REMAIN SANE. I WAS AGAIN SWEPT INTO COSMIC CHOAS ON A SCALE UNIMAGINABLE, CYCLOPEAN MADNESS IN FANTASTIC PROFUSION AND THROUGH IT ALL...
IT WAS APPARENT I WAS ABOUT TO ATTAIN KNOWLEDGE OF GREAT AND FEARSOME CONSEQUENCE.
NO MATTER, I PICKED UP THE MARVELOUS CRYSTAL AND GAZED TRANSFIXED...
AT A NIGHTMARE!
5

...I WAS IN A CONSTANT STATE OF GROWTH, SURGING IN EGO BLOATING EXPANSIVENESS I LOOMED LARGER THAN THE TITANIC FIERCE BURNING SUNS...
THEN, AS BEFORE, SUDDENLY THE HEAVENLY BODIES BLURRED, DIMINISHING, MOVING OFF ON A TIDAL DRIFT
LEAVING ME...
...TOWERING OVER STRANGE PLANETS I STALKED AMONG THE GALAXIES A VERITABLE GOD!
UTTERLY ALONE!
I WAS NOT THE SAME MAN WHO HAD ONCE HUMBLY SOUGHT KNOWLEDGE...I WAS QUITE ALTERED!
I HOLD THE UNIVERSE IN MY HAND!
6

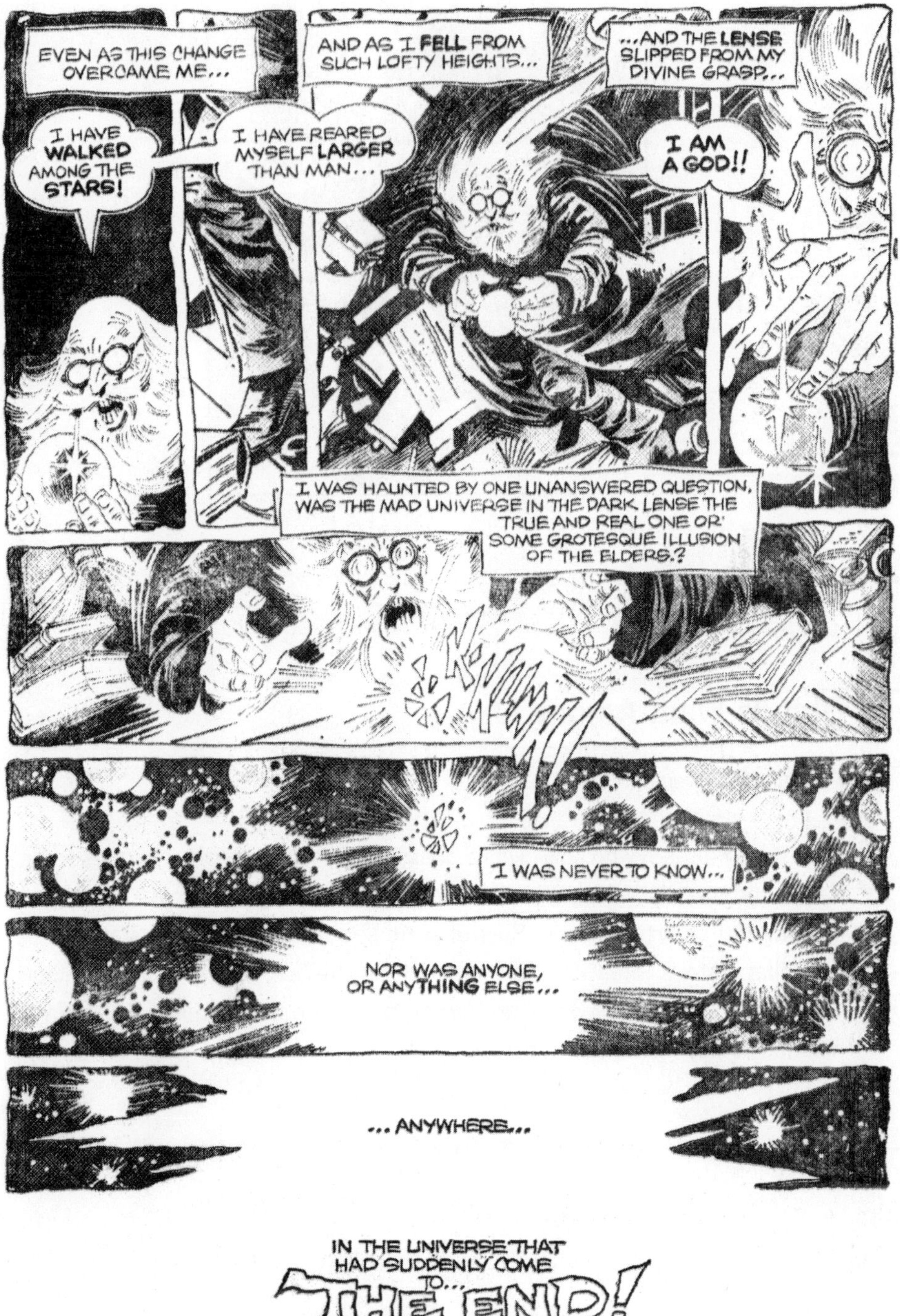

EVEN AS THIS CHANGE OVERCAME ME...

I HAVE **WALKED** AMONG THE **STARS**!

I HAVE REARED MYSELF **LARGER** THAN MAN...

AND AS I **FELL** FROM SUCH LOFTY HEIGHTS...

...AND THE **LENSE** SLIPPED FROM MY DIVINE GRASP...

I AM A GOD!!

I WAS HAUNTED BY ONE UNANSWERED QUESTION, WAS THE MAD UNIVERSE IN THE DARK LENSE THE TRUE AND REAL ONE OR SOME GROTESQUE ILLUSION OF THE ELDERS.?

I WAS NEVER TO KNOW...

NOR WAS ANYONE, OR ANY**THING** ELSE...

...ANYWHERE...

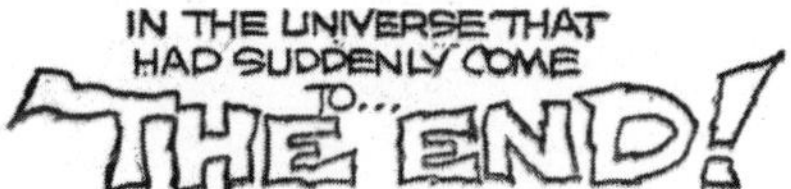

Ghouls Walk Among Us

Psycho 15, November 1973

Augustine Funnell, who now owns a bookstore, was in his early twenties when he penned this disturbing tale. Here you will find a very dark sense of humour at work and an artist, Ferran Sostres, who had a thorough understanding of his collaborator's intentions. Gus was one of the few people Alan Hewetson trusted to write scripts for the *Horrormood*; Skywald weren't always in a position to pay for new scriptwriters.

THE SOUND OF DARKNESS...AT FIRST JUST A THOUGHT... BUT THEN, WITH CREEPING, SLITHERING TERROR THE SOUND OF DARKNESS BECOMES A REALITY!

AND WITH REALITY COMES FEAR! THAT BLINDS AND BLOCKS OUT EVERYTHING!

NOW MORE THAN A THOUGHT, THE SOUND OF DARKNESS CAN BE HEARD! IT MOVES SLOWLY... BUT IT MOVES!

AND WITH MIND-SNAPPING FINALITY THE SOUND OF DARKNESS CAN BE SEEN! SEEN IN ITS AWFUL HORROR! SEEN AND FEARED LIKE NOTHING BEFORE IT!

A THOUGHT, A REALITY, A SOUND, A SIGHT, AND FINALLY PAIN! PAIN OF THE KIND THAT MEANS NOTHING LESS THAN DEATH! PAIN THAT TEARS THROUGH EVERY FIBRE, BURNING MORE HARSHLY THAN A FIERY COMET! AND NOW THE KNOWLEDGE, FIRST-HAND, THAT...
GHOULS WALK AMONG US
WRITTEN BY AUGUSTINE FUNNELL
ILLUSTRATED BY FERRAN SOSTRES
FERRAN SOSTRES-

MORNING, AS IT ALWAYS DOES, COMES... AND WITH IT COMES THE CHILL OF UNEXPLAINED HORROR.
GOOD LORD BILL! WOULD YOU LOOK AT THIS!?!
I KNOW CARL. IT'S NOT A PRETTY SIGHT. I THINK WE'RE DEALING WITH SOME KIND OF MANIAC. WHO FOUND IT ANYWAY?

THE GRAVEDIGGER. HE LIVES IN A SHACK JUST OVER THAT HILL.

BUT A NIGHT OF HORROR IS NOT ALWAYS EASILY EXPLAINED.
I DIDN'T HEAR A THING ALL LAST NIGHT. THEN, WHEN I WENT OUT THIS MORNING TO DIG A NEW GRAVE I FOUND THE BONES. CALLED YOU FELLOWS RIGHT AWAY.
WE CAN'T BE SURE, BUT THE SAME TYPE OF THING MIGHT HAPPEN AGAIN. IF YOU HEAR ANYTHING, LET US KNOW RIGHT AWAY.

AND A NIGHT OF HORROR IS EVEN HARDER TO EXPLAIN TO A CYNIC.
BUT CHIEF... AT FIRST WE THOUGHT IT WAS A HOMICIDAL MANIAC. BUT NO MAN COULD TEAR APART ANOTHER MAN LIKE THAT! IT'S IMPOSSIBLE!
AND I STILL SAY SOMEONE TOTALLY INSANE COMMITED THE MURDER. IF YOU WANT ME TO BELIEVE YOUR STORY, YOU'LL HAVE TO PROVE IT!

CHIEF... SOME OF THE BONES HAD TEETH MARKS IN THEM!

AGAIN THE SOUND OF DARKNESS, BUT THIS TIME THERE IS NO *LIVING* VICTIM.

BUT EVEN THOUGH THE PROOF IS BEFORE HIM, THE CYNIC REFUSES TO *BELIEVE*.
THERE'S A PICTURE OF THE *CORPSE* CHIEF. YOU CAN SEE THAT IT'S BEEN *HALF-EATEN!*
NONSENSE! THIS IS THE WORK OF A VERY *CLEVER* MAN. AN *INSANE* MAN, BUT A CLEVER ONE NEVERTHELESS. I WON'T ACCEPT YOUR RIDICULOUS STORIES. FIND THE *KILLER!*

BUT CHIEF... THIS IS A SMALL TOWN. WE'VE ONLY HAD *TWO* CRIMINAL OFFENCES IN THE LAST YEAR, AND BOTH THOSE GUYS ARE *LOCKED UP* OUT BACK. EVERYONE ELSE HERE IS LAW-ABIDING. WE *KNOW* THAT. IT'S GOT TO BE SOME KIND OF *FLESH-EATING CREATURE!*
I WON'T LISTEN TO ANOTHER WORD OF THIS *FOOLISHNESS!* I'M BEGINNING TO THINK BOTH OF YOU ARE LOSING YOUR *MARBLES!* *NOW GET THAT KILLER!*

A CYNIC HAS TO BE SHOWN CONCRETE FACT, HELD BEFORE HIS EYES. HE WILL ACCEPT NOTHING LESS...
I DON'T KNOW IF THIS WILL WORK BILL, BUT WE'VE GOTTA TRY IT. IF WE DON'T COME UP WITH SOMETHING SOON THE CHIEF ISN'T GOING TO BE OVERLY PLEASED...
I KNOW CARL... WE DON'T HAVE MUCH CHOICE... DO WE?

ONCE MORE THE SOUND OF DARKNESS... FOR THE THIRD TIME IN AS MANY NIGHTS. SOMEHOW THOUGH, THE SOUND OF DARKNESS CAN BE MUCH MORE HORRIBLE WHEN EXPERIENCED FIRST-HAND.
DAMMIT! I'M GETTIN' THE CREEPS FROM BEING IN THIS PLACE!
I KNOW EXACTLY WHAT YOU MEAN! IF SOMETHING DOESN'T HAPPEN SOON I'M GETTING THE HELL OUT OF HERE! IF THE CHIEF WANTS A KILLER, HE CAN GET HIM ALONE!

THERE'S SOMETHING IN THIS GRAVEYARD! I CAN FEEL IT!
WELL IT BETTER SHOW ITSELF SOON. I'M GOING NUTS WAITING!

...UGH... BILL?
HUH? WHAT IS IT?
LOOK... BE QUIET WILL YOU... AAAAHHHH!
HEY! WHAT'S GOING ON!?! I THOUGHT I HEARD...
AAAAAAHHHHHHH!
THEY LOOK AT EACH OTHER AND SMILE. THIS HAS BEEN A GOOD NIGHT. NO NEED AT ALL FOR THEM TO GO HUNGRY NOW.
NO, THEY WON'T GO HUNGRY THIS NIGHT.

EPILOGUE:

THEY HAVE FINISHED THEIR **MEAL**, AND ARE LEAVING, FOR THEY HAVE TO GO HOME. THE SOUND OF DARKNESS IS **QUIET** NOW, FOR THERE IS NO ONE AROUND TO HEAR IT.

BUT IT WILL BE HEARD AGAIN, FOR THE SOUND OF DARKNESS IS **ALWAYS** THERE, WAITING... WAITING... **WAITING!**

WE'LL STALK TO'MORROW NIGHT **BROTHERS...** REST WELL UNTIL THEN...

YES MRS. CRANSTON. WEIRD **NOISES** IN YOUR GARDEN TO-NIGHT, EH? WELL I'VE BEEN INVESTIGATING **ANOTHER** MATTER TO-NIGHT AND I'M AFRAID I WON'T BE ABLE TO GET OVER. TO-MORROW NIGHT FOR **SURE**. I'LL SEE YOU **THEN**. GOOD-BYE.

IT IS QUIET NOW. ALL IS PLEASANT, AND THE SOUND OF DARKNESS HAS FADED FOR ANOTHER NIGHT. BUT ONE OF THE CAUSES OF THAT SOUND SITS BACK IN HIS CHAIR, SMILES, CLOSES HIS EYES, AND LISTENS TO THE SOUNDS OF THE DEAD GRUMBLING WITHIN HIM...

Tradition of the Wolf

Nightmare 23, February 1975

This, the 1975 *Nightmare* Winter Special, was the finale for this title; a month later the *Psycho* Winter Special, its 24th issue, would herald the sad demise of the *Skywald Horrormood*. It wasn't a surprise behind the scenes at Skywald; Alan Hewetson hadn't been accepting anything new in terms of scripts and art for several months. His brief was to use what remained of the inventory and then, with the owners, fold the company. Thankfully, there was just enough time for Ed Fedory and Roberto Martinez to howl one more time before the moon. Roberto saw several stories appear in the latter months of the *Horrormood*; his work is often attributed to Robert Martin or Bob Martin.

THE SHARP CLANGING OF HAMMER AND ANVIL RINGS THROUGH THE QUIET AUSTRIAN VILLAGE... THE AIR SEEMS PREGNANT WITH EXPECTATION AS THE HOURS OF DAYLIGHT SOFTLY DRIFT TO A CLOSE.
ON MOST SUMMER EVENINGS WHEN THE WORK IS PLENTIFUL, THE SOUNDS OF THE BLACKSMITH AT WORK ARE HEARD LONG INTO THE NIGHT...
FOR WITHIN SHORT HOURS, THE FULL-MOON WILL RISE AND EVIL WILL STALK THE DARKENED WOODS!
LET THE COALS GROW COLD. WE HAVE DONE ENOUGH WORK THIS DAY!
WHAT WILL THE CAPTAIN SAY WHEN HE FINDS THAT THE SHOE HAS NOT BEEN REPLACED?
THE CAPTAIN BE DAMNED! THERE IS FAR MORE IMPORTANT WORK TO BE DONE THIS NIGHT!
...BUT THIS NIGHT IS FAR DIFFERENT THAN THE OTHERS--
FOR LONG YEARS YOU HAVE KNOWN OF MY HABITS, MY SON. WHEN THE MOON IS FULL WE VILLAGE MEN HUNT THE MOST HIDEOUS AND INTELLIGENT OF FOES--
--THE WEREWOLF!
TONIGHT SHALL BE NO DIFFERENT!
written by EDWARD FEDORY
illustrated by ROBERT MARTIN
TRADITION OF THE WOLF

LATER, AS THE RISING SILVER MOON REPLACES THE SUN ON THE NOW DARKENED HORIZON--
LAST MONTH WE LOST OLAF HAUSER! WHICH ONE OF US WILL IT SLAY TONIGHT!
TONIGHT HIS SKIN WILL BE STRETCHED ON THE SIDE OF MY SHOP! ALTHOUGH IT DOES NOT FEAR US--YET, WE SHALL TEACH IT THE THE MEANING OF-- --TERROR!
LET US SPREAD OUT SO WE CAN FIND HIM!
FROM WITHIN THE SHADOWS, QUICK, RED EYES FOLLOW THE SCENT OF MAN!
HE IS NEAR!
MEIN GOTT IN HEAVEN!

IN THE RAPIDLY FLICKERING LIGHT, BONE, TENDON AND MUSCLE ARE SLASHED AND TORN BY SHARP-NAILED CLAWS!
CHILD OF EVIL... SON OF THE NIGHT.. WITH PREY IN HIS GRASP HE SINGS HIS VICTORY TO THE MOON!
..A GROTESQUE, PRIMITIVE RITUAL BEFORE THE FEAST!

QUICKLY! IT CAME FROM THIS DIRECTION!
IN THE DIM LIGHT OF TORCH AND MOON, THE SEARCHERS ALMOST STUMBLE OVER THE GROTESQUE MESS THAT LITTERS THE FOREST FLOOR--
WHO WAS IT?
IT LOOKS LIKE JENSEN
MEIN GOTT-- WE MUST FIND THE WOLF BEFORE IT KILLS AGAIN! SEARCH THE AREA-- IT MUST BE NEAR!
SUDDENLY, AS THEY SEARCH THROUGH THE DENSE FOREST, A STRANGE MOVEMENT IS NOTICED--
THE WEREWOLF! HE HIDES AMONGST THE TREES WAITING FOR ME TO DRAW NEARER!
I SHALL NOT FALL PREY TO HIS CUNNING!
CLIKK
AS THE EXPLOSIVE CHARGE ECHOES THROUGH THE FOREST, A SILVER ANGEL OF DEATH TEARS THROUGH THE AIR!

WITHIN SECONDS THE RUSTIC STRIDES FORWARD WITH WARY STEPS TO VIEW THE CREATURE THAT HAS FALLEN VICTIM TO THE SILVER BULLET--
NO LONGER WILL MY VILLAGE LIVE IN FEAR-- --THE WEREWOLF-- IS DEAD!
DEAR GOD IN HEAVEN-- --WHAT HIDEOUS THING HAVE I DONE?
SERGE! SERGE!
I DIDN'T MEAN TO SHOOT HIM! I THOUGHT THE WEREWOLF WAS ON THE OTHER SIDE OF THE BRANCHES-- --NOT HIM!
WE MUST BRING HIM HOME BEFORE HE DIES! HE MUST NOT DIE ON THE GROUND LIKE-- --AN ANIMAL!

IT WAS AN ACCIDENT!
WHAT HAS HAPPENED?
IT IS YOUR FATHER-- --HE'S BEEN SHOT!
QUICKLY, BRING HIM TO HIS ROOM! HAS HE REGAINED CONSCIOUSNESS AT ALL?
AS WE HAVE BEEN CARRYING HIM, HE HAS CALLED YOUR NAME MANY TIMES-- --HE KEEPS REPEATING THAT THERE IS SOMETHING HE MUST TELL YOU.
USING UP WHAT LITTLE TIME AND ENERGY HE HAS, THE BLACKSMITH STRUGGLES TO SPEAK--HIS VOICE IS ONLY A VAGUE AND TATTERED REMNANT OF HIS ONCE POWERFUL THROAT!
...STEPHAN...
YES FATHER, I AM HERE.
...TELL THE OTHERS TO LEAVE... ...I MUST *COUGH* SPEAK WITH YOU ALONE...
EXCEPT FOR THE CRY OF AGONY AT HIS FATHER'S DEATH, NO SOUND BROKE FROM BEHIND THE CLOSED DOORS OF THE DEATH CHAMBER. A PALER, WEAKER FORM CAME TO THOSE DOORS AND ANNOUNCED HIS GRIM TIDINGS--
MY FATHER, SERGE GUNNARMANN IS DEAD-- --RETURN TO YOU HOMES!
SOME THOUGHT THAT HIS MIND HAD BECOME UNHINGED IN ITS GREAT SORROW, FOR THERE WAS A BURNING LIGHT OF INSANITY THAT SEEMED TO GLOW IN HIS EYES!

STEPHAN CONTINUED HIS FATHER'S TRADE, AND LIKE HIS FATHER, WAS VERY GOOD AT IT! --AND TRUE TO HIS FATHER'S EXAMPLE, ON NIGHTS OF THE FULL-MOON HE WOULD HUNT!
--BUT UNLIKE HIS FATHER, HE CHOSE TO HUNT ALONE!
THE SETTING SUN THREW HAUNTING SHADOWS ACROSS THE GRAVES OF THE LONG DEAD... AND THE PUNGENT SCENT OF ROTTING FLOWERS LACED THE AIR. HE FOUND IT SOOTHING TO ROAM AMONG THE DEAD, AND FOUND COMFORT IN HIS ONE-SIDED COVERSATIONS WITH HIS DEAD PARENT!
MANY TIMES HE HAD BEEN SEEN TALKING TO THE STONES... AND SOON ALL IN THE VILLAGE SHUNNED HIM AS ONE WOULD A LEPER. ONLY THE BRAVE DARED LOOK IN HIS EYES, FOR THEY WERE EYES THAT COULD PIERCE A MAN'S SOULD AND FREEZE HIS BLOOD
..THEY THOUGHT HIM MAD!

IT IS AT TIMES LIKE THESE-- BEFORE THE HUNT --THAT THE RESPONSIBILITIES I HAVE INHERITED SEEM TOO GREAT! IT IS TIMES LIKE THESE THAT YOUR APPROVING WORDS WOULD BE SO GREATLY WELCOMED--BUT YOU ARE DEAD, A MERE SHADOW OF WHAT YOU ONCE WERE!
RIP
1804 – 1858
THE WIND IS MOVING THROUGH THE THICK FOREST, CARRYING THE SCENT OF PINE AND OF THE ANIMALS HIDDEN IN THE GROWING DARKNESS! SOON, THE AIR WILL BE RAPT WITH STILL ANOTHER SCENT-- --THE ONE YOU KNEW SO WELL-- --THE SCENT OF MAN!
SOON TO BE FOLLOWED BY-- --THE SWEET TASTE OF... HUMAN FLESH!
NOSTRILS QUIVER AS THE SMELL OF SWEATING MEN LACES THE AIR! IT IS A SCENT THAT BRINGS SALIVA FLOODING THE MOUTH, AND RAISES LUPINE EARS FOR THE FAINTEST SOUND OF A DISTANT TWIG SNAPPING!
MANY ARE THE GIFTS THAT PASS BETWEEN FATHERS AND SONS, BUT NONE ARE SO STRANGE NOR SO INTIMATE AS THIS!

Sea of Graves

Web of Horror 2, February 1970

Michael W. Kaluta has become one of the most gifted creators in comic books. His modern-day fans associate him with covers he has produced for DC Comics, but three decades ago Michael was also revered for the pages he crafted. This tale comes from that creative phase beginning towards the end of the 1960s and lasting into the early years of the 1970s. Inspired by the likes of Frank Frazetta and Roy Krenkel, his technique has inspired a generation of artists. These pages are simple by comparison to his later achievements, but they are easy on the eye and reveal something of Roy Krenkel's influence. He would work regularly for DC and provide assignments for Marvel. His time applying his mastery alongside Bernie Wrightson, Jeff Jones and Barry Windsor Smith during the mid-1970s in what was known as The Studio saw him create posters and portfolios for which collectors still clamour. Long-time fans however will always remember the near-perfect six issues he produced for DC's *The Shadow*, although there were times when his pursuit of excellence made a mockery of deadline pressure.

art: MIKE KALUTA script: OTTO BINDER

GOLD, JEWELS, ARTIFACTS... PERHAPS EVEN SOME OF THEIR FABLED MEDICINAL ELIXIRS... WHAT A FIND THIS WILL BE FOR THE MUSEUM! WE'LL BOTH BE FAMOUS!
NOT FAMOUS, YOU OLD CREEP - RICH! AND NOT BOTH OF US...
...SINCE YOU DIED IN AN UNFORTUNATE BOATING ACCIDENT!
GHAAAAA!
WITH THE AID OF AN OLD SEA-ANCHOR, DENBY CONSIGNS CRAWFORD TO THE DEEP...
REST IN PEACE, OLD MAN... TEN FATHOMS DOWN! THE TREASURE IS DOWN THERE WAITING... WAITING FOR ME! GOLD, JEWELS... ALL MINE - MINE!
HIDING THEIR WEALTH UNDERWATER WAS A PRETTY CLEVER STUNT! THE SPANIARDS WOULD NEVER HAVE STUMBLED ACROSS IT... LUCKY THING I'VE GOT MY SCUBA GEAR WITH ME!
THIS MAYAN PARCHMENT IS TOUGH ENOUGH TO WITHSTAND A SOAKING, AT LEAST UNTIL I FIND THE TREASURE!

IN THE MURKY DEPTHS, WHERE NO MAN HAS BEEN FOR CENTURIES, THE STRANGEST TREASURE HUNT IN HISTORY BEGINS!
HMM! BY GOING DUE EAST, I'LL FIND THE FIRST LANDMARK... OR SEAMARK!
THERE IT IS! A TOTEM-POLE MADE OF TREATED CORAL SO THAT IT HAS SURVIVED THE AGES... AND THE ARROW SHOWS WHICH WAY TO GO!
BUT DENBY COMES UPON AN UNEXPECTED "SEAMARK"— ONE THAT SENDS SHIVERS OF TERROR DOWN HIS SPINE...
WH-WHAT'S THAT? ...YIPES! THE BODY OF OLD CRAWFORD! HOW DID IT DRIFT THIS FAR? OH WELL, FORGET IT AND GO ON. PLENTY OF AIR IN MY TANKS; THE TREASURE CAN'T BE TOO FAR AHEAD.
IN THE EERIE DEPTHS, DENBY SUCCEEDS IN FOLLOWING OTHER UNDERSEA MARKERS ON THE TREASURE TRAIL...
UNTIL...
THERE IT IS!

AN ANCIENT STRUCTURE LOOMS MYSTERIOUSLY IN THE WATER–
WHAT'S THAT INSCRIPTION? "DEFILERS OF THIS TEMPLE WILL MEET WATERY DOOM!" BAH! THE USUAL SILLY THREAT TO SCARE AWAY VANDALS!
HIDDEN COUNTER-WEIGHTS GROAN AS DENBY PULLS AN ORNAMENTED LEVER.
THAT STONE SLAB IS MOVING – THE DOOR IS OPENING! THIS IS A CINCH!
WINDING PASSAGEWAYS HONEYCOMB THE PYRAMID, YET DENBY KEEPS HIS SENSE OF DIRECTION UNTIL...
HOLY COW!! THE HIDDEN TREASURE OF THE MAYAN KINGS – LOST FOR ALL THESE CENTURIES! MINE FOR THE TAKING!
HIS MIND BURNING WITH A GOLDEN FEVER, DENBY HAULS PART OF THE TREASURE OUT OF THE PYRAMID... ONLY TO MEET A SHOCK.
NO! NO!
CRAWFORD'S CORPSE!

OUT OF MY WAY, YOU DRIFTING HORROR, AND STOP HAUNTING ME!
AFTER THE LONG SWIM BACK PAST THE UNDERSEA MARKERS...
THE BOAT! AND JUST IN TIME! I'M ALMOST OUT OF OXYGEN!
DRAT! ONLY ONE MORE AIRTANK. AFTER THIS TRIP I'LL HAVE TO GO ASHORE FOR A RE-FILL!
LATER, WHEN HE REACHES THE TREASURE CHAMBER, DENBY MAKES ANOTHER AMAZING FIND...
THAT INSCRIPTION! IT SAYS- "UNDERWATER ELIXIR! DRINK AND BE SAFE FROM DROWNING"! IT CAN'T BE TRUE, OR CAN IT? THAT FOOL CRAWFORD BABBLED SOMETHING ABOUT THE MAYANS' MYSTERIOUS ELIXIRS... MAYBE-?
DENBY BRINGS THE VIAL BACK WITH THE SECOND LOAD OF TREASURE, AND...
THE MAYANS MUST HAVE HAD SOME METHOD FOR BREATHING UNDER-WATER TO BUILD THAT PYRAMID! MAYBE I'M A FOOL, BUT...
GLUG
THE MAYAN VIAL LIES EMPTY ON THE DECK AS DENBY SHRUGS OUT OF HIS AQUALUNG.
NOW TO TEST THE "ELIXIR" AND SEE IF I'M "SAFE FROM DROWNING" AS IT SAYS!

IT WORKS! I CAN BREATHE UNDERWATER, LIKE A FISH! NO MORE CLUMSY TANKS TO WEAR! AND I CAN SEE PERFECTLY WITHOUT MY MASK!
MINUTES LATER DENBY IS ONCE AGAIN IN THE TREASURE CHAMBER.
IT'LL BE A CINCH NOW TO SWIM BACK AND FORTH WITH LOADS OF THE TREASURE UNTIL I'VE GOT IT ALL! HAAAA!
OUTSIDE THE PYRAMID, DENBY'S TRIUMPH IS SHARED BY AN UNWELCOME "GUEST"...
HIM AGAIN! HE SEEMS ALMOST AS IF HE'S FOLLOWING ME!
WELL... ONE MORE TRIP AND I'LL BE RID OF HIM, FOREVER!
WITH HIS GREED KNOWING NO BOUNDS, DENBY MAKES THE RETURN TRIP IN RECORD TIME...
I CAN SIMPLY DUMP EACH LOAD INTO THE TRAWLING NET WITHOUT WASTING TIME GOING UP ON DECK! NOW FOR THAT LAST LOAD!

AS DENBY MAKES HIS FINAL TRIP TO THE PYRAMID, THE MUTILATED CORPSE SEEMS TO FOLLOW HIM. IT LEERS HIDEOUSLY, AS IF LAUGHING AT SOME UNKNOWN JOKE...
I'LL SURE BE GLAD TO GET ASHORE AND AWAY FROM HIM! THERE'S THE PYRAMID...
BUT SOON THE TREASURE IS SAFE IN THE TRAWLING NET, AND DENBY PREPARES TO CLIMB ON BOARD...
ALL DONE! NOW TO ENJOY A LIFE OF LUXURY!
ONLY TO MEET A GHASTLY SURPRISE!
I-I CAN'T BREATHE! CHOKE WHATS WRONG? IT'S ALMOST AS IF I'M- DROWNING IN AIR!
FOR THE FIRST TIME SINCE DRINKING THE ELIXIR DENBY'S THOUGHTS WERE NOT ON THE TREASURE... HE LOOKED WILDLY AT HIS WEBBED HANDS - HIS WEBBED FEET, HIS SLIME COVERED BODY - AND HE COULD ONLY IMAGINE THE HORROR THAT WAS HIS FACE!
LATER, A HALF-MAD FIGURE SITS FORLORNLY ON THE STEPS OF THE ANCIENT PYRAMID - PEERING INTO A HIDEOUS AND ENDLESS FUTURE...
THE WARNING CAME TRUE! 'WATERY DOOM'! THE ELIXIR ONLY WORKS ONE WAY! I CAN BREATHE WATER - BUT NOT AIR!
MY TREASURE IS USELESS HERE. AND CRAWFORD'S BODY, GRINNING AT ME - FOREVER!
IT LOOKS LIKE HAL DENBY TURNED OUT TO BE A REAL WEBBED HORROR! HE AND POOR PROFESSOR CRAWFORD SHOULD MAKE QUITE A PAIR. MAYBE THEY'LL TURN UP AGAIN IN ANOTHER ONE OF MY LITTLE TALES,
WHO KNOWS?

The Faithful Few

1980s and 1990s

Comic book horror didn't entirely vanish after the implosion of 1975, but there were very few titles to interest serious horror fans. Warren's three black-and-white terrors survived, although they adopted science fiction themes following the success of films such as *Star Wars, Alien* and *Close Encounters of the Third Kind.* Eerie Publications continued with their exploitative debauchery, but it had begun to wear a little thin. Marvel carried on with *Tomb of Dracula* for a few more years, but Marvel *Preview* was put to use to exhaust what little remained of their horror inventory. DC continued to publish *Ghosts, House of Mystery* and *The Unexpected* beyond the decade; but *House of Secrets* and *The Witching Hour* went to meet their maker in 1978. By the end of 1983 not a single one of these titles was still in existence; each and every one of them had been laid to rest as a new generation beckoned.

As 1980 came to an end, with the eventual failure of *Tomb of Dracula*, Marvel turned away from horror: for them this was to be the age of the superhero. DC however revived the creation of Len Wein and Bernie Wrightson from ten years before, *Swampthing*, in May 1982 following the release of Wes Craven's languid excuse of a movie. The early issues were devoid of impact, not unlike the film, and it looked as if *The Saga of the Swampthing* would face cancellation at the same time as *House of Mystery* and *The Unexpected.* But the introduction of artist Steve Bissette with issue 16 and script writer Alan Moore, four issues later, heralded a miraculous change in the title's fortunes. Termination was forgotten as it began to terrorize its readers in a way few comics had done before, or would after. The axe wasn't to fall until 1996 after a laudable run of 171 issues. Alan Moore had already proved himself an adept writer with *V for Vendetta* and *Marvelman*; his vision had little to do with the sanguinary morsels enjoyed by the comics of the

1950s. His was a more psychological terror, an exploration of the frailties of the human psyche, which would take the horror comic in a markedly different direction, one more commonly associated with the literary horror story than the pages of a disposable comic book.

In 1988 DC added to their line of horror comics with John Constantine Hellblazer, a character who had debuted in the *Swampthing* series three years earlier. Hellblazer was a very British affair, borne out of the repressive Thatcher years. Events in this title would develop Alan Moore's psychological terror, and furnish it with the hellish accoutrements to last into the twenty-first century.

Away from DC, horror was only just contriving to hold its own during the polished years of the 1980s, largely thanks to the success of a revived craze in the horror movie. Freddy Krueger (of *A Nightmare on Elm Street*), Jason Voorhees (*Friday the 13th*) and Michael Myers (*Halloween*), each made it possible for these comic book terrors to ply their foul trade, albeit in a very different guise to that which had been seen during the previous thirty years.

In the early 1980s Bruce Jones, after several years of success with Jim Warren, presented a set of his ideas to a new West Coast publisher, Pacific Comics. He had never lost his love for Bill Gaines' legendary EC mythos; it was his dream to capture the creative excitement from that halcyon period. *Alien Worlds* was to be his short-lived homage to *Weird Science* and *Weird Fantasy*. *Twisted Tales* would follow in the tainted footsteps of *Tales from the Crypt* and its gruesome companions. From the outset it looked every bit like a horror comic, with the logo combining the impact that came with EC and the insanity of the underground horrors of ten years past. Bruce already had a reputation as a storyteller with an ability to spring a surprise or two. He supplemented this with a gathering of some of the finest artists of the day, Richard Corben, Bernie Wrightson, Mike Ploog, Mike Hoffman, Alfredo Alcala and Tim Conrad. The series had often had an adult undercurrent and was not afraid to cause a stir.

However, Pacific Comics had turned into an uncontrollable monster of its own kind, which its owners could not control. Bankruptcy ensued and *Twisted Tales* moved to another relatively new publisher, Eclipse Comics. With the closure of Pacific so too went their full-colour reprint collections from Bernie Wrightson, Richard Corben and Arthur Suydam. *Twisted Tales* lasted only another couple of issues before bowing out on its tenth appearance, but in a short space of time it made a considerable impact.

With the evolution of the direct sales market many new comic publishers came into being. The expanding range of publishers promoted a remarkable diversity in the styles of comic available to their insatiable public. Eclipse were just one of these aspiring companies. They provided a home for Michael T. Gilbert's *Mr Monster* before he moved on to yet another recently established company, Dark Horse. Michael was a creator who had a great affection for and understanding of the world of horror, but chose to lampoon it in his own inimitable way. Eclipse also published thirteen issues of *Tales of Terror*, but unless such anthologies carried the DC symbol of ownership, they didn't seem able to endure for more than a couple of years. There was an obvious interest in tales from the grave, but it was going to take something extraordinary to create a series with the capacity to persevere.

It came with a zombie-infested creation published by Arrow Comics called *Deadworld.* Its arrival on the shelves of the comic stores was not widely announced. Many potential readers were oblivious of its existence for quite some time. *Deadworld*, however, managed to maintain a regular publishing schedule from its inception in 1986 through into the early Nineties when it was under the Calibre imprint, and then only a matter of years ago crawled from the grave with Image Comics. This really is the horror comic that refuses to die. Twenty years ago zombies didn't have the draw they have now, so this title was unique; it also ran variant covers depicting the regular zombie fun and the more extreme "not for wussies" edition. With Gary Reed's engaging storytelling and Vince Locke's graphic zombie artwork, *Deadworld* just kept on going.

Deadworld remained the exception. With so many small companies keen to make use of the direct sales market and get straight into the growing number of comic shops, competition was fierce. These outfits may have had the creative inspiration and the ability to conjure up nightmares, but they didn't have the resources of Marvel or DC. Projects were often short-lived. For many readers it was a frustrating situation that went on throughout the 1980s and the 1990s. There was some very interesting material to be uncovered, but it wasn't always easy to find.

Some publishers had success in reprinting pre-Code material; there was a new generation of comic book readers who had never had access to these abominable tales. Of note were Dark Horse's reprints of Basil Wolverton's work in *Gateway to Horror*; Eclipse published six issues of *Seduction of the Innocent* and all of EC's horror tales saw a further release, proving almost as popular as they ever were. George Suarez's *Tales Too Terrible To Tell* was the one that stole the show. He offered a variety of pre-Code tales in a title that was originally seventy-two pages long. It was backed up with highly informative articles and cover galleries that would have more collectors searching for such obscurities from decades past.

As the genre entered the 1990s, comics gradually became more daring than they had been in almost forty years. There no longer seemed to be any boundaries, as the fiction of Clive Barker was translated to the comic book format and Steve Bissette and John Totleben exposed some of the forbidden aspects of this ever-darkening domain. Their anthology *Taboo* was banned in the United Kingdom; it was never to make it through Customs. Maybe they had ventured to lay open too many of our innermost demons.

Killer Planet

Death Rattle Vol. 2 No. 1, October 1985

"Killer Planet" first appeared in the 1978 edition of *Fog City Comics 2*, published by Canada's Stampart, before being reprinted in *Death Rattle*. Just as the film *Alien* did a year after this tale's first appearance, it merged horror with the realm of science fiction. Creator Rand Holmes was an exceptional talent. His pages showed his admiration for the accomplishment of EC veteran Wallace Wood, as had his covers for Last Gasp's *Slow Death* several years before. As a teenager he used to copy the tales once drawn by Wally and Will Eisner; there could have been no better tutors. His work regularly appeared in the underground comix of the 1970s and his counterculture creation, *Harold Hedd*, continues to delight and arouse great amusement. He passed away in 2002.

Death Rattle, which had first appeared as an underground comic a quarter of a century before, was the dream child of Denis Kitchen. This second series presented an eclectic mix of horror and the absolute weird. There was no telling what would appear on an issue-to-issue basis.

KILLER PLANET
COPYRIGHT © 1985
BY RAND H. HOLMES
ALL RIGHTS RESERVED
EXCERPT
CAPT'S LOG
INTERPLANETARY
FREIGHTER-ORION
17-6-2683:
WE WERE TWO PARSECS FROM THE ANTARES CLUSTER-EN ROUTE TO THE NEXUS RIMWORLDS-WHEN THE LIGHT DRIVE BLEW.....
...IT CAME AS NO PARTICULAR SURPRISE. EVERYTHING ON THIS OBSOLETE TUB WAS LONG OVERDUE TO MALFUNCTION, BREAKDOWN OR JUST QUIETLY DISINTEGRATE
WHEN I REACHED THE BRIDGE, WALDRING-MY FIRST OFFICER-INFORMED ME THAT WE'D POPPED OUT OF HYPER SPACE INTO THE MIDDLE OF A SMALL SOLAR SYSTEM
I CAN'T FIX THIS CAP'N... ...CASING'S CRACKED CLEAN THROUGH
VERY WELL MR. GREELB
CONTACT THE PATROL SCARF..
..WE'LL SIT TIGHT TIL THEY BRING US NEW PARTS
WELL MR. WALDRING ...WHAT HAVE YOU GOT ON THIS PLACE?
SEEMS TO BE A FRINGE STAR SIR.. ...TECHNICALLY BELONGS TO THE RIM I GUESS BUT IT'S WAY OUT HERE IN THE GULF BY ITSELF
...I'LL HAVE A COMPUTER SCAN-OUT IN A FEW MINUTES
CAPTAIN?
...I'M GETTING A FLAT READING ON ALL COMMUNICATOR CHANNELS
AAAAHH.. ..BLOODY HELL!
GREELB!
...FIND OUT WHAT'S WRONG WITH THE BUGGERING COMMUNICATION SYSTEM...
..I'LL GO EXPLAIN THIS MESS TO THE PASSENGERS

IN THE PASSENGER'S WARDROOM I EXPLAINED THAT, WITHOUT A LIGHT-DRIVE WE WERE STUCK IN THE RELATIVE CONFINES OF AN APPARENTLY UNINHABITED SOLAR SYSTEM.... THE VOICE PIPE INTERRUPTED THE GREENY'S OUTRAGED HISSING
CAPTAIN?... ...I'VE GOT THE SURVEY READ-OUT HERE
GO AHEAD MR. WALDRING
THE STAR'S A YELLOW DWARF... DESIGNATED THETA ON THE CHARTS... ONLY TWO PLANETS, ONE'S A GASBALL THE OTHER - GET THIS - IS ONE OF THE SURVEY CONDEMNED KILLER PLANETS!

MELISSA, THE HUMAN PASSENGER, HAD BEEN DRINKING AS USUAL
HEY SHOULDERS... ..WHAT'S ALL THIS KILLER PLANET STUFF
AHEM... EVERY ONCE IN A WHILE ...AH.. MELISSA... MAYBE ONE IN A THOUSAND PLANETS EXPLORED TURNS OUT TO BE SO DANGEROUS TO HUMAN LIFE THAT IT'S MARKED QUARANTINE IN THE SURVEY DATA BANKS

WELL... ..MR. GREELB?
CAPTAIN... ..THE COMMUNICATIONS SYSTEM...
...IT'S A COMPLETE WRITE-OFF ...FUSED AT THE MAINS... NO WAY WE SIGNAL ANYBODY!
SOUNDS LIKE A FUN PLACE.. EH SCALY?

DO YOU MEAN WE'RE TRAPPED HERE!?
CAPTAIN SSSSTRAWN! ...I HOLD YOU DIRECTLY RESPONSSSIBLE ...SSSS...
HOLD IT A MINUTE!
THE SURVEY TEAMS PLANTED SIGNAL BEACONS ON ALL THESE KIL... AH... ..QUARANTINE PLANETS... WE'LL SIMPLY HOME IN ON IT... LAND... ACTIVATE THE DAMN THING AND WAIT FOR A PATROL SHIP... SO EVERYBODY JUST RELAX!

I RETURNED TO THE BRIDGE AND ORDERED ZLEEN - OUR NAVIGATOR - TO PUNCH-IN PLANETARY APPROACH CO-ORDINATES WHILE I SCANNED THE ORIGINAL SURVEY REPORT. THETA II TEEMED WITH PLANT AND ANIMAL LIFE.. NONE OF IT INTELLIGENT.... ALL OF IT SAVAGELY CARNIVOROUS!
EXCUSE ME CAPTAIN ...I DIDN'T WANT TO SAY IT IN FRONT OF THE PASSENGERS...
ENTERING ATMOSPHERE
...BUT THE DAMAGE WAS DELIBERATE
WHAT!?

ENTERING CLOUD LAYER
YESSIR... ...SO THEN I CHECK THE LIGHT DRIVE DAMAGE A LITTLE CLOSER AN FOUND BITS OF A TIMING DEVICE!
A BOMB?!
..YOU AMAZE ME MR. GREELB
..WHO'D WANT TO PUT A BOMB IN THIS WRECK?

WITHOUT WARNING THE SHIP LURCHED VIOLENTLY THRUSTING GREELB'S DISCOVERY FROM MY MIND AND FLINGING US TO THE DECK

WE WENT IN LIKE A ROCK
UNNHH...KEE-RIST!!
ZLEEN!
...SHITSAKE MAN... ..WHAT HAPPENED?
..POUCH... THE GREEN LEATHER POUCH...HAVE TO GET... THE... POU..
CONCUSSION..
ZLEEN..C'MON ...SNAP OUT OF IT
WHA... ..STRAWN!
JEEZUZ...NO RESPONSE FROM THE STARBOARD LANDING ROCKETS...TRIED TO CUSHION OUR FALL...NOT ENOUGH POWER...
MY GOD!... STRAWN, WHAT HAPPENED!?
THE GREENORLIAN EMBASS-S-Y S-S-SHALL GET A FULL REPORT OF THISS-S-S... ..OUTRAGEOUSSSS
WE'VE CRASHED ON THE SURFACE
SHIP SEEMS TO BE HOLDING ATMOSPHERE BUT I WANT EVERYONE IN SUITS JUST IN CASE
HOW DO WE GET TO THE SIGNAL BEACON NOW CAP'N?
YOU, ME AN ZLEEN ARE GONNA WALK TO THE DAMN THING!
THE OTHERS WILL STAY HERE IN SAFETY UNTIL WE GET BACK WITH A RESCUE SHIP
CHEER UP MR. GREELB... AN EASY JAUNT FOR A MAN BORN IN SIX GRAVITIES LIKE YOURSELF
I HAD THE COMPUTER PREPARE A MAP FROM THE AERIAL PHOTOS SIR. WE'RE APPROXIMATELY 35 KILOMETRES FROM THE BEACON
THANK YOU MR. WALDRING
MR. GREELB ...BREAK OUT THE ARMS CHEST IF YOU PLEASE
CAPTAIN! THE SHIP..IT'S.. ...WE'RE SINKING!
IT WAS TRUE... WE HAD LANDED IN A SORT OF THICK VISCOUS BOG AND THE SHIP WAS SLOWLY SETTLING IN THE GLUEY MASS.. THERE WAS NO CHOICE. I GAVE THE ORDER TO ABANDON SHIP.
..SPARE OXYGEN SCARF?
GOT IT HERE SIR
BLORP
AS THE DAMNED PLANET LITERALLY SWALLOWED THE SHIP BEFORE OUR EYES I HASTILY DIVIDED THE SMALL ARMS AMONGST PASSENGERS AND CREW
HERE GREELB ...KEEP IT SET AT MAXIMUM
SCARF...SCARF! ...WHERE THE HELL...
THERE HE IS... ...BUT... WHAT'S THAT THING?!

TURNING, I SAW SCARF ADVANCING-AS THOUGH MESMERIZED-INTO THE WAITING FANGS OF ONE OF THE PLANET'S MORE LOATHESOME MONSTROSITIES
SCARF.. ..NO!!
I RECOGNIZED IT AT ONCE FROM THE SURVEY READOUT: A DREAMWEAVER ... TECHNICALLY A PLANT SINCE IT WAS ROOTED IN THE SOIL AND UNABLE TO MOVE.

ABLE TO EXTRACT FROM THE MIND OF ITS INTENDED MEAL HIS MOST HEARTFELT DESIRE - IT THEN PROJECTS THAT IMAGE DIRECTLY TO THE VICTIM'S OPTIC NERVE SO THAT THE CREATURE ITSELF APPEARS AS THE DESIRED OBJECT

SCARF STILL APPEARED DAZED AS HE EXPLAINED WHAT HE'D SEEN. KNOWING HIS ALL ABIDING PASSION I SHOULD HAVE GUESSED
FOR CHRISSAKE SCARFUPSKI!..USE YOUR HEAD!
I KNOW.. ..I KNOW... ..STUPID!...BUT.. IT LOOKED SO DAMNED REAL!

LEAVING BEHIND A VARIETY OF BLOATED VINES-WHICH HAD BEEN GROWING WITH ALARMING RAPIDITY IN OUR DIRECTION-WE COMMENCED OUR TREK TOWARDS THE BEACON
MR. S-S-SCARFUPSKI.. ..HOW DID YOU INTEND TO EAT THAT MEAL WITH YOUR S-S-SUIT ON??
HA!...THAT WOULDN'T STOP HIM!.. ..HE HAD ONE OF THOSE DE-CONTAMINATION UNITS INSTALLED IN HIS SUIT JUST SO'S HE COULD EAT GEEK-WORLD CHOW...
...AINT THAT RIGHT SCARFY?
AAAH... ..BLOW IT OUT YER ASS YA PHILISTINES!

WITHIN MINUTES WE ENCOUNTERED THE FIRST ANIMAL LIFE...
SPUK

...AND FROM THAT POINT ON FACED CONTINUAL ASSAULT FROM AN APPARENTLY ENDLESS ARRAY OF RAPACIOUS LIFE FORMS
DAMMIT!...THESE THINGS JUST LIVE TO EAT!
POT CALLING THE KETTLE BLACK EH SCARFY?..HA HA

WE HAD JUST SURVIVED AN ATTACK BY A HUGE FLYING CREATURE AND MR. WALDRING WAS SLIGHTLY AHEAD...
HEY CHIEF! THERE'S A FUNGUS AMONG US.. NYUK
SO I OBSERVE.. ..AND I'M GIVING IT A WIDE BERTH

GLURCH
AAA..
HOLY FUCK!!

EEEAAAAAAAA A
CHUG

HE WAS DEAD WHEN WE REACHED HIM-HIS SUIT RUPTURED-FUNGUS GROWTHS ALREADY BLOSSOMING AT MOUTH, EYES AND NOSTRILS.
GET HIS PERSONAL EFFECTS SCARF
HIS SUIT.. ...IT'S EATEN CLEAN THRU
MUST HAVE DIGESTIVE JUICES LIKE SULPHURIC ACID

IT'S NOT JUST HIS SUIT THAT'S CORRODING!..
..ALL OF YOU.. ..LOOK AT YOUR BOOTS!

EXAMINING MY PITTED BOOTS I REALIZED THAT EVEN THE DAMNED GRASS WAS TRYING TO ABSORB US
SEEMS WEAKER THAN THAT THING
BUT IT'S BOUND TO EAT THROUGH EVENTUALLY
AND IT GROWS EVERY- -WHERE

EVERYWHERE...IT COULDN'T GROW EVERYWHERE.... ..SOMETHING NAGGED AT MY MEMORY . . . . I FUMBLED FOR THE MAP

I KNEW IT! ..THERE'S A DESERT NEAR HERE

WE'D BEEN ON THE DESERT ABOUT 3 HOURS AND THE ONLY VISIBLE LIFE FORMS WERE SOME APPARENTLY HARMLESS CACTUS-LIKE GROWTHS
SAY.. THIS'S ALLRIGHT CAP'N.. ..NO GRASS AND NO UGLY NASTIES
SHIT GREELB... THEM THINGS WOULDN'T EAT A HOMELY BUGGER LIKE YOU ANYWAY

CAPTAIN!
EVEN AS I ATTEMPTED TO ROLL CLEAR I KNEW I'D *NEVER* MAKE IT.!
UNHHH!
CAPTAIN... ..GET OUT!
CRUNCH
KILL IT! ...KILL IT! ..I CAN'T HOLD...
CHUG
CHUG
CHUNGN
THE GIGANTIC *CLAM-THING*, IN ALL ITS MINDLESSNESS, WENT ON CRUSHING THE LIFE OUT OF GREELB LONG AFTER ITS MINISCULE BRAIN HAD BEEN *BLASTED* TO *VAPOR*
LOOK!...
CAPTAIN?... IT'S THE *BEACON!*
THE BEACON - SET IN SOLID GRANITE, ATOP A SMALL PLATEAU - WAS STILL A GOOD 10 KILOMETRES AWAY... *SCARF* HAD SEEN THE SUN GLINTING OFF ITS *FORCEFIELD*
STRAWN..?
...C'MON... ...YOU CAN'T HELP HIM NOW
HUNH?.. ..OH YEAH... S'ALLRIGHT..
..JUST GETTING HIS PERSONAL STUFF
..HE HAD FAMILY ON REGA IV
45 MINUTES LATER WE LEFT THE *COMPARATIVE SAFETY* OF THE DESERT AND-ONCE MORE-ENTERED *THE JUNGLE*

JEEZUZ.. THAT FRUIT LOOKS GOOD!... AND I'M BLOODY STARVING!

WHAT THE HELL... THE DECONTAMINATOR WILL TAKE CARE OF ANY BACTERIA OR FUNGUS SPORES
HMMMMM
CLICK

I DON'T UNDERSTAND.. ..IF SOMEONE WANTED TO DESTROY THE SHIP WHY NOT PUT A BOMB IN THE HULL INSTEAD OF JUST DAMAGING THE LIGHT DRIVE?
GREELB SEEMED TO THINK IT WAS SOMEONE ABOARD... ONE OF US

THAT MAKES EVEN LESS SENSE ..UNLESS..
UNLESS?
WELL..WITH THE COMMUNICATION SYSTEM SABOTAGED WE HAD NO CHOICE BUT TO COME HERE TO CALL FOR HELP ..RIGHT?..
..SUPPOSE WHOEVER DID IT WANTED US TO COME TO THIS PLANET

HANH!... COULDN'T BE SCARFUPSKI THEN... HE LIKES PLANETS WHERE HE CAN EAT THINGS... NOT PLANETS WHERE THINGS EAT HIM!..
... EH SCARF?

WHAT THE...?
SCARF! NO DON'T!
CHOMP CHOFF
AS WE STARED IN HORROR SCARFUPSKI VIRTUALLY EXPLODED WITHIN THE CONFINES OF HIS SUIT
EEEAAAAA

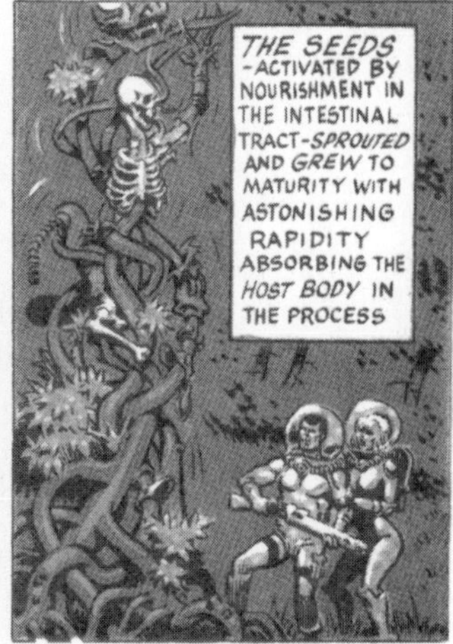
THE SEEDS -ACTIVATED BY NOURISHMENT IN THE INTESTINAL TRACT-SPROUTED AND GREW TO MATURITY WITH ASTONISHING RAPIDITY ABSORBING THE HOST BODY IN THE PROCESS

I HAD SALVAGED SCARF'S PERSONAL POSSESSIONS AND STARTED AFTER THE OTHERS WHEN MY ATTENTION WAS RIVETED BY A SUDDEN MOVE-MENT WITHIN A HOLLOW

I WAS PREPARED FOR ANYTHING EXCEPT THE SIGHT OF MELISSA-NUDE AND BECKONING SENSUOUSLY-HER SOFT SKIN SEEMINGLY IMPERVIOUS TO THE CORROSIVE GRASS ON WHICH SHE RECLINED

IT WAS ONE OF THE DREAMWEAVERS OF COURSE ... I WAS BACKING AWAY SHOCKED-NOT SO MUCH BY THE CREATURE'S PRESENCE AS BY ITS REVELATION OF THE DEPTH OF MY FEELINGS FOR MELISSA-WHEN SUDDENLY...

THE PERIHELION: A FEDERATION STARSHIP... HAD BEEN HIJACKED -IN THE GULF- OVER A YEAR AGO
....IT CARRIED-AT THE TIME AN EMISSARY FROM A RECENTLY CON -TACTED ALIEN CIVILISATION OF SOME COMPLEXITY

THE HIJACKERS-APPARENTLY MEMBERS OF THE CREW-HAD KILLED THE GORKLIAN AMBASSADOR AND STOLEN A SINGLE PRICELESS GEM...

THEY THEN DISABLED THE SHIPS DRIVE AND LIFEBOATS EXCEPTING ONE IN WHICH THEY MADE THEIR ESCAPE...
ZL-V.6J

THE DIPLOMATIC REPERCUSSIONS ARISING FROM THE INCIDENT HAD BROUGHT THE FEDERATION AND THE GORKLIANS TO THE BRINK OF WAR... ... THE HIJACKERS VANISHED WITHOUT A TRACE
THEN... YOU WERE ONE OF THE HIJACKERS!?
OH NOT ME STRAWN...
...THEY ALL DIED ON THIS GODFORSAKEN PLANET..AFTER THEY STUPIDLY MANAGED TO CRASH THE LIFEBOAT...
...ALL BUT ONE THAT IS

THE PATROL-ANSWERING THE DISTRESS SIG-NAL FROM THIS SAME BEACON-FOUND HIM SAFE-BUT DELIRIOUS-WITHIN THE FORCEFIELD ...I FOUND HIM IN A SPACEPORT BAR DRUNK AND TALKATIVE...
THE PATROL HAD MADE NO CONNECTION BETWEEN HIM AND THE PERIHELION HE DIDN'T HAVE THE GEM BUT HE RE-MEMBERED WHERE THE MAN WHO'D CARRIED IT HAD DIED...
...HE MADE AN EXCELLENT MAP JUST BEFORE I KILLED HIM

THEN YOU SABOTAGED THE LIGHT DRIVE AND THE COMMUNICATION SYSTEM JUST SO WE'D BE FORCED TO COME TO THIS BEACON!
...OF COURSE... ..ONLY YOU-THE NAVIGATOR-COULD HAVE TIMED IT SO PRECISELY...
...BUT.. WHY THE CRASH?

ACCIDENT!... ..THAT DAMNED SCOW!... THE BOMB MUST HAVE DAMAGED THE STARBOARD THERMOCOUPLINGS
I'D MEANT TO LAND HERE AT THE BEACON THEN QUIETLY RETRIEVE THE GEM WHILE AWAITING RESCUE ...PERHAPS IT'S BETTER THIS WAY THO... NO MESSY EVIDENCE AT ALL

SO NOW YOU KILL US... AND WAIT FOR THE PATROL TO RESCUE YOU..
...AFTER YOU'VE FOUND THE GREEN LEATHER POUCH OF COURSE...

I HAD SEEN NO SIGNIFICANCE IN ZLEEN'S SEMI-CONSCIOUS REMARKS AT THE TIME OF THE CRASH... AND I WAS STILL ONLY GUESSING
HOW... HOW COULD YOU KNOW!?...
...YOU'VE FOUND IT!

HIS REACTION WAS ALL I'D HOPED FOR
WHERE IS IT!? YOU BASTARD!
IF... IF I TELL YOU... WILL YOU LET US LIVE UNTIL THE RESCUE SHIP ARRIVES?

MMM... THAT'S NOT AN UNREASONABLE REQUEST STRAWN...
...OKAY.. DEAL!
NOW WHERE IS IT?!

FEIGNING RESIGNATION I MADE THE FINAL GAMBLE...
IT'S IN THAT HOLLOW

I HELD MY BREATH AS ZLEEN - BLASTER LEVELED IN OUR DIRECTION - CAUTIOUSLY APPROACHED THE DREAMWEAVER'S LAIR...
...SUDDENLY HIS FEATURES RELAXED IN A SMILE AS HE BEHELD THAT WHICH HE DESIRED MOST

HE WAS STILL SMILING AS THE SUCKERED TENTACLES WITH THEIR VENOM-TIPPED BARBS PUNCTURED HIS SUIT

...I MADE NO EFFORT TO RETRIEVE ZLEEN'S PERSONAL EFFECTS.
END

Over His Head

Twisted Tales 2, April 1983

Bruce Jones' EC homage *Twisted Tales* was only just under way, but already he had assembled a fine collection of artists. Aficionados of Marvel horror comics of the early 1970s were delighted to see Mike Ploog return to comics, albeit only briefly. The previous few years had seen him move to film and animation, but comic book fans knew him better for his revered *Werewolf by Night*, *Ghost Rider*, *Manthing*, *Frankenstein*, *Planet of the Apes* and *Weirdworld*. This tale is a reminder of his early days working with the esteemed Will Eisner, particularly owing to the degree of caricature. There was no effort to strive for realism here; rather, as with so much of Mike's memorable contribution to comics, a stylized world was embellished.

The past twenty years have seen him continue to work in animation, and provide storyboards for television and film. The work he produced for Abadazad, published by the sadly defunct Crossgen, marked a welcome return to comics. Apparently more comic-related projects are in the pipeline.

Story: BRUCE JONES Art: MIKE PLOOG
Colors: STEVE OLIFF

ONE MONTH EARLIER...
--LOTTA NUTS IN THE NEIGHBORHOOD SO'S I GOTTA BE CAREFUL WHO I RENTS TO, KNOW WHAT I MEAN? CAN'T NEVER TELL THESE DAYS, PEOPLE SHAKE YOUR HAND ONE MINUTE CUT OUT YOUR GIZZARD THE NEXT, KNOW WHAT I MEAN? I'M ALL ALONE NOW THAT MR. SANCHEZ DIED, GOTTA BE CAREFUL. YOU AIN'T A HOMO ARE YA?
NO, I--
ROOM FOR RENT

NOT THAT I GOT NOTHIN' AGAINST FAGGOTS YOU UNDERSTAND. MY OWN SISTER'S KID IS A LITTLE LIGHT ON HIS FEET IF YOU KNOW WHAT I MEAN BUT I ALWAYS SAY: WHAT A PERSON DOES IN THE PRIVACY OF HIS OWN ROOM IS HIS BUSINESS. YOU AIN'T WITH AA ARE YA?
NO, I--

MY YOUNGEST NEPHEW WAS A DRINKER. WRAPPED HIS BRAND NEW PORCHE AROUND A TELEPHONE POLE AT SIXTH AND MAPLE, HAD TO PRY HIM OFF THE WINDSHIELD AND POUR HIM INTO A BAG. I DON'T HAVE TO TELL YOU THAT THEY KEPT THE CASKET CLOSED ON THAT FUNERAL, KNOW WHAT I MEAN? YOU AIN'T INTO DRUGS I HOPE?
NO, I--

GOTTA TENANT IN 4B THAT'S SHOOTING IT INTO HIS ARMPIT--COVERS UP THE TRACKS, KNOW WHAT I MEAN? OH, HE DON'T ADMIT IT, AND I CAN'T PROVE NOTHIN' BUT HE'S A HOPHEAD ALL RIGHT, I KIN SMELL IT ON HIS BREATH.
THAT'S TWENTY-FIVE IN ADVANCE, BY THE WAY.

YOU WANT THAT TANK? LAST TENANT LEFT IT. COST ME TO HAVE IT HAULED OFF--I'LL KNOCK THREE BUCKS OFF YER RENT IF YOU'LL KEEP IT.
YEAH... SURE... I ALLUS WANTED A FISH TANK...

DON'T SUPPOSE YOU'D WANT THE TREE TOO?...WON'T DO YOU MUCH GOOD IN JULY I GUESS. OR ARE YOU JEWISH?
NO, I...
NOT THAT I GOT ANYTHING AGAINST JEWS. MY BROTHER'S DAUGHTER MARRIED ONE. NICE CLEAN-CUT YOUNG MAN. SMART TOO. SO WHAT IF HE HAD A NOSE JOB? SO WHO CARES? NOT THAT HE'D ADMIT IT...

WHACK!
SPLAT

2

RENT IS DUE THE FIRST OF EACH MONTH. NO EXCUSES. YOU DON'T PAY UP, YOU FIND YER DOOR LOCKED. I KEEP YER STUFF TILL YOU PAY. I DON'T LIKE TO BE A HARD ASS, BUT A WOMAN ALL ALONE LIKE ME HAS GOT TO BE CAREFUL, KNOW WHAT I MEAN? YOU LOOK KINDA PUNY, YOU GOTTA COLD?
NO, I...
NO RADIOS OR TV AFTER 10 P.M. TRASH DAY IS TUESDAY. ENJOY YOUR STAY.

IF YOU WUZ REAL I'D ASK YOU OUT ON A DATE. I AIN'T NEVER BEEN ON A DATE BEFORE...

...IF YOU WUZ REAL...

--GIVE ME A BREAK, ROSIE AND SERVE THE NEXT BEER OVER AT MY PLACE! WHAD YA SAY?
I'D SAY YER LITTLE HEAD'S TALKIN' FOR YER BIG HEAD AGAIN, AL.

LOOK, SHORTY. THIS AIN'T NO CREDIT UNION! YOU GET SOME BREAD AND I'LL GIVE YOU A DRINK, OTHERWISE--
BUT I GOT THE BREAD THIS TIME, PETE! SEE? I GOT THE BREAD! SEE THE BREAD, PETE. SEE IT?
HE SEES IT, DOLL-FACE. WE BOTH SEE IT. YOU GONNA DRINK UP ALL THAT CASH, YOURSELF?
...UH...MAKE THAT TWO BEERS, PETE!
MAKE IT TWO BOURBONS INSTEAD, PETE. MY NAME'S LILA...
YOU, UH, YOU'RE SUPPOSED TO TELL ME YOUR NAME NOW...
HUH? OH, I'M JOE BECKMAN. UH...ARE YOU REAL?
HA-HA! AS REAL AS ANYTHING IN THIS PHONY BURG! HOW FAR AWAY IS YOUR PAD, SWEETS?
LIQUOR
THIS IS YOUR --PAD?
YEAH! NICE, HUH?
TELL YOU WHAT, DOLL, WHY DON'T YOU HUSTLE ON DOWN TO THE ALL-NIGHT THRIFT SHOP AND BUY US A NEW MATTRESS, THEN HUSTLE BACK HERE AND LILA WILL MAKE THE EARTH MOVE FOR YA! UH, FOR FIFTY BUCKS, OF COURSE...
FIFTY? WELL, I...
SOON...
I (GASP) ONLY GOT FORTY BUCKS LEFT NOW, LILA (GRUNT), MEBE YOU COULD JUST MAKE THE EARTH TREMBLE A LITTLE BIT...
IT TREMBLED ALL RIGHT, LILA, IT SURE DID TREMBLE ALL RIGHT! HOW 'BOUT TOMORROW NIGHT? MEBE WE COULD MAKE IT TREMBLE SOME MORE!
SUGAR, YOU GOT THE MONEY AND LILA'S GOT THE TIME!
4

AN ADVANCE? FER PUSHIN' A BROOM? ARE YOU KIDDIN'?
SEE, BERNIE, I GOT THIS GIRL NOW, AN--
LOOK, KID, TELL YOU WHAT: I JUST LOST MY REGULAR COOK. YOU EVER SLUNG HASH BEFORE?

WELL, I--
TRY YOU OUT FOR TONIGHT. YOU DON'T MAKE NOBODY THROW UP, AND YOU GOT YER ADVANCE. DEAL?

SEE, LILA, I GOT THE DOUGH! I'M THE NEW COOK AT BERNIE'S PLACE AN--
YEAH, YEAH, SURE, ONLY IT'LL COST YA DOUBLE THIS TIME, JOE, AN' A NEW BED.

WILL YA MAKE THE EARTH TREMBLE AGAIN TONIGHT, LILA, HUH, WILL YA?
TOOTS, WE'LL SHAKE YER FRONT TEETH LOOSE!
YOU KNOW, THIS PLACE COULD USE SOME CURTAINS, JOE...

COITINS?
JUST A LITTLE ADVANCE, BERNIE, JUST A LITTLE ONE!
WELL... TO TELL THE TRUTH, THIS CHILI AIN'T BAD...

I LOVE YOU, LILA... I LOVE YOU MORE THAN MY PET HAMSTER HARVEY THAT DIED LAST WINTER AND STUCK TO THE BOTTOM OF THE CAGE. I LOVE YOU MORE THAN--
YEAH, SURE, JOE... YA KNOW, WE COULD USE SOME FURNITURE AROUND HERE...

YOU LIKE THE NEW CHAIR, LILA? IT DON'T TRY TO COP A FEEL LIKE THE OLD ONE, DOES IT?
IT'S SWELL, JOE. THIS SLIP IS GETTING KINDA FRAYED THROUGH... AND REMEMBER THAT FUR COAT WE SAW AT BULLOCK'S YESTERDAY?

WORLD FAMOUS MASTER
CHEF JOSEPH
AT BERNIE'S BAR
CHILI KING

I TOOK ON EXTRA HOURS LIKE YA ASKED, LILA, NOW COULD WE--
SURE HON, SOON AS YOU GET THAT COLOR TV I WANTED AND THAT NEW SOFA AND--
5.

--STEREO, TOASTER, THAT BROOCH AT BERGDORF'S, THE NAUTILUS COURSE--
LILA
HUH?
I WANT WE SHOULD GET MARRIED, LILA...

HA-HA-HA-HA-HA-HA-HA!

HA-HA-HA-HA-HA-HA-HA!

HA-HA-HA-H-(ULP!)

LILA? I'M SORRY, HONEY! I DIDN'T MEAN IT! YA SHOULDNTA LAUGHED LIKE THAT! I DON'T LIKE IT WHEN PEOPLE LAUGH. LILA? YOU AIN'T GONNA BE DEAD NOW ARE YA, LILA, LIKE HARVEY? LILA?
6.

MR. BECKMAN? OPEN UP PLEASE, IT'S MRS. SANCHEZ, THE LANDLADY!
ARE YOU IN THERE, MR. BECKMAN? OPEN UP PLEASE, I HAVE AN OFFICER WITH ME!
MR. BECKMAN? YOU'VE BEEN IN THERE FOR WEEKS! MR. BECKMAN!
GOT TO WEIGHT YOU, LILA...YEP...
...GOT TO WEIGHT YOU DOWN SO'S THEY CAN'T FIND YOU...YOU DOWN HERE, LILA?
...AH, THERE YOU ARE!
...JUST GOTTA TIE THOSE WEIGHTS 'ROUND YA, HONEY, GOTTA--
--HAIR...HAIR ALL OVER THE PLACE...TOO MUCH HAIR!...ALL TANGLED...
...TANGLED UP!... CAN'T GET AWAY. I--LILA! HONEY, DON'T ...C-CAN'T BREATHE!... LILA...LILA!
7.

BECKMAN! YOU *IN* THERE?
KA-RUNCH!

HOLY JUMPIN' *JE-ZUZZ!*

AND HE NEVER BROUGHT *ANYONE* UP HERE, YOU SAY?
ONLY THEM LITTLE PIECES OF *DOLL FURNITURE* HE GOT DOWN AT THE THRIFT SHOP...I SEEN HIM!
CRIPES, I SHOULDA *KNOWN* BETTER--WHOLE *NEIGHBORHOOD'S* FULL O' *NUTS*...
YEAH, *TELL* ME ABOUT IT!
LILA
PLOOG '82
8

Christmas Carol

Demon Dreams 1, February 1984

This was one of Pacific Comics' finest moments before their regrettable demise. *Demon Dreams* reprinted a couple of Arthur Suydam's dark tales from his recent past. Arthur's sense of innovation during the 1970s was characteristic of that exciting time. He used the techniques learned from more classical styles and the achievement of members of his own artistic family and worked them into the comic he was assigned. He also worked on *Heavy Metal* and for *Last Gasp*, Marvel and DC. Not only has his draughtsmanship gained him recognition in the world of comic books, it led to various commissions illustrating children's books. In comic books, he has deservedly once more entered the limelight following his cover art for the Marvel *Zombies* series.

BY CHRISTMAS, THE FOG HAD BEEN SQUATTING OVER LONDON FOR WEEKS, ERODING THE SPIRITS OF THE SEASON. THEN, ON THE AFTERNOON OF THE TWENTY-FOURTH, THE STORM CAME. BUT HOWEVER THE STORM AND THE FOG AFFECTED THE SPIRITS OF OTHERS, IT DIDN'T MATTER ONE WHIT TO ME, FOR I KNEW CAROL WAS WAITING FOR ME.

SEEKING SHELTER, I ABANDONED THE BROAD AVENUES FOR THE NARROW BACK ALLEYS, WHERE LONDON'S FACADE OF MERCHANT STREETS GIVES WAY TO CRUMBLING WALLS AND SINKING TENEMENTS.
AS I EXPECTED, THEY WERE NOW DESERTED...
...ALMOST...

I WOULD HAVE IGNORED THE INHUMAN WHINE AND THE OUTSTRETCHED HAND, BUT... PERHAPS IT WAS THE SPIRIT OF CHRISTMAS THAT MOVED ME. I REFUSED HIS REQUEST FOR SILVER, AND IN-STEAD, COURTEOUSLY DEMANDED THAT HE ACCOMPANY ME HOME...
Christmas Carol
...WHERE HE WOULD RECEIVE A HOT MEAL.
SUYDAM 73

APPROACHING OUR RESIDENCE, I CAUGHT A GLIMPSE OF CAROL AT THE WINDOW. IT WAS EASY TO SEE THAT SHE WAS EXPECTING ONLY ME.
CAROL, DARLING, I HAVE A SURPRISE FOR YE!

CAROL MET US AT THE DOOR IN A HASTILY DONNED GOWN. IN AN ATTEMPT TO RELIEVE HER OBVIOUS DISAPPROVAL, I CHEERFULLY EXPLAINED THE EVENTS THAT LED TO THE INVITATION OF OUR GUEST.
MY GOD, JAMES, WHATEVER POSSESSED YOU TO INVITE THAT THING INTO OUR HOME?
WELL, I COULDN'T VERY WELL LEAVE HIM IN THE STORM. BESIDES, IT'S CHRISTMAS.

HAD I ONLY NOTICED THE PROFANE STARE THAT RAVAGED CAROL'S BODY.
FOOL THAT I WAS FOR NOT SEEING THAT UNBLINKING EYE CAPTURING HER EVERY MOVEMENT.

AFTER DINNER:
YOU WOULD THINK THAT THE GOOD LORD WOULD AT LEAST WATCH OVER HIS OWN SON'S BIRTHDAY. AT LEAST THAT. SUCH RAIN! PERHAPS IT WILL LET UP!
BUT IT NEVER DID.

I COULD NOT FIND IT IN MYSELF TO SEND THE CREATURE INTO THE STORM. AND SO...
YE CAN SLEEP ON THE COUCH TILL MORNING.

WE WERE AWAKE WHEN THE RAIN TURNED INTO SNOW, AND AGAIN WHEN NIGHT LIFTED ITS VEIL LIKE A SCULPTOR REVEALING HIS LATEST WORK. LONDON HAD BEEN SILENTLY REMADE. BUT THOUGH PRESENTING ITSELF IN HOLIDAY DRESS, IT STILL EXACTED THE SAME RITUAL FROM ALL BUT THE WEALTHIEST OF ITS POPULATION, AMONG WHOM I WAS NOT ONE.
RELUCTANTLY I FORCED MYSELF OUT OF BED (DISENTANGLING MYSELF FROM CAROL'S ARMS) AND GOT DRESSED FOR WORK.
JUST A FEW MINUTES LATER I WAS OUT THE DOOR. I PREVAILED UPON CAROL TO ALLOW OUR GUEST THE LUXURY OF THE SOFA FOR A FEW MORE HOURS.
GIVE HIM A FEW SHILLINGS WHEN HE WAKES, MY PET. AND THEN SEND HIM ON HIS WAY.
GOOD-BYE.
IF ONLY I HAD FORGOTTEN SOMETHING...
OOHHHHH... KEEP AWAY.
...JUST BY SOME STROKE OF LUCK TO HAVE FORGOTTEN SOME PAPERS, OR PERHAPS POCKET CHANGE...
NO! PLEASE DON'T!... OH!
UH...UH...UH...
3.

HAVING RUSHED THROUGH MY WORK, I WAS ON MY WAY HOME. AS I HURRIED THROUGH THE SNOW-COVERED STREETS, HOW COULD I HAVE KNOWN THAT THE IMAGES OF THE NIGHT BEFORE HAD BEEN BRUTALLY DISPLACED FROM HER MIND. ALL I WOULD KNOW IS WHAT SHE HERSELF WOULD TELL ME WHEN I ARRIVED HOME.
FOR REASONS OF HER OWN, SHE CHOSE TO HIDE HER VIOLATION.

I COULD SEE THAT SHE WAS UPSET. BUT I COULD NOT PERCEIVE THE HORRORS THAT HAD TRANSPIRED.
HOW WAS YOUR DAY, DEAR?
FINE.
WELL THEN, SHALL WE SIT BY THE FIRE?

BUT SHE DIDN'T COME. NOR DID THINGS EVER REALLY RETURN TO NORMAL IN THE MONTHS THAT FOLLOWED. SHE TOOK TO BROODING IN SILENCE. INSTEAD OF NIGHTS AT HOME, THERE WERE EVENINGS AT THE THEATER. AND IT WAS THERE THAT SHE TOLD ME...
I WENT TO SEE THE DOCTOR AGAIN LAST WEEK.
THE PAINS AGAIN?
YES... I SUPPOSE. BUT THAT'S NOT ALL.
SOMETHING ELSE, TOO?

WE'RE GOING TO HAVE A BABY.

MY JOY WAS SOON REPLACED BY APPREHENSION. THE CHILD WAS DUE IN SEPTEMBER...

BUT IN OCTOBER, AFTER TWO MONTHS OF BEDRIDDEN PAIN AND SEVERAL FALSE LABORS, WE WERE STILL WAITING.
NOVEMBER CAME AND WENT.
FINALLY, THE YEAR DREW TO A CLOSE. ON CHRISTMAS EVE, THE DOCTOR ARRIVED IN RESPONSE TO MY URGENT MESSAGE.
BOIL SOME WATER...
...AND GET ME SOME CLEAN TOWELS!...
...AND HURRY!...

I WAITED DOWNSTAIRS, ALMOST AFRAID THAT THE CHILD MIGHT FINALLY BE BORN... HOPING THAT THIS PERHAPS WAS ANOTHER FALSE ALARM. WITH THESE FEARS, I WAITED.
AT FIRST, I COULD HEAR CAROL'S SOBS.

BUT THEN ALL FELL SILENT.
I WAITED FOR THE CRY OF A NEWBORN CHILD, BUT MY EXPECTATIONS WERE BETRAYED AND MY FEARS NURTURED.

I WALKED TO THE FOOT OF THE STAIRS TO LISTEN MORE CLOSELY. STILL SILENCE...

I WAS HARDLY AWARE OF CLIMBING THE STAIRS. INSTEAD, IT WAS THE DOOR THAT SEEMED TO BE MOVING CLOSER TO ME.
5.

AND CLOSER...

MY TREMBLING HAND FUMBLED WITH THE LOCK, WHICH YIELDED A TINY CRACK THROUGH WHICH I EAGERLY PEERED. IT WAS THEN THAT I SAW...

THE ROOM ROSE BEFORE ME, THE FLOOR TILTING MADLY, UNTIL I WAS SURE I WOULD FALL BACKWARDS INTO SOME ENDLESS ABYSS THAT YAWNED OPEN BEHIND ME. VIOLATED BEYOND REASON, TRANSPORTED BY HORROR, MY SENSES WERE REELING. WHAT I SAW WOULD HAVE MADE BLINDNESS A BLESSING, INSANITY A SALVATION. BUT IT WAS TOO LATE FOR BLINDNESS OR INSANITY. ONLY DEATH ITSELF COULD HAVE STRUCK THE IMAGE FROM MY BRAIN. SERPENTINE LEECHES, SUMMONED INTO BEING BY THE WRETCHED NIGHTMARES OF SOME BEFOULED AND BEFOULING FIEND, CLUNG TO THE GLISTENING FORM OF MY DEAR EXHAUSTED WIFE. THE HEAT WAS UNBEARABLE. MY CLOTHES STUCK TO ME LIKE SLIME. I WAS NAUSEOUS, UNBALANCED. BEFORE ME, TO THE RIGHT, THE DOCTOR LAY IN HIS OWN BLOOD, SILENT AND STILL, HIS EYES STILL OPEN TO THE HORROR OF HIS OWN DEATH.
6

I HEARD MYSELF SPEAK...
MY SON... WHERE IS MY SON?

WE'VE BEEN BLESSED WITH MANY CHILDREN.

I WANTED TO BEG AND PLEAD, TO ABJECTLY SURRENDER, TO DIE... WHEN SHE SPOKE AGAIN, I SCREAMED.
COME EMBRACE THEM.
MOTHER OF GOD! THESE ARE NO CHILDREN OF MINE!

SEE, JAMES-YOUR SON APPROACHES. FONDLE AND STROKE HIM. DO NOT BETRAY HIS LOVE.
7.

ISN'T HE BEAUTIFUL? A SON WHO NEEDS A FATHER.

!?!
IT WAS TOO MUCH TO ASK. MY BODY HEAVED IN REVOLT.

NO!
SPLAT

NOOAARGHHH!
HER SCREECH CUT THROUGH MY SUDDEN ANGER LIKE A KNIFE. I WAS STUNNED BY HER FURY.

CAROL!

IT WAS WHEN THE FLOOR SLAMMED INTO MY BACK THAT I REALIZED I HAD FALLEN.

I TRIED TO CRAWL AWAY. I NEEDED A BRIEF RESPITE TO CLEAR MY THOUGHTS, TO THINK CLEARLY. BUT THERE WAS NO RELIEF TO BE HAD. FISTFALLS RAINED LIKE HAMMERS ON MY ALREADY POUNDING SKULL.

TINY FINGERS WITH NAILS LIKE NEEDLES CLAWLED AT MY LIPS AND EYELIDS... AND THEN I SAW THE LAMP.

8.

DESPERATELY, I REACHED FOR IT... GRABBED IT AND...

AN INSANE STRENGTH SURGED THROUGH MY LIMBS.

MY ARMS FLAILED WILDLY IN ALL DIRECTIONS, THE LAMP A BURNING BLUDGEON THAT SMASHED AND SCORCHED THE VICIOUS SPAWN. THEY FLED BEFORE MY MINDLESS FURY, BUT I COULD NOT KILL THEM ALL.

THROUGH THE GAPING WINDOW, THEY ESCAPED INTO THE SNOWY NIGHT.

WHEN IT WAS OVER, CAROL WAS LEFT, HORRIBLY BURNED... AND DEAD.

WHAT MEANING COULD LIFE HOLD FOR ME AFTER WHAT I HAD SEEN AND DONE? *DEATH* WOULD BE MY SALVATION.

BUT THEN, I REALIZED... *THEY WERE FREE!* AND AS CAROL'S CHILDREN, THEY WOULD GIVE ME A REASON TO LIVE.

THEY WERE FREE, BUT MY LUST FOR VENGEANCE WOULD GROW AND RIPEN WITH THEM. IN THE BIBLE, IT IS SAID THE VOWS OF THE FAITHFUL COULD MAKE THE RULERS OF HELL TREMBLE. BUT ALL THESE VOWS WOULD PALE BEFORE MY OWN.
AND NO DEVIL WOULD EVER HAVE MORE TO FEAR OF RIGHTEOUS FURY THAN THESE SPAWN WOULD HAVE TO FEAR OF MY OWN.
9.

·THE END·

Mr Monster: His World

Dark Horse Presents 14, January 1988

Originally created by Fred Kelly for Canadian publisher Bell Features, Mr Monster alias Doc Stearne made only one appearance in June 1947's *Super Duper Comics 3*. Many years later when the character had long since been forgotten, Michael T. Gilbert resurrected him for Pacific Comics. He returned in their anthology title *Vanguard's* seventh appearance. Then, as Pacific Comics filed for bankruptcy, Michael was approached by Eclipse to continue the crusade of his larger-than-life creation. The full-colour adventures became popular, but further moves followed, this time to Dark Horse, and later on to Atomeka Press and Tundra Publications.

Michael has had an enjoyable career working for *Heavy Metal*, *Star Reach*, *Quack* and *Slow Death*. He also worked on Batman and Walt Disney's comics and stories. If this wasn't enough, he has established himself as a regular columnist for Roy Thomas's *Alter Ego* magazine.

~His World~
-A MR. MONSTER ADVENTURE-
So don't believe me! I don't care. They exist! (THEY DO!)
BONG! BONG! BONG! BONG
flap flap flap flap
And they wait! (OH YES!) They wait! In the dark. To suck the marrow from your bones. To scoop the soft tasty parts from your skull (FOR DESSERT!)
Creatures of mist and memory...
The nightmare people.
And... they're coming, brother! They're coming...
...for you!
And only one man can stop them...

Mr. MONSTER!!
DROP HER, BLOOD-SUCKER!
CRASSH
ART ASSIST: K. HOOPER/ C. KIRKHAM
IMMERSED IN A RIVER OF MOLTEN GOLD BY A DEN OF MUTATED MILK-SPIDERS--DOCTOR STRONGFORT STEARNY MIRACULOUSLY SURVIVED HIS ORDEAL UNSCATHED! HORRIFIED BY THE EXPERIENCE, HE EXACTED SWIFT VENGEANCE ON HIS GHASTLY TORMENTERS... AS MR. MONSTER!! SINCE THEN HE HAS WANDERED THE EARTH, SEARCHING OUT OTHER SUCH ABOMINATIONS... AND DESTROYING THEM!!!
Script/Art/Editing: MICHAEL T. Gilbert
(DONE AT THE STROKE OF MIDNITE)
© 1987, 2007

This is Mr. MONSTER... and this is his world.
It is a world of good and evil – vampires and ghouls. Giant flesh-eating blobs.
I SAID...
DROP HER!
CRAKK!
WHAM!
SCREEEEEE
And nightmare people!
SCREEEEEE
CCRAKK!!
EEEEEEEEEEKK!

TOO SLOW, FOOL--TOO SLOW!

CRAK!

C'CRASH!!

clatter

YOU'VE GAINED NOTHING! THE GIRL MAY BE SAFE--BUT LOOK BELOW!!

THOUSANDS JUST LIKE HER. MEN, WOMEN-- EVEN JUICY LITTLE CHILDREN!

INNOCENTS, WHOSE BLOOD WILL TASTE JUST AS SWEET!

TONIGHT, WHILE YOU'RE TRAPPED EARTHBOUND, I'LL GORGE ON THE BLOOD OF BABES!

AND THINK OF YOU!

HA! HA!

LIKE BLOODY HELL YOU WILL!

KA-BOOM!

The nightmare people quietly wait in the dark corridors of his world. But it's ours that keeps them fat!
They feed on fear, you see!
FIRE EXIT
HA! HA! HA!
In our real world of apathy and quiet terrors.. they are invincible!
BOOM! BOOM!
BOOM!
BOOM!
In our world of psychos and scientologists, deficits and dioxins--who is left to challenge them?
BOOM!
BOOM!
BOOM!
BOOM!
What have they to fear?
Who would dare oppose them?

WHO
WOULD
DARE?!
CCRASSHH!!
PUNCH! PUNCH! PUNCH! PUNCH!
SO...
...YOU LIKE BABIES, HUH?
ARRRRR!
ARRR! GET OFF! GET OFF!
PUNCH
PUNCH
NO! STOP! OWW!
NOOOOOOO
In the safety of our world, these guys have it soft.
CERUMPP!

But this isn't our world! Not tonight. Tonight...
...it's his!
PUFF! PUFF!
KA-CHINK!
EEAAAAAAA!
SPLOOT!
SPLORK!
BLAM!
BLAM!
BLAM!
BLAM!
KILL KILL
AKK! NO PLEASE.. *SOB!*
SPLOOT!
BAD NIGHT TO BE OUT, FRIEND!
AHHHH! NO!
N--: MR. MONSTER? OH, THANK GOD! *SOB!*

His world is sudden death...
GOD BLESS YOU!
GOD BLESS YOU, MR. MONSTER!
Sniff! Sniff!
HHH!!!!
WHOOSH
SSCRRAPE!!
WHOOOOOOSHEBB
!
SLAM!
MONSTERS!!
ROAR
QUISSH
CRUSH
BLAM!
BLAM!
BLAM
...and swift retribution!!

A world of impossible odds...
!
...met...
...head on!
BONG!
BONG!
°oOOOo° BROTHERS-LOOK! HIS GUNS GROW COLD... °oOOOOo°
BLAM!
click! click! click!
BLAM
BLAM
click! click! click!
sploosh!
sploosh!
sploosh!
But more than that--it's a world in which one man with courage and conviction can make a difference!

NOW AND FOREVER-- HE IS OURS!
AT LAST! OURS!
OURS!
OURS!
OURS!
OURS!
OURS!
OURS!
A man of unwavering faith in a world of despair. One brave man, to whom the black, endless night holds promise...
OURS! HA! HA! OURS ;, eh?
NO! NOT NOW! NOT WHEN WE WERE SO... SO...
CLOSE...!
SSIZZZLE!!
BONG BONG BONG
...of a bright new dawn!
Yes..this is Mr. Monster. And, for better or worse...

...this is his world!
BONG! BONG! BONG! BONG!
NO PARKING
VVVROOM!
GET IN!
SCREEECCH!!!
MORNING, DOC! ROUGH NIGHT?
NOT TOO BAD. A LITTLE SLOW, ACTUALLY. IT'S TOMORROW THAT CONCERNS ME, KELLY.
TOMORROW? WHAT'S SO SPECIAL ABOUT TOMORROW?
FIRST NIGHT OF THE FULL MOON, KELLY...
THINGS'LL REALLY BE HOPPIN' THEN!
~The End?~

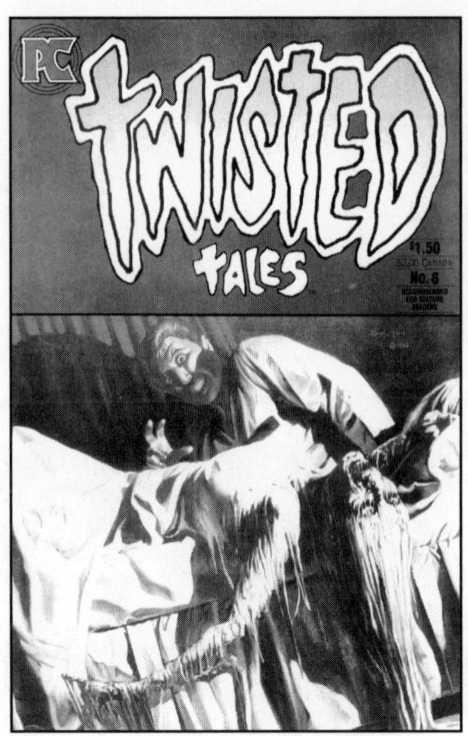

Home Ties

Twisted Tales 6, January 1984

There was an unusually restrained terror in this piece penned by Bruce Jones suggestive of the adult, as opposed to sensationalist nature, of this title; it was also beautifully illustrated by Mike Hoffman. Mike's style is usually imbued with the spirit of those luminary giants Frank Frazetta and Wally Wood. Like Bruce, Mike shares a great love of the EC tradition, but these pages are notably different and appear impressed by a European aesthetic.

His luscious work has been seen on magazine covers, portfolios and CDs as well as comic books. His own title *Lost Worlds of Science Fiction* ran for ten issues and his adaptation of the "Cabinet of Dr Caligari" for Fantagraphics' short-lived Monster Comics imprint met with critical acclaim.

HOME TIES

IT HADN'T BEEN A GREAT WEEK. EVERYTHING WAS SET FOR "THE LEFT-HANDED GUN"; THEY'D HIRED THIS BOY-GENIUS FROM TV NAMED PENN TO DIRECT AND, AFTER MONTHS OF NEGOTIATION, DEAN HAD COME OFF HIS "GIANT" HIGH-HORSE LONG ENOUGH TO CONSENT TO PLAY THE LEAD. WE'RE GOING FOR COLOR, SCOPE, THE WHOLE WORKS, SOLLY TELLS ME...THEN PRESTO, DEAN WRAPS HIS PORSCHE AROUND AN OLD FORD, WARNER'S GETS SCARED AND OUT GOES THE COLOR AND BIG BUDGET ALONG WITH THE STAR. BRANDO SAYS NO WAY AND HOLDEN IS DOING SOME INGE THING ABOUT A MID-WESTERN PICNIC. THEY STICK US WITH SOME NEW KID NAMED NEWMAN. FORGET IT, I TELL SOLLY, YOU CAN SHOVE YOUR BILLY THE KID EPIC, I'D RATHER WORK WITH JOSH ON THE MID-WESTERN PICNIC THING. "YOU WON'T LIKE IT", SOLLY WARNS ME, "IT'S LOCATION SHOOTING..." "I *LOVE* THE MIDWEST," I REPLY. HMPH. YOU EVER BEEN TO SALINA, KANSAS?...

STORY: BRUCE JONES ART: MIKE HOFFMAN
Letters: Carrie McCarthy Colors: Joe Chiodo

AH, WELL, NICE TO BE OUT OF THE L.A. SMOG AWHILE. AND IN ITS OWN QUAINT WAY, SALINA ISN'T SO BAD, I GUESS...
WHAT? NO LIMOUSINE?

KNOCK IT OFF, BROOKS: YOU'RE JUST THE PRODUCTION ASSISTANT, NOT THE HEAD WRITER...

SAY, PAL, WHERE DOES A GUY CATCH A CAB AROUND HERE?
YOU GOTS TO CALL ONE, MISTER! THIS AIN'T NEW YORK CITY!
I NOTICED.

THE WILSHIRE HOTEL. UH... IT DOES HAVE HOT AND COLD RUNNING WATER...?
IT DOES NOW.
OH BROTHER!

HARRY CHESTER STILL MISSING
HOTEL

THAT'S WHEN IT HAPPENED! I WAS JUST PASSING THE COFFEE SHOP WHEN I SAW HIM... HARRY CHESTER, THE GUY ON ALL THE FRONT PAGES...
SALINA A
COFFEE SH
HOLY--

HARRY! HARRY! IT'S ME! PHILIP BROOKS!
COFFEE
I COULDN'T BELIEVE IT! HARRY WAS ALIVE AND WELL! I DASHED INSIDE, BRIMMING WITH QUESTIONS...
HARRY, I--
WHAT TH-- GONE...HE'S GONE!
I CHECKED INTO MY ROOM... THEN I CHECKED INTO THE LOCAL PHONE BOOK...
HE WAS THERE, ALL RIGHT, THAT MEAL WAS ONLY HALF EATEN!

I DIDN'T REALLY EXPECT TO FIND ANYTHING. I WENT DOWNSTAIRS, HAD DINNER, THEN RENTED A CAR AND DROVE AROUND JUST TO GET OUT OF THE STUFFY HOTEL...
ONE OF THE HOTTEST DIRECTORS IN HOLLYWOOD AND SUDDENLY HE JUST ISN'T THERE ANYMORE...THAT MAKES IT TWICE I'VE SEEN HIM DISAPPEAR...

THAT T-BIRD! THAT'S HARRY'S! I'D BET ANYTHING ON IT!
FEELING SOMEWHAT FOOLISH, I WALKED UP TO THE VICTORIAN DOOR AND KNOCKED AWAY...
HARRY...IT IS YOU!
HELLO, PHIL...I SUPPOSE YOU'LL WANT TO COME IN...YES...WHY NOT.
WHERE THE DEVIL HAVE YOU BEEN, OLD MAN? YOUR WIFE--THE POLICE--
I LIVE HERE NOW...WITH ANGELIQUE...

ANGELIQUE—?
SHE'LL BE DOWN IN A MINUTE... CARE FOR A DRINK?
I'D CARE FOR SOME EXPLANATION IS WHAT I'D CARE FOR!

I DON'T SUPPOSE YOU'D CONSIDER SIMPLY CLIMBING BACK INTO YOUR CAR AND DRIVING AWAY, WOULD YOU?
NO, I DON'T SUPPOSE I WOULD.
I THOUGHT NOT. (SIGH) OKAY, HERE IT IS... THE WHOLE STORY... SIT BACK...

"I WAS IN TOWN ON BUSINESS--A WESTERN--THREE YEARS AGO WHEN I HAPPENED BY THE HOUSE IN MY CAR."

"I SAW A LOVELY FEMALE FIGURE SILHOUETTED IN THE UPSTAIRS WINDOW. I ALSO NOTICED THAT THE DOWNSTAIRS DOOR WAS AJAR..."

"I STOPPED AND APPROACHED THE HOUSE, INTENDING TO WARN THE OWNERS THAT THEIR DOOR HAD BEEN LEFT OPEN. I KNOCKED BUT NO ONE ANSWERED ...SO I PUSHED OPEN THE DOOR AND STEPPED INSIDE..."

"AS I STARTED ACROSS THE FOYER, A FIGURE APPEARED ON THE STAIRCASE..."
"THE LOVELY FIGURE OF THE WOMAN I SAW IN THE WINDOW..."

"SHE WAS RAVISHING...THE MOST BEAUTIFUL CREATURE I'D EVER LAID EYES UPON..."

AH, HERE SHE IS NOW! MEET ANGELIQUE!

I LOOKED UPON THE MOST INTOXICATINGLY BEAUTIFUL WOMAN I HAD EVER SEEN...
NO NEED TO STAND FOR ANGELIQUE, PHIL...
LOVELY, ISN'T SHE?
EXQUISITE!

NEVER MIND, OLD MAN, ANGELIQUE CAN LIGHT HER OWN CIGARETTE...

NO MATTER WHAT HAPPENS NOW, PHIL, DON'T MOVE OR INTERFERE IN ANY WAY...

THERE WAS A SUDDEN KNOCKING AT THE DOOR. IMMEDIATELY ANGELIQUE ROSE TO ANSWER IT...

A TALL DARK MAN IN FORMAL EVENING ATTIRE STOOD THERE. ANGELIQUE BADE HIM ENTER. THEY EMBRACED...

W-WHO IS IT? HER BROTHER?
BE PATIENT, YOU'LL SEE...

SILENCE FOR A FEW MOMENTS. THEN--SHOCKINGLY--THE UNMISTAKABLE SOUNDS OF LOVEMAKING...

HARRY, WHAT THE DEVIL--??

AFTER A TIME, THE YOUNG MAN IN EVENING ATTIRE DESCENDED THE STAIRS AGAIN, STRAIGHTENING HIS TIE. ANGELIQUE APPEARED AT THE UPSTAIRS BANNISTER A MOMENT LATER ...BUT THERE WERE TEARS STREAKING HER LOVELY FACE...
PETER...

IT ALL HAPPENED IN SECONDS...
BLAM!

JESUS...
PHIL, DON'T--

NO!
BLAM!

OH GOD...OH CHRIST, I'M GOING TO BE SICK...

I DASHED PAST THE CRUMPLED RAG DOLL AT MY FEET, SEARCHING DESPERATELY FOR AN UPSTAIRS BATHROOM...

WHEN I'D FINISHED WRETCHING...
SORRY, OLD MAN. I WANTED TO SPARE YOU THAT... COME, LET'S HAVE A DRINK...

BUT WHEN I LOOKED AT THE SPOT WHERE ANGELIQUE HAD LAIN...
WHAT TH-- GONE! SH-SHE'S VANISHED!!
YES...THE MOST VIVID, DETAILED, CLEARLY DISCERNABLE HAUNTING IN THE HISTORY OF GHOSTS AND SPECTRES. I WATCH IT EVERY NIGHT...

BUT THIS IS FANTASTIC! YOU'VE GOT TO TELL THE POLICE--TH-THE PRESS! WE'VE GOT TO GET THIS THING ON TELEVISION!
I THOUGHT OF ALL THAT...

A COLD LIGHT FORMS IN HARRY'S EYES...
--I EVEN TRIED TO CALL THE POLICE AFTER THE FIRST TIME...BUT I COULDN'T. I COULDN'T. I'M IN LOVE WITH HER, PHIL...

IN LOVE...BUT SHE'S A--A PHANTOM! ARE YOU INSANE? WHAT ABOUT YOUR WIFE, YOUR HOME?
I'VE TRIED TO LEAVE... REALLY TRIED...BUT I CAN'T GET HER FACE OUT OF MY MIND...SHE'S HAUNTING ME ALL RIGHT, PHIL, MORE THAN YOU'LL EVER KNOW...AND IT'S WORTH IT, EVEN IF I CAN ONLY SEE HER FOR THOSE FEW MINUTES EACH NIGHT...

YES, I KNOW WHAT YOU'RE THINKING: HARRY CHESTER, BIG-SHOT MOVIE DIRECTOR, PHOTOGRAPHED, SLEPT WITH THE MOST BEAUTIFUL WOMEN IN THE WORLD! BUT NONE OF THEM ARE LIKE ANGELIQUE. NONE OF THEM...
YOU'VE SEEN HER, PHIL, YOU KNOW IT'S THE TRUTH...
BUT--

OH, I'VE THOUGHT OF WHAT WOULD HAPPEN IF I CHANGED THE PATTERN, LOCKED THE DOOR, PERHAPS. AT LEAST THAT WAY I WOULDN'T HAVE TO WATCH HIM KISS HER ...WATCH HER DIE... PERHAPS SHE'D EVENTUALLY COME TO ME! BUT WHAT IF IT BROKE THE CHAIN? WHAT IF SHE MERELY VANISHED? I COULDN'T TAKE THAT, I'D DIE. I DON'T WANT HER TO REST IN PEACE!

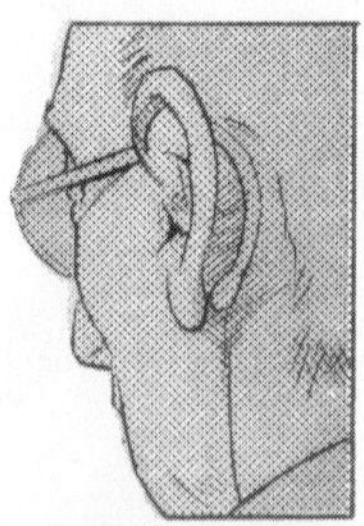

LATER ON, HARRY WOULD TELL ME THAT HE'D NEVER SEEN SUCH A DESPERATE, PATHETIC LOOK ON ANYONE'S FACE BEFORE ...ANYONE'S BUT HIS OWN, THAT IS...

COME IN, PHIL...

Hollywood Times

SEPTEMBER 12, 1955

ANOTHER DISAPPEARANCE PLAGUES HOLLYWOOD COMMUNITY

HOLLYWOOD, CA — Police are still baffled by the sudden disappearance of Philip C. Brooks, last seen at the Los Angeles train depot heading east on a business trip . . .

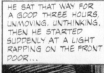

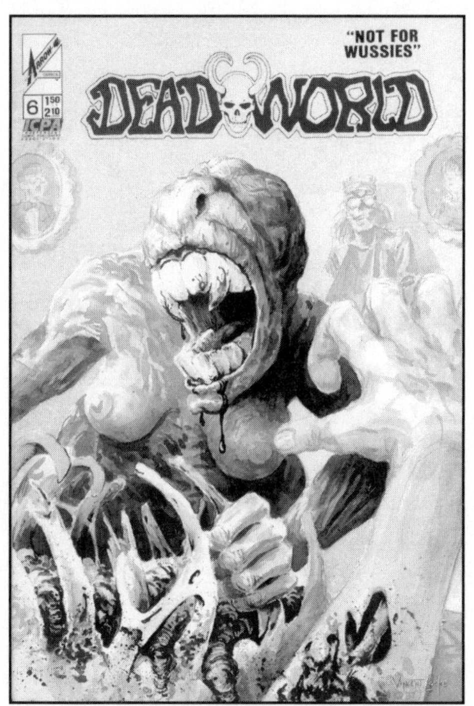

One of these Days

Deadworld 6, December 1987

At a time when superheroes once again reigned supreme, Arrow Comics had the strength of conviction to release one of the finest zombie comics of any era of comic book publishing; in its day it was the only zombie comic of its kind. It's hard to believe, but the dead, recently risen from the grave and intent on taking a chunk out of your arm, didn't have a mass appeal back then. While there was plenty of gore to be had throughout this series, there was also a very intelligent storyline accompanied by a cast of characters with whom the reader could readily empathize. There hadn't been an ongoing story of this depth since *Tomb of Dracula* and nor would there be for some time to come.

Deadworld later moved to Gary Reed's Caliber, a publisher who seemed intent on steering clear of anything remotely mainstream. Their back catalogue is still eagerly sought out. Gary would eventually take on the scriptwriting to work alongside artist Vince Locke. After an overly long hiatus from the mid-1990s, *Deadworld* has recently made a welcome return to Image Comics.

...WHAZZA
WHISZHAHENMM
...
...WHERZAT
NECRONOMICONNN
...
HMF
NOTS...
...NOTSSSAFFE...
UH...NOT...

...UMFF...
PLEEEEZ...
...NNOOOO...
...GOOUOO
--PLEEEEZ...
SNORT!
...NOOOOOO...
...UMFF
...HMFF...
Girl's Room! Keep Out!

KEEP IT DOWN, WORMHEADS, YOU'LL WAKE THE PREY.
CLUNK!
OH, YEAH, BIG FUN TONIGHT. REAL BIG FUN.

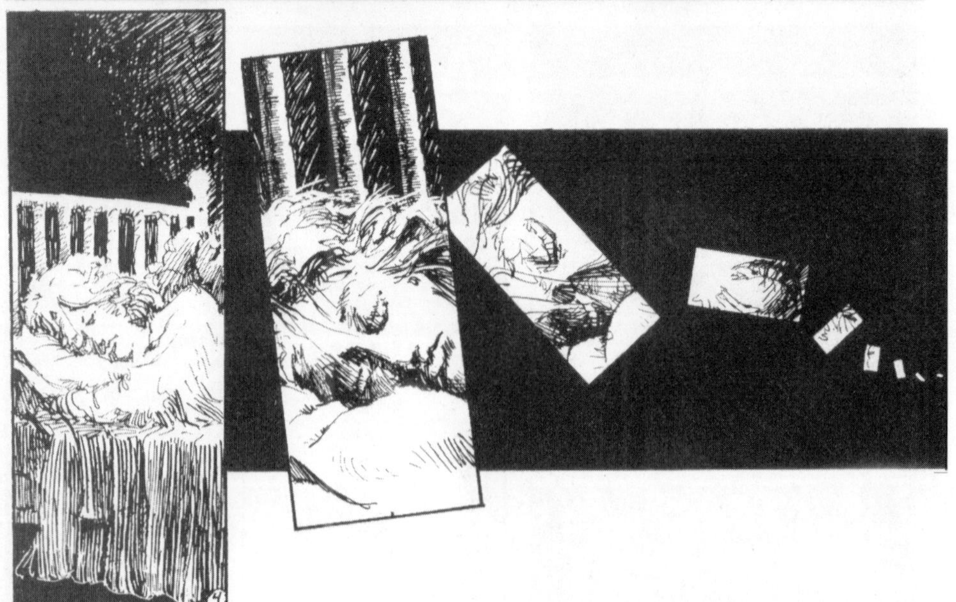

PUNCH KICK
KNEE
CLOBBER
KICK BITE
SCRATCH
GNAW
"DANNY?"
"OH, DANNY..."
5

"IT'S A DREAM."
"A DREAM..."
CHOCK!

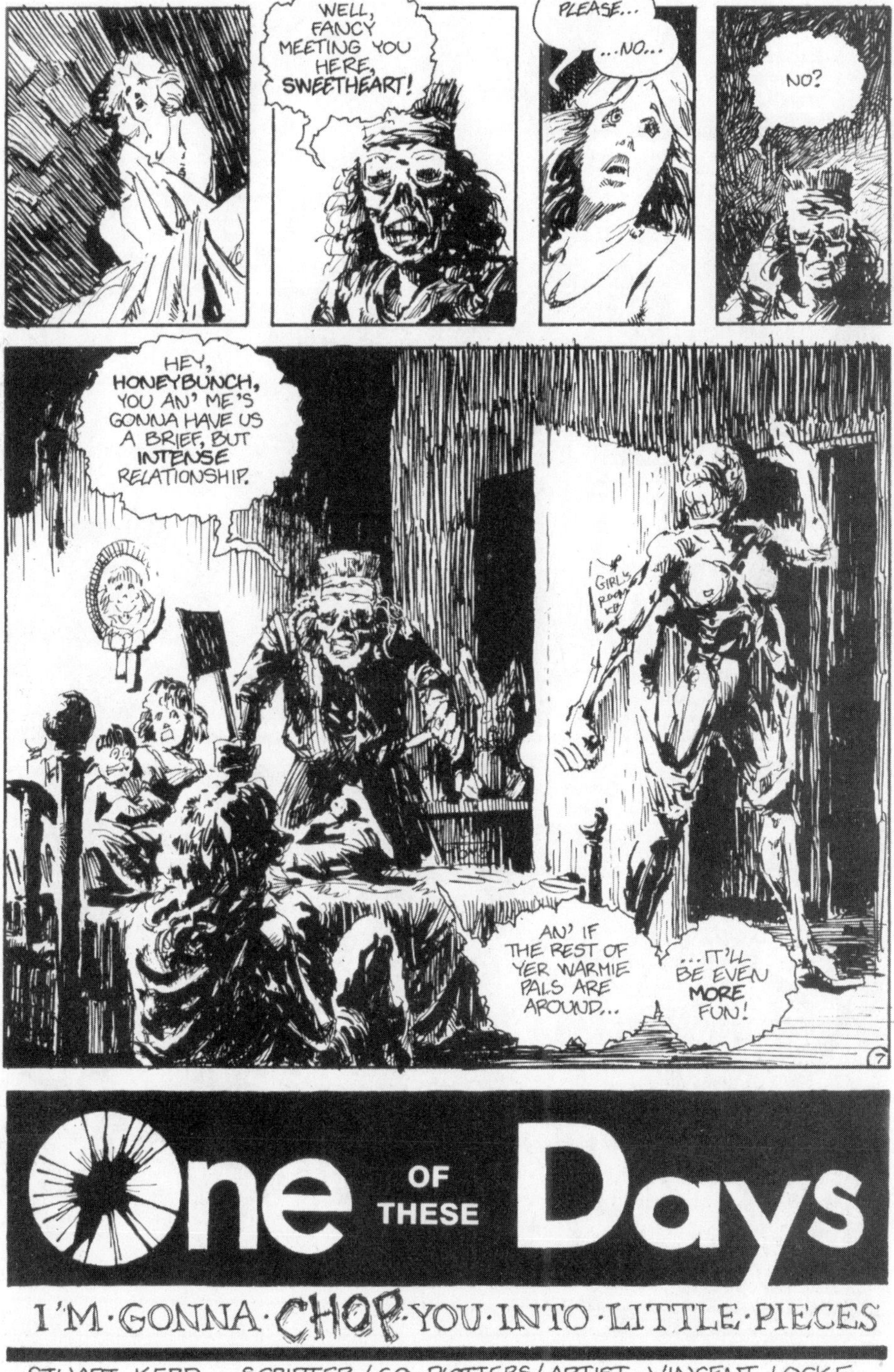

I'M·GONNA·CHOP·YOU·INTO·LITTLE·PIECES

STUART KERR · SCRIPTER/CO-PLOTTERS/ARTIST · VINCENT LOCKE

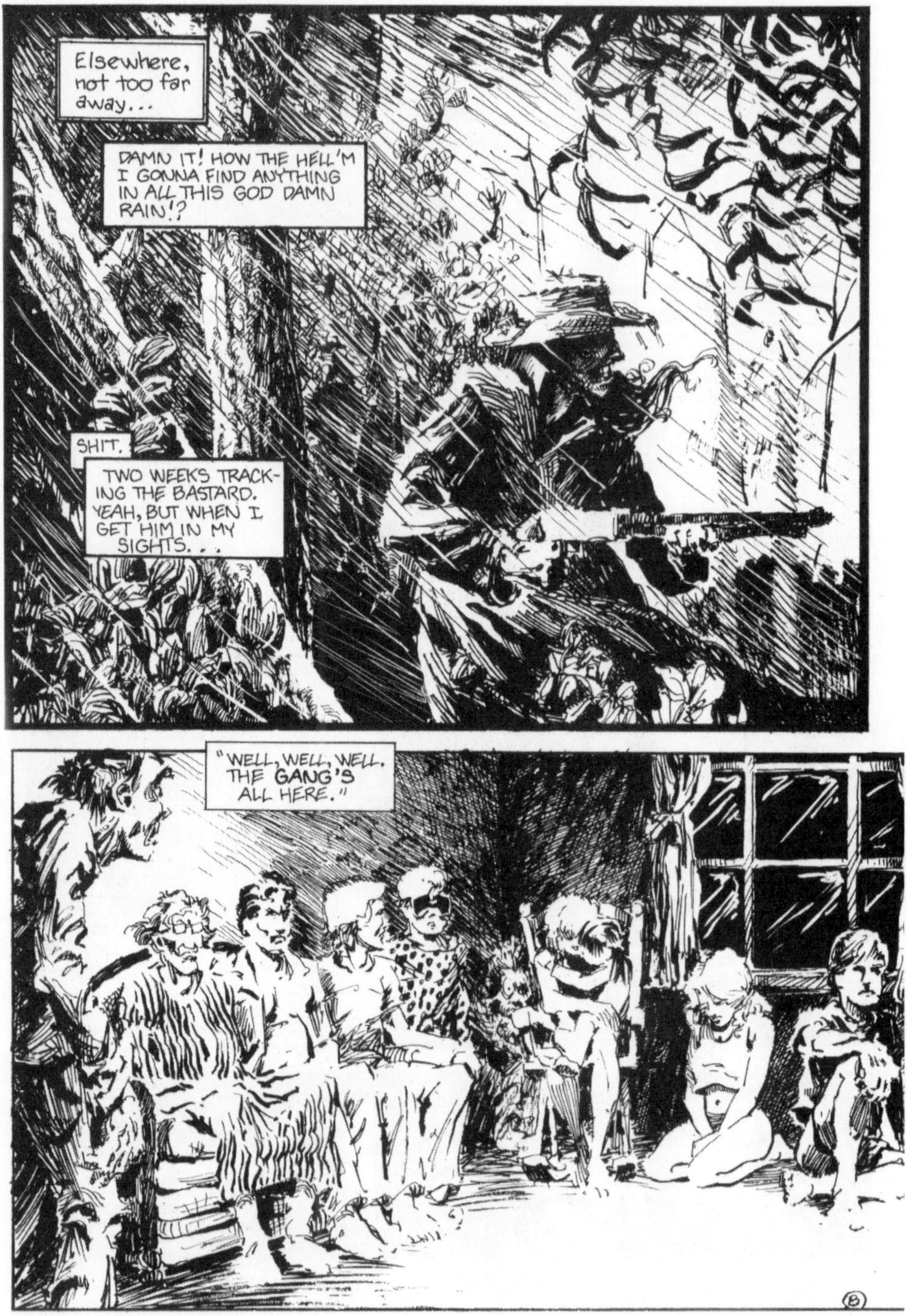

Elsewhere, not too far away...
DAMN IT! HOW THE HELL'M I GONNA FIND ANYTHING IN ALL THIS GOD DAMN RAIN!?
SHIT.
TWO WEEKS TRACKING THE BASTARD. YEAH, BUT WHEN I GET HIM IN MY SIGHTS...

...'CEPT FOR YER BUDDIES I TOOK CARE OF BACK ON THE RIVERBOAT, THAT IS. HA HA HA!
ELMER LAWS SUCK
YOU JUST KEEP QUIET, SPUD. NO SMART ALECK REMARKS.
I AIN'T EVEN THINKIN' ABOUT IT!
WHEN I SAY THE WORD, GET YER ASS OUT THAT DOOR AND INTO THE WOODS. AND DON'T LOOK BACK. THAT'S AN ORDER
GOTCH YA.
YOU GUY'S BEEN A REAL PAIN IN THE ASS FOR ME. MAKIN' ME LOOK BAD WITH THE BOSS. I DON'T LIKE THAT.
YOU'DA BEEN BETTER OFF IF YA'D JUST LAID DOWN AN' GONE QUIET AT THE RIVERBOAT. NOW I'M GONNA HAVE TA--
GET!
GET THEE HENCE, SATAN!
DIS'N BE A HOUSE WHAT'S BEEN SANCTEE-FIED BY DE LORD GOD! AN' DERE AIN'T NOT ENOUGH ROOM'N FOR DE BOTH OF YAS!
OH, SHUT UP, YA OL' FART.

SLAP!
UNGH!
ANTAGONIZING THE SON OF A BITCH WON'T BRING MARY BACK, PA.
MUMBLE GRUMBLE
AS I WAS SAYIN' BEFORE THE GEEZER STUCK HIS TWO CENTS IN... SINCE I ALREADY SPENT THIS MUCH TIME FOLLOWIN YOUR ASSES, I MIGHT AS WELL GIVE MYSELF A LITTLE TIME TO ENJOY THE FRUITS OF MY LABORS. SPEND A LITTLE QUALITY TIME WITH YA, YA MIGHT SAY.
WE'RE GONNA HAVE SOME FUN!
YOU MIGHT HAVE US, GEEK, BUT YOU'LL NEVER TAKE EARTH. IT'S WINTER NOW. ALL YOUR SOLDIERS ARE FREEZING IN THE COLDER REGIONS.
SILLY BOY, YOU DON'T KNOW WHAT YOU'RE TALKIN' ABOUT. TOO BAD YOU WON'T BE AROUND LONG ENOUGH TA BE EDUCATED.
...

MAN, DID I JUST HEAR SOMETHIN' OR IS THIS BITCHIN' WIND MESSIN' WITH MY EARS?
COULD BE THE END OF THE RAINBOW IF MY LUCK'S RUNNIN' HIGH.
THIS IS IT, MAN. COME ON, LET THIS BE IT.
AAAAARRGH!
11

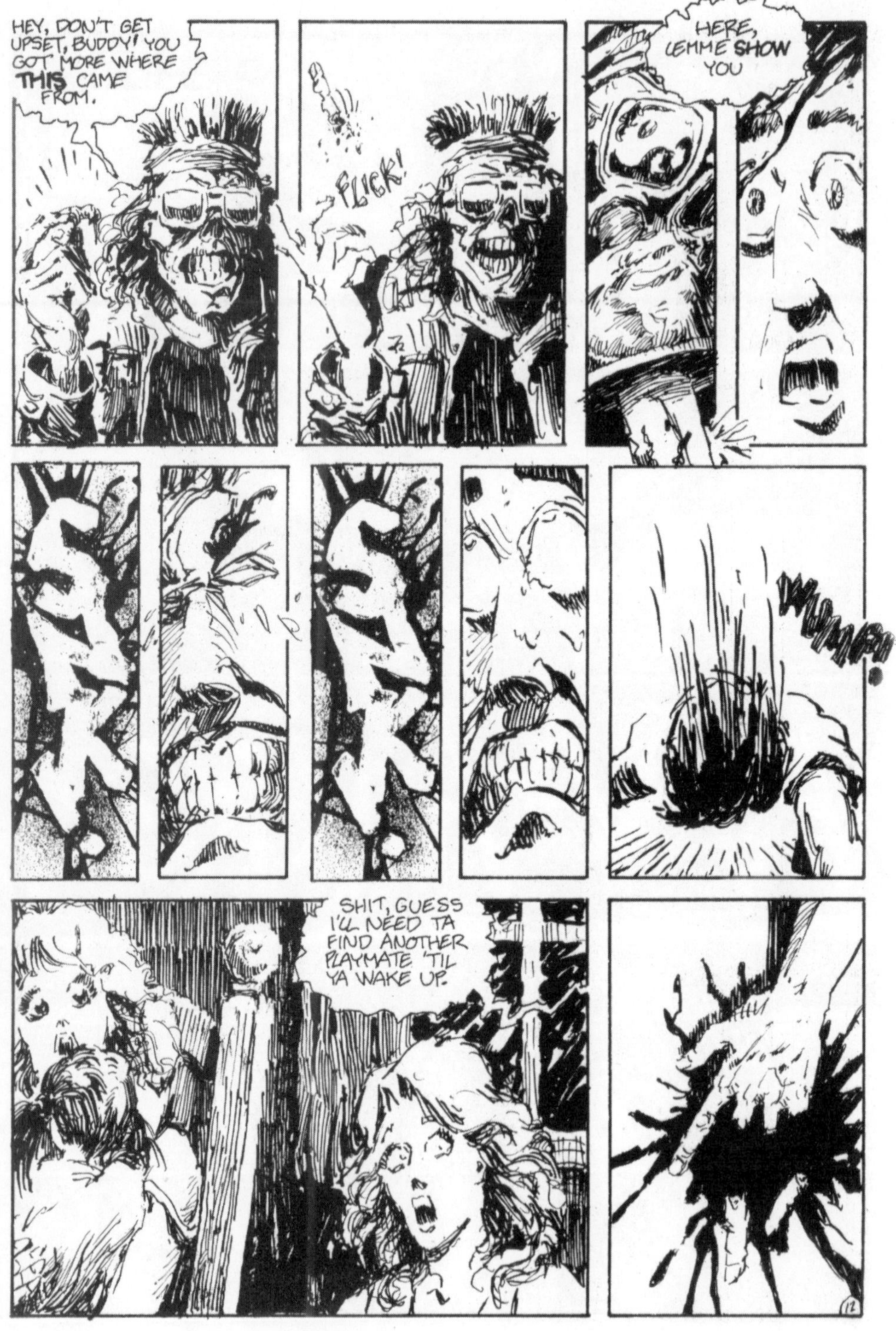
HEY, DON'T GET UPSET, BUDDY! YOU GOT MORE WHERE THIS CAME FROM.
FLICK!
HERE, LEMME SHOW YOU
WUMP!
SHIT, GUESS I'LL NEED TA FIND ANOTHER PLAYMATE 'TIL YA WAKE UP.
12

DEFINITELY SOMEBODY IN THERE. GOTTA GET A CLOSER LOOK.
I GOT A FEELIN' ...
...YEA...
YER TIMES COME, MOTHERFUCKER.

PSHAW! I TOL' YAS, DEAKE. YAS AN ABOMINATION AN' YAS BROUGHT EVIL INTA OUR GOD-FEARIN' HOME!
SHHH! SIT DOWN!
WHAT!?
SUFFER YE NOT A WITCH TA LIVE, AN HERE I IS LETTIN' A SATAN-WORSHIPPER SHARE M' ROOF!
HEY, SHHH! KEEP--
DE LORD HAS TURN HIS BACK ON DIS HOUSE F'SHUR, AN' IT'S ALL COME DOWN ON US CUZZA YOU! BLASPHEMER AN' CORRUPTER!
YER SOUL IS A CERTAIN GOAN' TA BURN IN HELL, YA DEVIL!
NO... SHHH... PLEASE... QUIET--
YOU!
DEAKE? COME HERE.

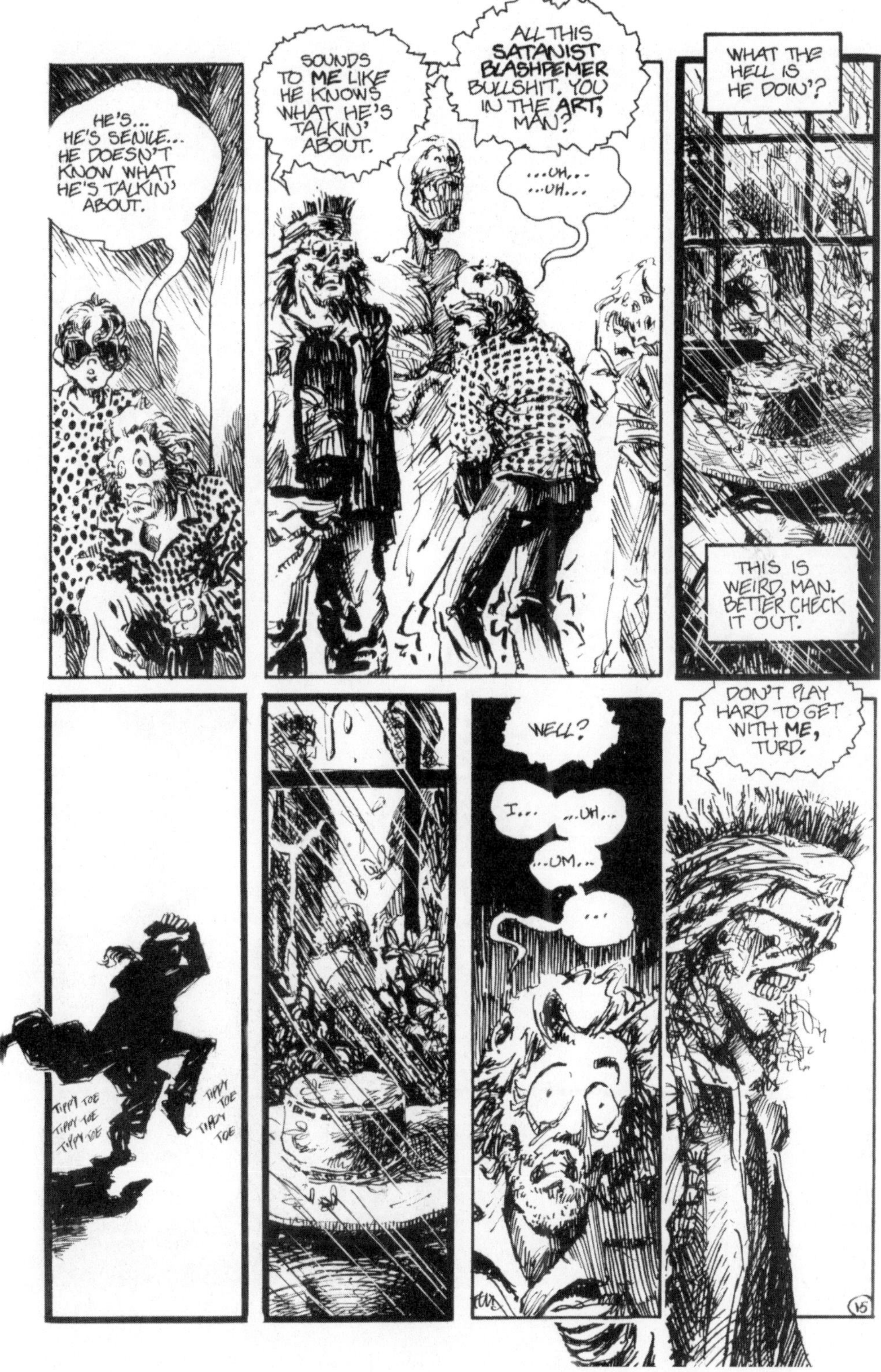
HE'S... HE'S SENILE... HE DOESN'T KNOW WHAT HE'S TALKIN' ABOUT.
SOUNDS TO ME LIKE HE KNOWS WHAT HE'S TALKIN' ABOUT.
ALL THIS SATANIST BLASHPEMER BULLSHIT. YOU IN THE ART, MAN?
...UH... ...UH...
WHAT THE HELL IS HE DOIN'?
THIS IS WEIRD, MAN. BETTER CHECK IT OUT.
TIPPY TOE TIPPY TOE TIPPY TOE
TIPPY TOE TIPPY TOE
WELL?
I...
...UH...
...UM...
...
DON'T PLAY HARD TO GET WITH ME, TURD.
15

OR MAYBE I'LL HANG YA WITH YER OWN INTESTINES. I'M SURE I CAN THINK OF SOMETHING JUST RIGHT FOR YOU.
NO! NO, PLEASE, I CAN... HELP YOU. I'M THE ONLY ONE
I KNOW ABOUT THE GATE. I HAVE POWER.
IF YA DON'T FEEL LIKE TALKIN' MAYBE I'LL JUST HAVTA CUT OFF YER TOES AND JAM 'EM DOWN YER THROAT SO YA DON'T TALK NO MORE AT ALL.
I... WE OPENED IT. I CAN... OPEN IT AGAIN.
JUST DON'T... DON'T HURT ME! I'LL DO ANYTHING...
ANYTHING!

NOW THIS IS INTERESTING. DID I REALLY COME ACROSS MY FAVORITE WARMIES AND FIND THE NUMBER ONE WARMIE ON THE KEEP ALIVE LIST?
THIS IS EVEN WORTH CUTTIN' THE PARTY SHORT FOR.
GUESS I'LL HAV'TA QUICKEN THE PACE A LITTLE, BUT NOT TOO MUCH.
YEAH, THE BOYS ARE GONNA SHIT BRICKS WHEN THEY HEAR ABOUT DEAKE!
YOU, THE ONE WITH THE TITS. YOU LOOK LIKE YOU'LL BLEED A LOT. YOU'RE FIRST.
NO NEED TO THANK ME.
WHAT'S UP NOW?
OH, MAN. CAN'T LET HIM CUT UP A NICE PIECE OF ASS LIKE THAT.
17

'EY, DON'T SWEAT IT BABE. THIS AIN'T GONNA HURT MORE'N A FEW SECONDS, AN' IT'LL ALL BE OVER.
'COURSE, IF YA SQUIRM TOO MUCH, IT'S BOUND TO TAKE MORE'N ONE SLASH.
SO, LIKE MR. WELK SAYS, 'A ONE AN' A TWO AN' A--'
18

HE KNOWS I'M HERE, BUT GODDAMNIT, I KNOW HE CAN'T SEE ME!
OH, SHIT--

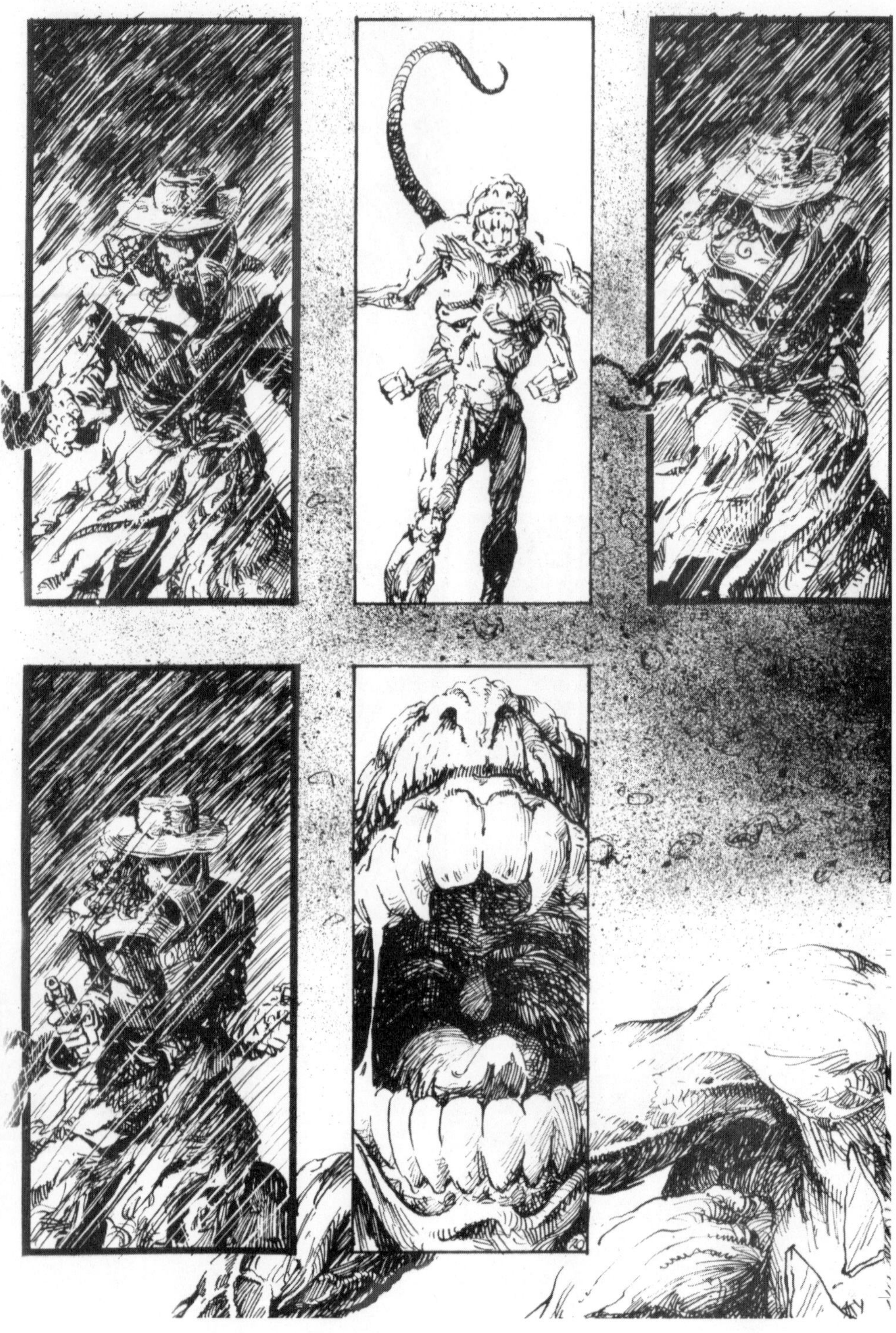

BLAM!
CRASH!

SHIT!
KICK ASS!
DOWN!
SPRAK!
YEOW!
C'MERE, YOU. I AIN'T LETTIN' YOU OUTTA MY SIGHT, TURD.
LOOKS LIKE IT'S TIME FOR A STRATEGIC WITHDRAWL.
ZIP
BLAM

BAM!
MOTHERFUCKER'S SHOOTIN' BACK!
BAM!
WE'RE OUTTA HERE. C'MON, ROVER!
23

BLAK!
BORF!
BLEK!
IT'S QUIET. THE SHOOTING'S STOPPED.

MAN! WHO WAS THAT DUDE? MACK BOLAN?
FAR OUT!
IS MIKE... OKAY?
HE'LL BE ALRIGHT, BUT WE BETTER GET SOMETHING ON HIS HAND BEFORE IT GETS INFECTED.
SHHH!
25

DANNY!
Meanwhile, not yet a hundred yards away...
I'D BE PRETTY PISSED OFF ABOUT THIS TIME IF I HADN'T MAN-AGED TO GRAB YOU, TURD.
26

YOU DON'T KNOW HOW MUCH YOU'RE WORTH, TURD. YOU'RE THE GOD DAMN MOST VALUABLE TURD EVER SHIT, THAT'S WHAT. YER GONNA OPEN UP DAT GOLDEN GATE, TURD. HEH HEH HEH!
AN' THEN YER GONNA FIND OUT WHAT ALL HELL BREAKIN' LOOSE REALLY MEANS. HA HA HA!
WHAT'VE I DONE, WHAT'VE I DONE, WHAT'VE I DONE?!
I'M A TRAITOR AGAIN. I'M GONNA KILL EVERYBODY THIS TIME.
PLEASE, PLEASE, LET ME DIE NOW. I CAN'T... I CAN'T HELP MYSELF.
PLEASE LET ME DIE....
YEAH, IT'S BEEN A LONG, LONG DAY, TURD, BUT M'JOB'S FINALLY ABOUT OVER. WITHIN A FEW DAYS ...
"...EVERYBODY DIES."
27

The Dunwich Horror

The Haunter of the Dark and Other Grotesque Visions, 1999

When critics combine words such as "shocking", "harmful", "harrowing" and "brilliant" to describe an artist, the seeker of the abstruse will do all they can to search out his or her work. This collection of graphic interpretations uncovering the imaginings of H. P. Lovecraft from Oneiros Books is a mystical treasure; its odious perception suggests it to have been forged from the Necronomicon itself. This version of "The Dunwich Horror" first saw print as early as 1988 when published by Caermaen Books; it is a truly hideous, although meticulous vision and as such is closer to Lovecraft's terrifying dreamscape than anything ever seen in a comic-related publication. John Coulthart has a rare gift – some may call it a curse.

His work has been seen on the covers of Hawkwind albums, along with Cradle of Filth, and more avant-garde comic readers will have seen his maniacal rendering in Savoy's tantalizing *Lord Horror*.

THE DUNWICH HORROR
BY H.P. LOVECRAFT

GENERAL STORE

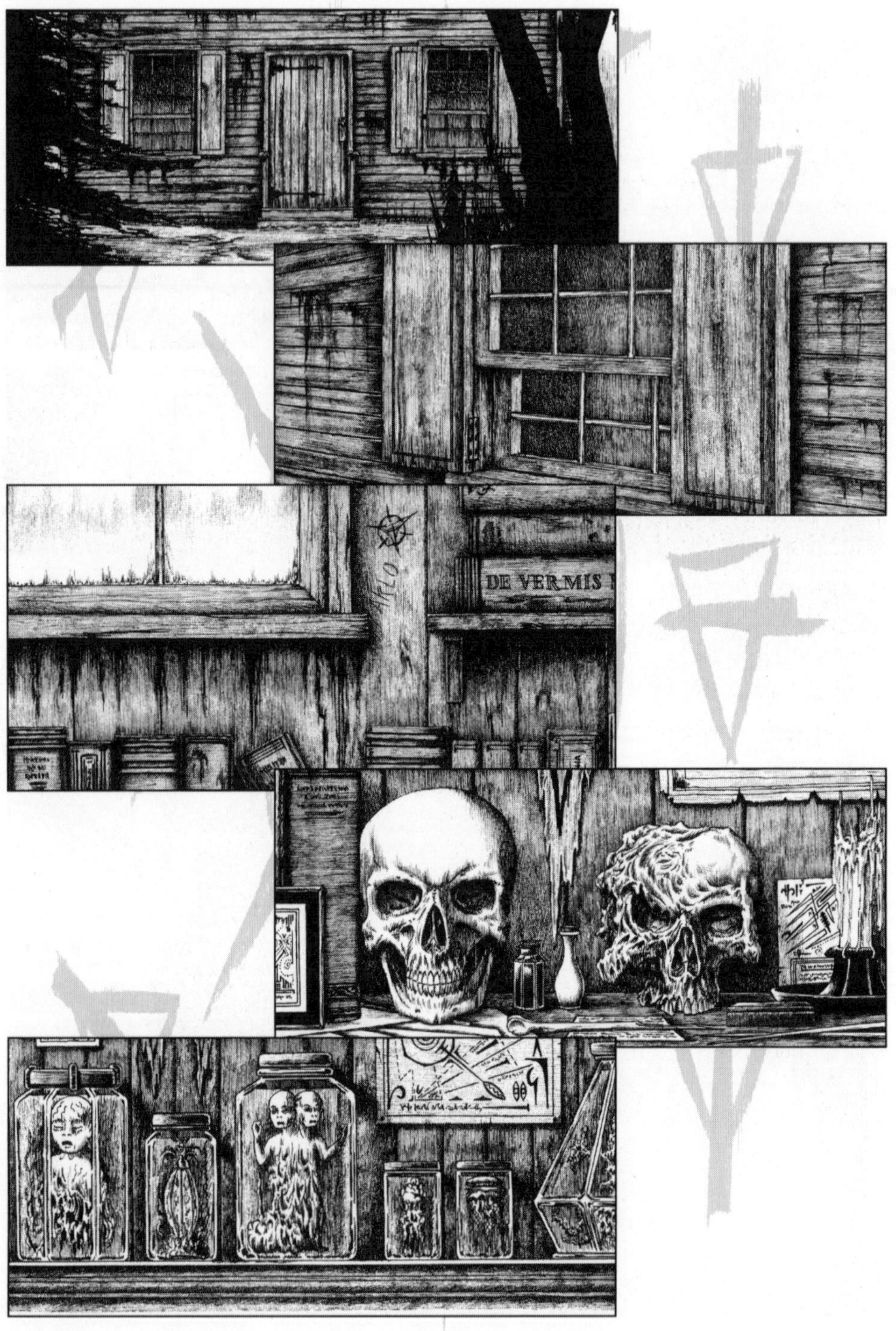
DE VERMIS

Ungrund

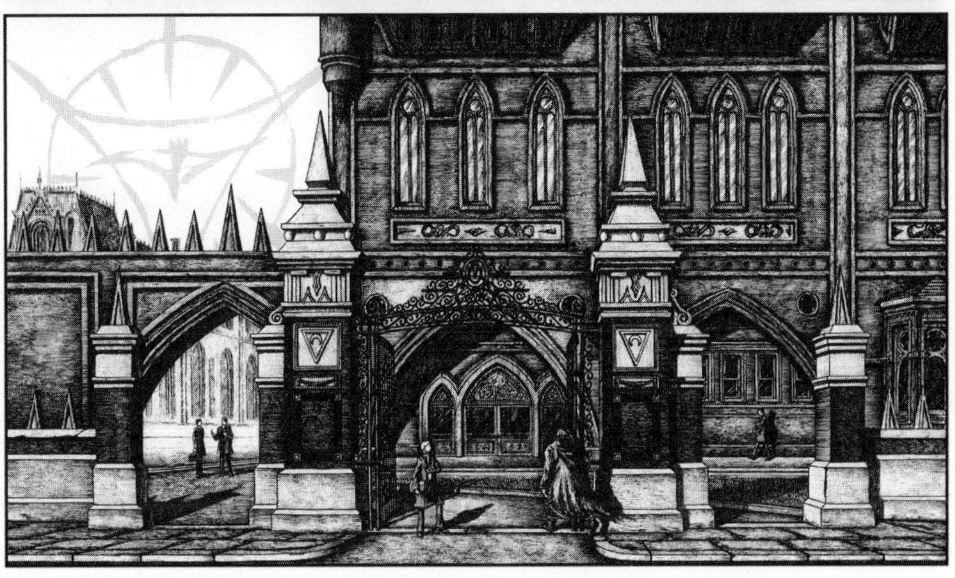

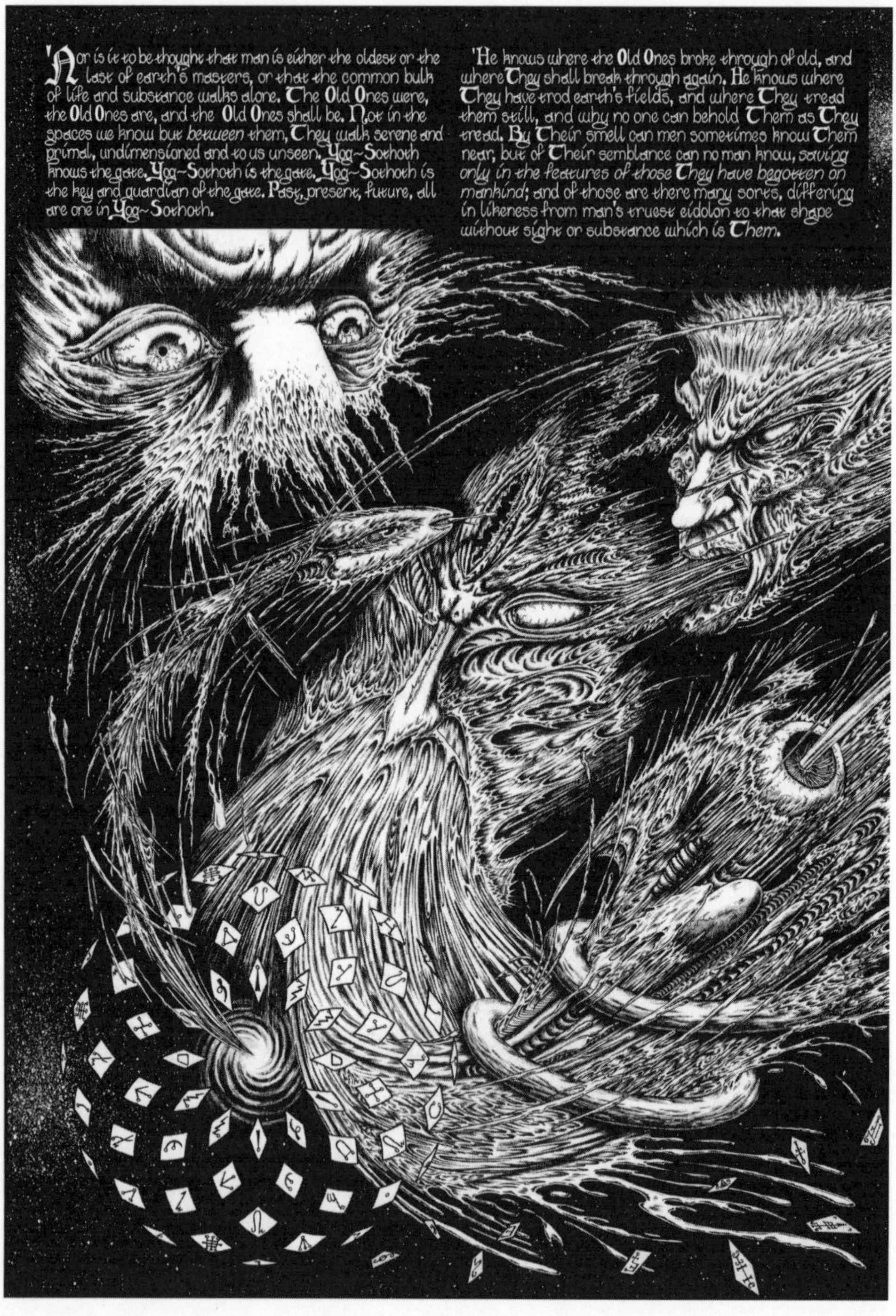
'Nor is it to be thought that man is either the oldest or the last of earth's masters, or that the common bulk of life and substance walks alone. The Old Ones were, the Old Ones are, and the Old Ones shall be. Not in the spaces we know but *between* them, They walk serene and primal, undimensioned and to us unseen. Yog-Sothoth knows the gate. Yog-Sothoth is the gate. Yog-Sothoth is the key and guardian of the gate. Past, present, future, all are one in Yog-Sothoth.
'He knows where the Old Ones broke through of old, and where They shall break through again. He knows where They have trod earth's fields, and where They tread them still, and why no one can behold Them as They tread. By Their smell can men sometimes know Them near, but of Their semblance can no man know, *saving only in the features of those They have begotten on mankind*; and of those are there many sorts, differing in likeness from man's truest eidolon to that shape without sight or substance which is *Them*.

'They walk unseen and foul in lonely places where the Words have been spoken and the Rites howled through at their Seasons. The wind gibbers with Their voices, and the earth mutters with Their consciousness. They bend the forest and crush the city, yet may not forest or city behold the hand that smites. Kadath in the cold waste hath known Them, and what man knows Kadath? The ice desert of the South and the sunken isles of Ocean hold stones whereon Their seal is engraven but who hath seen the deep frozen city or the sealed tower long garlanded with seaweed and barnacles?
'Great Cthulhu is Their cousin, yet can he spy Them only dimly. Iä! Shub-Niggurath! As a foulness shall ye know Them. Their hand is at your throats yet ye see Them not; and Their habitation is even one with your guarded threshold. Yog-Sothoth is the key to the gate, whereby the spheres meet. Man rules where They ruled once; They shall soon rule where man rules now. After summer is winter, after winter summer. They wait patient and potent, for here shall They reign again.'

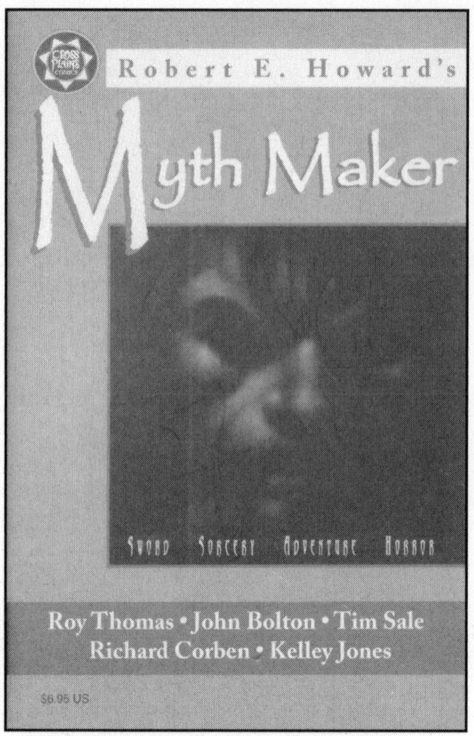

Robert E. Howard's
Myth Maker
Roy Thomas • John Bolton • Tim Sale
Richard Corben • Kelley Jones
$6.95 US

Dream Snake

Robert E. Howard's Myth Maker, 1999

Almost forty years ago Roy Thomas championed the writings of Robert E. Howard while working as editor for Marvel Comics, although he insists it wasn't entirely his idea to bring Conan to the pages of a comic book. Roy found himself in a position where even as editor he wouldn't delegate it away so ended up writing the character.

In 1999 Roy worked with a small publisher by the name of Cross Plains, who have since folded operations, to introduce more of Robert E. Howard's creations to an ever-eager comic-buying public. *Myth Maker* revealed Howard as an eminent writer of horror stories. Tim Sale, more recently the art consultant on the hit NBC television series *Heroes*, embellished this script with his unusually stark delineation, conveying perfectly the horror at hand.

THE NIGHT WAS STRANGELY STILL.
Dream Snake
Adapted by
Roy Thomas Tim Sale
and Matt Hollingsworth
AS WE STOOD UPON THE WIDE VERANDA, GAZING OUT OVER THE BROAD, SHADOWY LAWNS, THE SILENCE OF THE HOUR ENTERED AND SPIRITS AND FOR A LONG WHILE NO ONE SPOKE.
THEN FAR ACROSS THE DIM MOUNTAINS THAT FRINGED THE EASTERN SKYLINE, A FAINT HAZE BEGAN TO GLOW...

...AND PRESENTLY A GREAT GOLDEN MOON CAME UP, MAKING A GHOSTLY RADIANCE OVER THE LAND AND ETCHING BOLDLY THE DARK CLUMPS OF SHADOWS THAT WERE TREES.

A LIGHT BREEZE CAME WHISPERING OUT OF THE EAST, AND THE UNMOWED GRASS SWAYED BEFORE IT IN LONG, SINUOUS WAVES, DIMLY VISIBLE IN THE MOONLIGHT...

AND FROM AMONG THE GROUP ON THE VERANDA THERE CAME A SWIFT GASP...

...A SHARP INTAKE OF BREATH THAT CAUSED US ALL TO TURN AND GAZE.
FAMING WAS LEANING FORWARD, CLUTCHING THE ARMS OF HIS CHAIR, HIS FACE STRANGE AND PALLID IN THE SPECTRAL LIGHT...
...A THIN TRICKLE OF BLOOD SEEPING FROM THE LIP IN WHICH HE HAD SET HIS TEETH.
THERE'S NO NEED OF GAWKING AT ME LIKE A FLOCK OF SHEEP!
WE STOOD BEWILDERED, SCARCELY KNOWING WHAT SORT OF REPLY TO MAKE, AND SUDDEN-LY HE BURST OUT AGAIN:
NOW I GUESS I'D BETTER TELL THE WHOLE THING...
...OR YOU'LL BE GOING OFF AND PUTTING ME DOWN AS A LUNATIC.
DON'T INTERRUPT ME, ANY OF YOU! I WANT TO GET THIS THING OFF MY MIND.
YOU ALL KNOW I'M NOT A VERY IMAGINATIVE MAN, BUT THERE'S A THING, PURELY A FIGMENT OF IMAGINATION, THAT HAS HAUNTED ME SINCE BABYHOOD.
A DREAM!
AND GOD, WHAT A DREAM!

THE FIRST TIME
NO, I CAN'T REMEMBER THE FIRST TIME I EVER DREAMED IT-- I'VE BEEN DREAMING THE HELLISH THING EVER SINCE I CAN REMEMBER.

NOW IT'S THIS WAY...

"THERE IS A SORT OF BUNGALOW, SET UPON A HILL IN THE MIDST OF WIDE GRASSLANDS NOT UNLIKE THIS ESTATE BUT THIS DREAM IS SET IN AFRICA, AND I AM LIVING THERE WITH A SORT OF SERVANT, A HINDOO.

"JUST WHY I AM THERE IS NEVER CLEAR TO MY WAKING MIND, BUT I THINK I AM A FUGITIVE FROM JUSTICE... AND THE HINDOO IS ALSO A FUGITIVE.

"THE GRASSLANDS STRETCH TO THE HORIZON IN EVERY DIRECTION... KNEE-HIGH IN SOME PLACES, WAIST-HIGH IN OTHERS.

"NOW THE DREAM ALWAYS OPENS AS I AM COMING UP THE HILL, JUST AS THE SUN IS BEGINNING TO SET.

"I AM CARRYING A BROKEN HUNTING RIFLE AND I HAVE BEEN ON A HUNTING TRIP.
"I COME UP THE HILL AND THE FIRST THING I AM COGNIZANT OF THAT IS OUT OF THE ORDINARY, IS A SORT OF TRACK LEADING UP THE HILL IN AN IRREGULAR WAY.
"THE GRASS IS MASHED DOWN AS IF SOMETHING HEAVY HAD BEEN DRAGGED OVER IT.

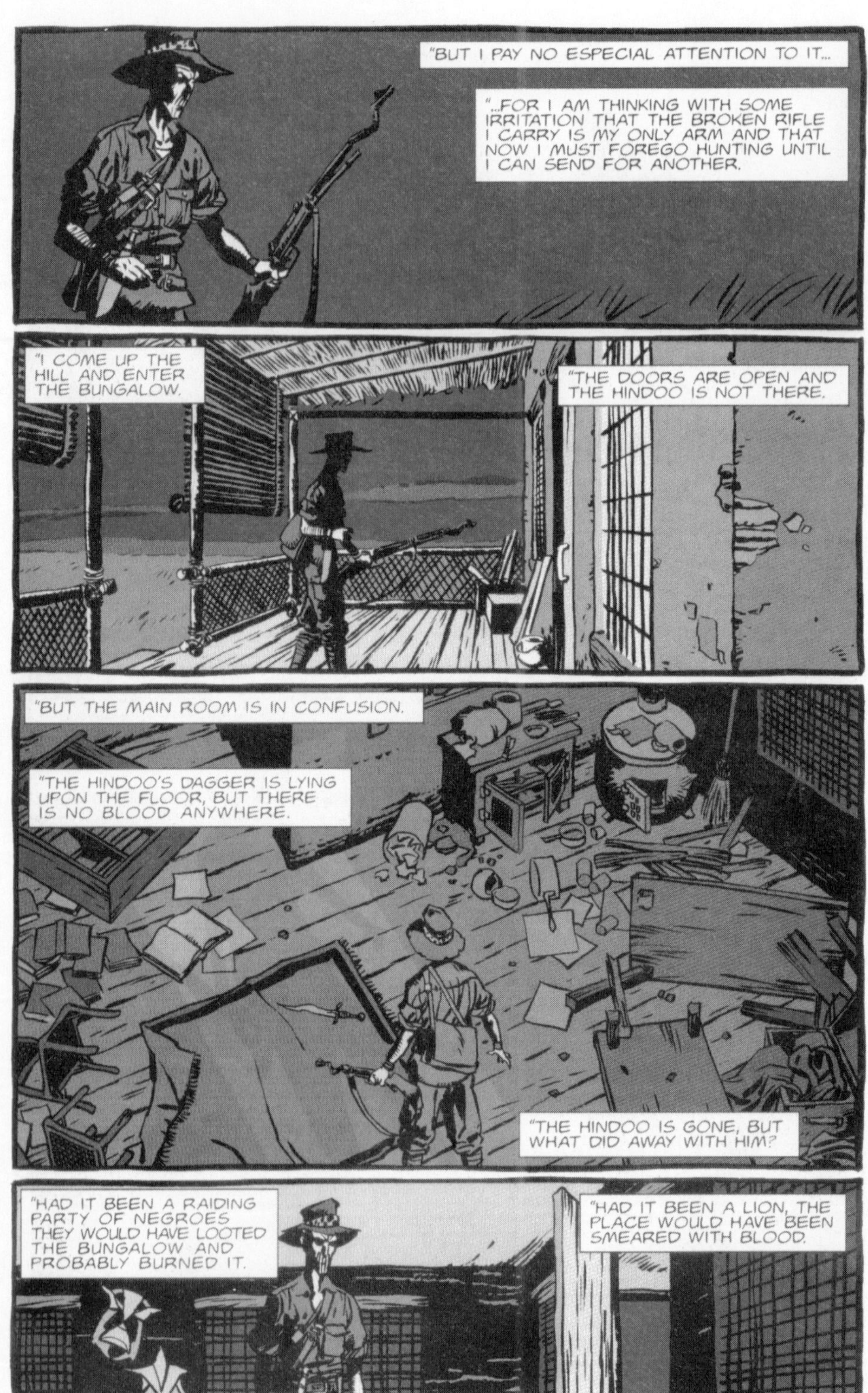
"BUT I PAY NO ESPECIAL ATTENTION TO IT...
"...FOR I AM THINKING WITH SOME IRRITATION THAT THE BROKEN RIFLE I CARRY IS MY ONLY ARM AND THAT NOW I MUST FOREGO HUNTING UNTIL I CAN SEND FOR ANOTHER.
"I COME UP THE HILL AND ENTER THE BUNGALOW.
"THE DOORS ARE OPEN AND THE HINDOO IS NOT THERE.
"BUT THE MAIN ROOM IS IN CONFUSION.
"THE HINDOO'S DAGGER IS LYING UPON THE FLOOR, BUT THERE IS NO BLOOD ANYWHERE.
"THE HINDOO IS GONE, BUT WHAT DID AWAY WITH HIM?
"HAD IT BEEN A RAIDING PARTY OF NEGROES THEY WOULD HAVE LOOTED THE BUNGALOW AND PROBABLY BURNED IT.
"HAD IT BEEN A LION, THE PLACE WOULD HAVE BEEN SMEARED WITH BLOOD.

"THEN SUDDENLY I REMEMBER THE TRACK I SAW GOING UP THE HILL...
"...AND A COLD HAND TOUCHES MY SPINE.
"THE THING THAT CAME UP FROM THE GRASSLANDS AND BROUGHT HAVOC IN THE BUNGALOW...
"...COULD BE NAUGHT ELSE EXCEPT A GIANT SERPENT.
"AND AS I THINK OF THE SIZE OF THE SPOOR, COLD SWEAT BEADS MY FOREHEAD AND THE BROKEN RIFLE SHAKES IN MY HAND.
"MY FIRST THOUGHT IS TO MAKE A DASH FOR THE COAST...
"BUT THE SUN HAS SET AND DUSK IS STEALING ACROSS THE GRASSLANDS.
"AND OUT THERE SOMEWHERE...
"...LURKING IN THE TALL GRASS...
"...IS THAT GRISLY THING
THAT HORROR.
GOD!

ALL OF US STARTED AT HIS OATH, NOT REALIZING THE TENSION WE HAD REACHED.
SO I BOLT THE DOORS AND WINDOWS...

"...I LIGHT THE LAMP I HAVE...
"...AND TAKE MY STAND IN THE MIDDLE OF THE ROOM.

"AND I STAND LIKE A STATUE.
"WAITING.
"LISTENING.

"AFTER A WHILE THE MOON COMES UP AND HER HAGGARD LIGHT DRIFTS THROUGH THE WINDOWS.
"AND I STAND STILL IN THE CENTER OF THE ROOM.
"THE NIGHT IS VERY STILL SOMETHING LIKE THIS NIGHT.
"THE BREEZE OCCASIONALLY WHISPERS THROUGH THE GRASS...

"AND EACH TIME I START AND CLENCH MY HANDS
"UNTIL THE NAILS BITE INTO THE FLESH AND THE BLOOD TRICKLES DOWN MY WRISTS
"AND I STAND THERE AND WAIT AND LISTEN.

"BUT IT DOES NOT COME THAT NIGHT!
"I AM DETERMINED, IF I LIVE THE NIGHT THROUGH, TO START FOR THE COAST EARLY THE NEXT MORNING, TAKING MY CHANCE OUT THERE IN THE GRIM GRASSLANDS
"WITH IT.

BUT WITH MORNING, I DARE NOT RISK COMING UPON HIM IN THE OPEN, UNARMED AS I AM...

"SO, AS IN A MAZE, I REMAIN AT THE BUNGALOW.
"*GOD!* IF I COULD BUT HALT THE SUN IN THE SKY!

"THEN THE SUN ROCKS DOWN THE SKY AND THE LONG GRAY SHADOWS COME STALKING ACROSS THE GRASSLANDS.

"I HAVE BOLTED THE DOORS AND WINDOWS AND LIGHTED THE LAMP LONG BEFORE THE LAST FAINT GLOW OF TWILIGHT FADES.

"THE LIGHT FROM THE WINDOWS MAY ATTRACT THE MONSTER, BUT I DARE NOT STAY IN THE DARK.
"THERE IS NO KNOWING HOW LONG I SIT THERE IN THE CENTER OF THE ROOM WAITING.

"THEN *GOD!* BUT WHAT IS *THAT?*

"NOT THE NIGHT BREEZE THIS TIME.

"SOMETHING MAKES THE GRASSES SWISH-SWISH AS IF A GREAT, LONG, PLIANT WEIGHT WERE BEING DRAGGED THROUGH THEM.

"ABOVE THE BUNGALOW IT SWISHES AND THEN CEASES IN FRONT OF THE DOOR.

"THEN THE HINGES *CREAK CREAK!*
"THE DOOR BEGINS TO BULGE INWARD A SMALL BIT THEN SOME *MORE!*
"AND I KNOW I SHOULD LEAN AGAINST THE DOOR AND HOLD IT SHUT, BUT I DO NOT.
"I CANNOT MOVE.

"I STAND THERE, LIKE A SHEEP WAITING TO BE SLAUGHTERED
"BUT THE DOOR HOLDS!

"AND ALL NIGHT I STAND MOTIONLESS, EXCEPT TO TURN SLOWLY
AS THE SWISS-SWISH OF THE GRASSMARKS THE FIEND'S COURSE ABOUT THE HOUSE.

"EVER I KEEP MY EYES IN THE DIRECTION OF THE SOFT, SINISTER SOUND.

"SOMETIMES IT CEASES FOR AN INSTANT, OR FOR SEVERAL MINUTES...

"...AND THEN I STAND SCARCELY BREATHING.

"THEN THE SOUNDS COMMENCE AGAIN
"AND I FREEZE MOTIONLESS.

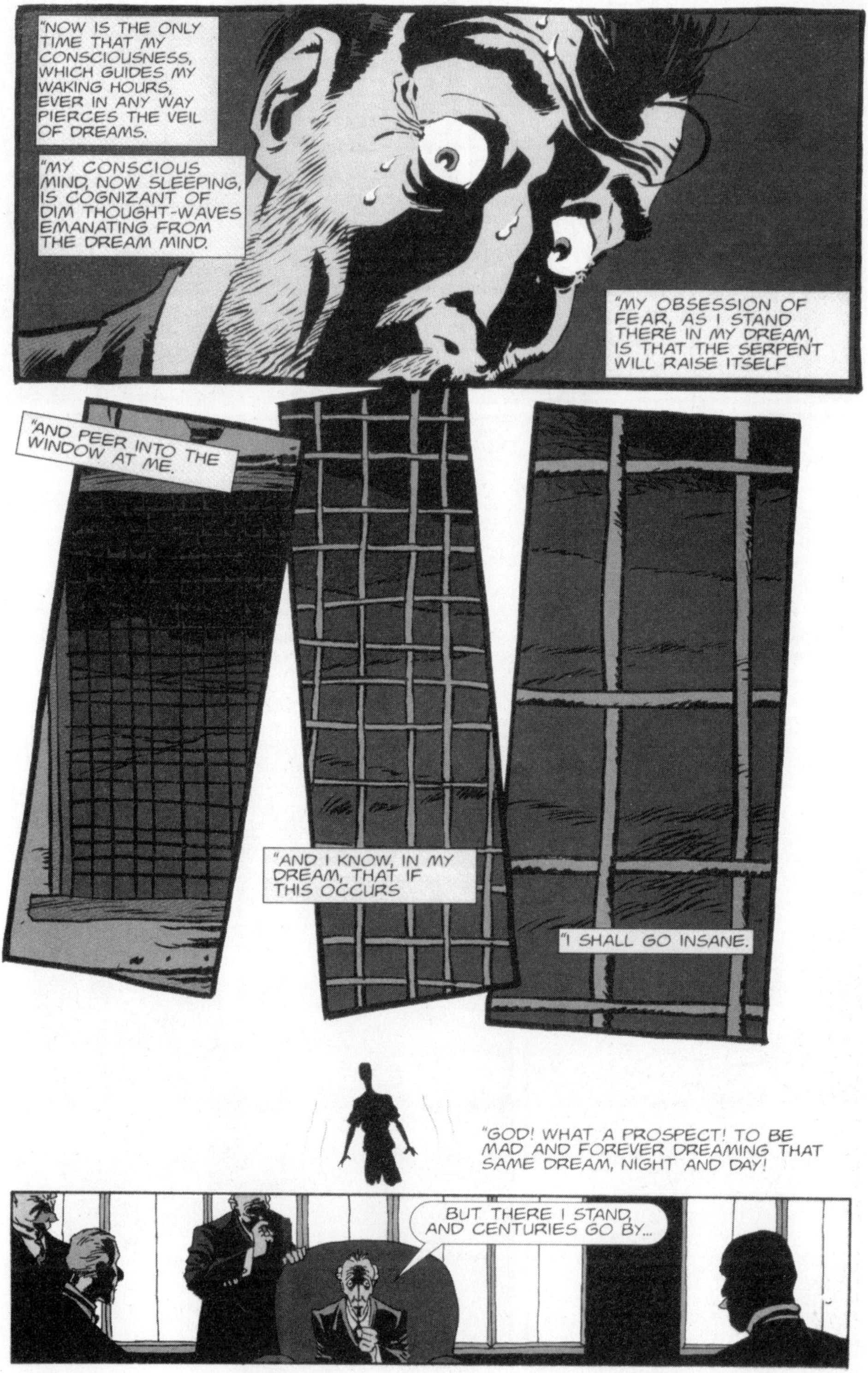

"NOW IS THE ONLY TIME THAT MY CONSCIOUSNESS, WHICH GUIDES MY WAKING HOURS, EVER IN ANY WAY PIERCES THE VEIL OF DREAMS.

"MY CONSCIOUS MIND, NOW SLEEPING, IS COGNIZANT OF DIM THOUGHT-WAVES EMANATING FROM THE DREAM MIND.

"MY OBSESSION OF FEAR, AS I STAND THERE IN MY DREAM, IS THAT THE SERPENT WILL RAISE ITSELF

"AND PEER INTO THE WINDOW AT ME.

"AND I KNOW, IN MY DREAM, THAT IF THIS OCCURS

"I SHALL GO INSANE.

"GOD! WHAT A PROSPECT! TO BE MAD AND FOREVER DREAMING THAT SAME DREAM, NIGHT AND DAY!

"AT LAST THE SWISHING DIES AWAY IN THE DISTANCE, AND PRESENTLY A RED, HAGGARD SUN CLIMBS THE EASTERN SKY.
"THEN I TURN ABOUT AND GAZE INTO A MIRROR...
"...AND MY HAIR HAS BECOME PERFECTLY WHITE.
"I STAGGER TO THE DOOR AND FLING IT WIDE.
"THERE IS NOTHING IN SIGHT BUT A WIDE TRACK LEADING AWAY DOWN THE HILL THROUGH THE GRASSLANDS
"IN THE OPPOSITE DIRECTION FROM THAT WHICH I WOULD TAKE TOWARD THE COAST.
"WITH A SHRIEK OF MANIACAL LAUGHTER, I RACE OFF ACROSS THE GRASSLANDS.
"I RACE UNTIL I DROP FROM EXHAUSTION, THEN I LIE UNTIL I CAN STAGGER UP AND GO ON.
"ALL DAY I KEEP THIS UP, WITH SUPERHUMAN EFFORT...
"...SPURRED ON BY THE HORROR BEHIND ME.

"HOW SWIFTLY THE SUN TRAVELS WHEN A MAN RACES IT FOR LIFE!
"A LOSING RACE IT IS, AS I KNOW WHEN I WATCH THE SUN SINKING TOWARD THE SKYLINE, AND THE HILLS WHICH I HAD TO GAIN ERE SUNDOWN...
...SEEMINGLY AS FAR AWAY AS EVER.
THEN THE SUN SETS... AND THE SHADOWS COME ON.
"THE MOON COMES UP...
"AND I LOOK BACK THE WAY I HAVE COME.
"AND FAR BACK
I
SEE
THE
GRASS
WAVING.
"THERE IS NO BREEZE, BUT THE TALL GRASS PARTS AND SWAYS IN THE MOONLIGHT, IN A NARROW, SINUOUS LINE...
"...FAR AWAY...

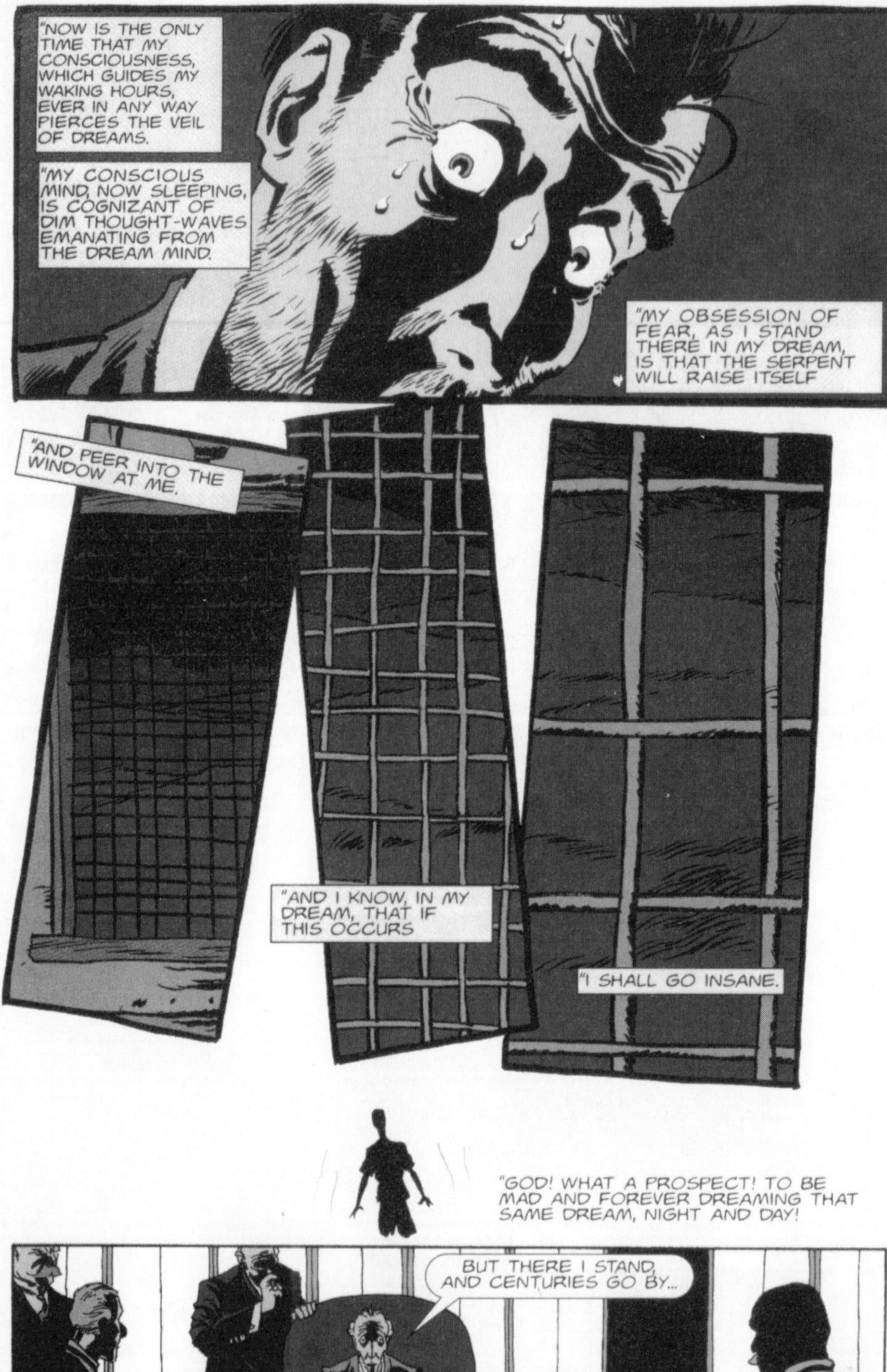
"NOW IS THE ONLY TIME THAT MY CONSCIOUSNESS, WHICH GUIDES MY WAKING HOURS, EVER IN ANY WAY PIERCES THE VEIL OF DREAMS.
"MY CONSCIOUS MIND, NOW SLEEPING, IS COGNIZANT OF DIM THOUGHT-WAVES EMANATING FROM THE DREAM MIND.
"MY OBSESSION OF FEAR, AS I STAND THERE IN MY DREAM, IS THAT THE SERPENT WILL RAISE ITSELF
"AND PEER INTO THE WINDOW AT ME.
"AND I KNOW, IN MY DREAM, THAT IF THIS OCCURS
"I SHALL GO INSANE.
"GOD! WHAT A PROSPECT! TO BE MAD AND FOREVER DREAMING THAT SAME DREAM, NIGHT AND DAY!
BUT THERE I STAND, AND CENTURIES GO BY...

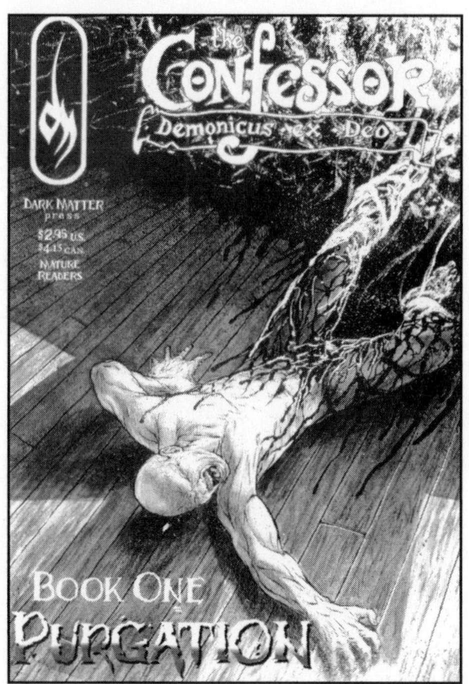

Purgation

The Confessor Demonicus-ex-Deo, 1996

Imagine a horror comic so dark that its shadow drags you deep into a world of inescapable nightmare, leaving you screaming at the blackest hour of night. This tale did exactly that following my first encounter with it just over ten years ago. Writer and artist Chuck Regan was delighted when he heard of the trauma his powerful tale had evoked. Dark Matter Press was one of those talented outfits which had the ability but lacked the powerful media machine of companies like Marvel and DC. Alongside Chuck, Tony Garofalo, Chuck Tooley and Dan Hirsch poured themselves into this project, becoming immersed in the characters that traverse its tormented landscape. Take your time with these pages because they move very much like a film, a medium by which Chuck Regan was influenced.

Chuck continues to produce comics and ideas under his Maelstrom Graphics imprint.

SAINT GERHAINE BE PRAISED!
THE FIFTH OF THE FIVE IS COMPLETE!

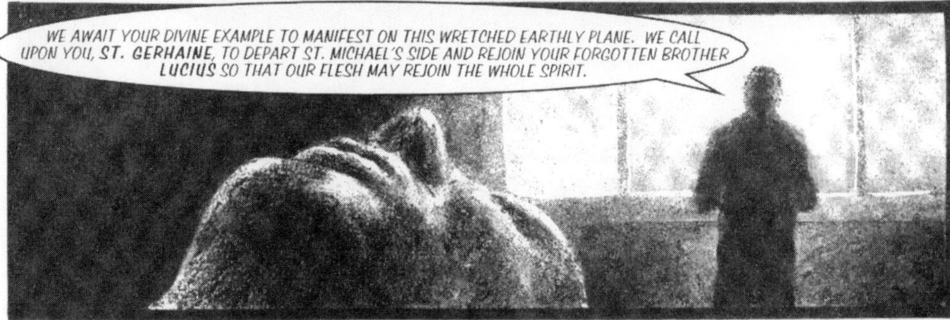
WE AWAIT YOUR DIVINE EXAMPLE TO MANIFEST ON THIS WRETCHED EARTHLY PLANE. WE CALL UPON YOU, ST. GERHAINE, TO DEPART ST. MICHAEL'S SIDE AND REJOIN YOUR FORGOTTEN BROTHER LUCIUS SO THAT OUR FLESH MAY REJOIN THE WHOLE SPIRIT.

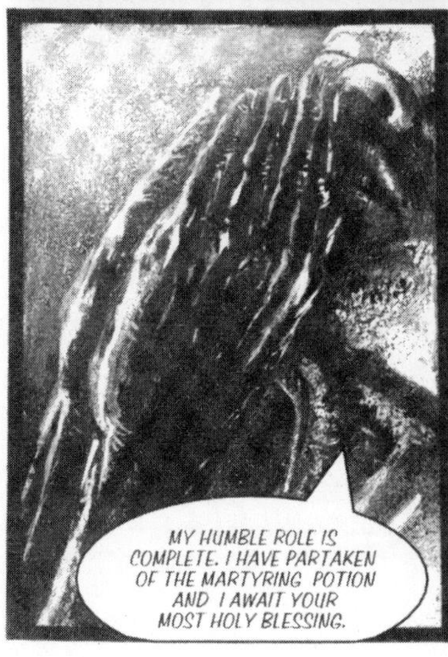
MY HUMBLE ROLE IS COMPLETE. I HAVE PARTAKEN OF THE MARTYRING POTION AND I AWAIT YOUR MOST HOLY BLESSING.

MY SOILED FLESH HOLDS FEAR. PURGE ME OF THE GUILT OF MY ANCESTRY. TEAR ME FROM THIS EARTHLY CELL SO THAT I MAY BE PURIFIED!

ST. GERHAINE BE PRAISED! THE FIFTH OF THE FIVE IS COMPLETE.
PURGE ME OF MY FEARS. PURGE ME OF MY FEARS.
PURGE ME OF MY FEARS.
plp.
splk!!
plk.
plp.
spplk!
spk.
splk!
PURGE ME
spIp.
PURGE ME OF MY FEARS.
PURGE ME OF MY FEARS.
plkl
plk.
spplk!
plk.
plpk.
PURGE
AAAAAIIIIEEEEEEEE

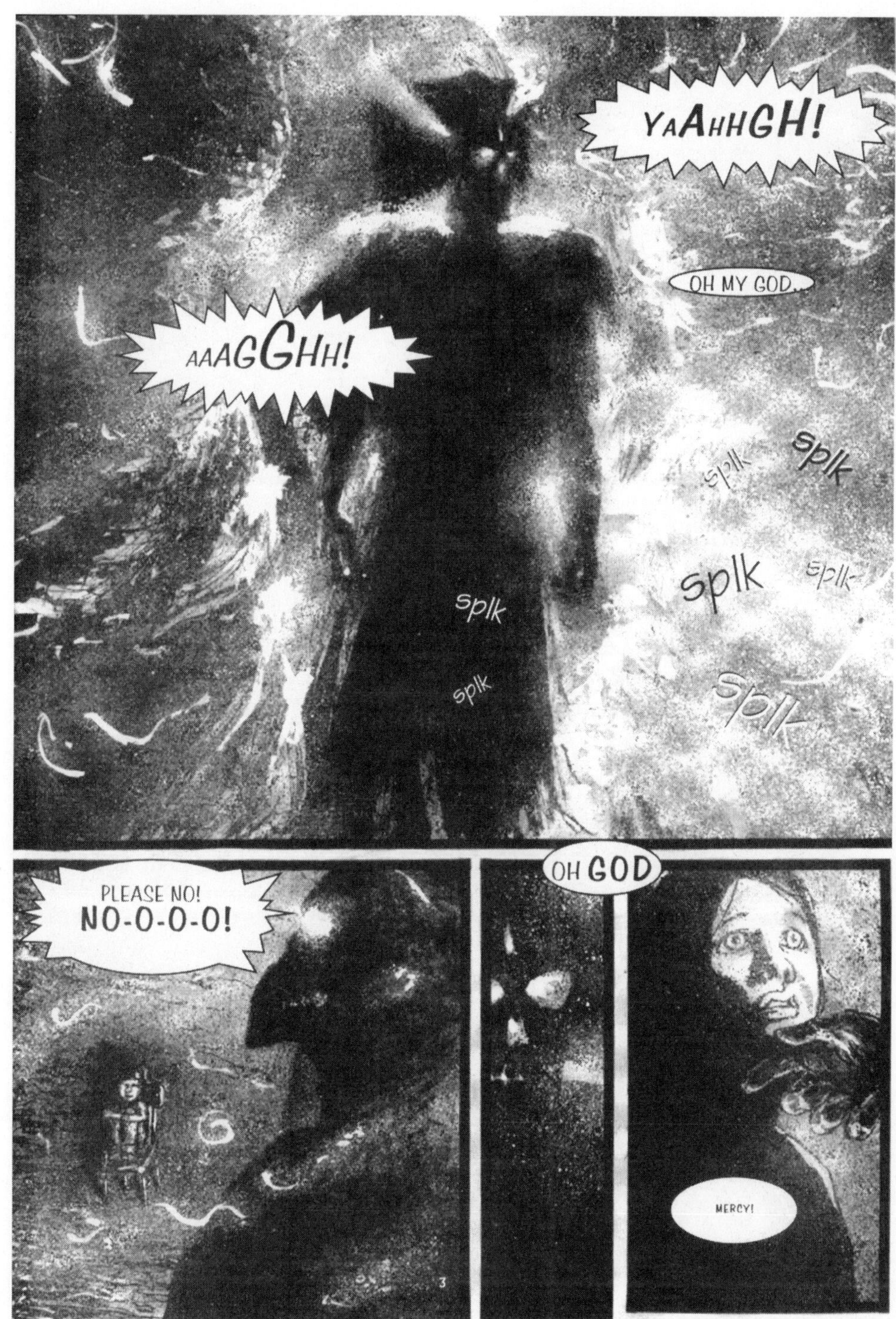
YAAHHGH!
OH MY GOD...
AAAGGHH!
splk
splk
splk
splk
splk
splk
splk
PLEASE NO!
NO-O-O-O!
OH GOD
MERCY!

IN THROUGH HERE

AND THERE THAT'S WHERE WE FOUND THE LITTLE GIRL.

JUST... SITTING THERE.

AND THAT'S IT?
SHE HADN'T BEEN PHYSICALLY HARMED IN ANY WAY?

CUT ON HER KNEE - THAT SORT OF THING. THOUGH WHAT SHE SAW! CHRIST!

SHE WOULDN'T UTTER A WORD. NOT EVEN A SOUND. WHAT SHE SAW PUSHED HER OVER THE EDGE. LEFT HER CATATONIC. THEY TOOK HER TO MERCY.
WELL G., IT'S THE SAME M.O. 'CEPT FOR THE KID. LET'S ZIPPER IT UP.
MMMH....
NOT SO FAST.
HEAR ME OUT, POOLE. LOOK AT THIS BODY.
THINK ABOUT THE OTHER THREE.WHAT'S SO DIFFERENT?
YOU'RE LOSIN' ME.
THERE'S THE SAME SYMMETRICAL ARRANGEMENT WITH EACH BODY. THE SYMBOLS ARE THE SAME. BUT THE PENMANSHIP...
THE SYMBOLS HAVE A DIFFERENT... FLAIR. A VARIANCE IN THE RENDERINGS.
LIKE THERE ARE TWO PSYCHOS AT WORK. OR MAYBE SOME CULT'S INVOLVED. WHATEVER IT IS - I'D SAY WE'RE IN A WHOLE NEW BALL GAME.
YEAHHH. AND THE WHOLE THING'LL BE OUT OF OUR HANDS.
THEY'LL GIVE IT TO CHAUNCEY AND ELDER.
CULT SHIT LIKE THIS IS THEIR BAG.

...CLASSIC AUTISTIC SYMPTOMS. SHE STARES MOSTLY AT THE CEILING AND REFUSES TO ACKNOWLEDGE ANYONE.
I'M SO VERY SORRY, BUT I CAN'T SEE HOW SUSAN CAN BE OF ANY HELP TO YOU.
MAYBE WE'LL GET LUCKY. WE'LL BE KEEPIN' TABS ON HER.SO DOC, IF THERE'S ANY SORT OF CHANGE - ANY KIND -GIVE US A CALL.
MOST ASSUREDLY. BUT KNOW THAT THESE THINGS TAKE TIME.
WE GOT A PLANE TO CATCH, PARTNER.
WELL SUSIE, WOULD YOU LIKE A NICE DRINK OF MILK?

VACATION TIME?

LOOK, THIS ONE TOOK A LOT OUT OF ME, POOLE.
I'M GOING TO FIND ME A GOOD FISHING HOLE AND GET SOME R&R..
YEAH... SURE! AND LEMME KNOW WHAT THE KID CATCHES FOR YOU.
YOU ALWAYS READ ME LIKE A BOOK, POOLE.
AWRIGHT G. YOU'RE OVERDUE FOR A BREAK. JUST DON'T DO ANYTHING THAT I WOULDN'T DO...
AND WHAT WOULDN'T YOU DO?
YOU READ ME LIKE A BOOK, HAYES. LATER!

DOLLS
LEGO

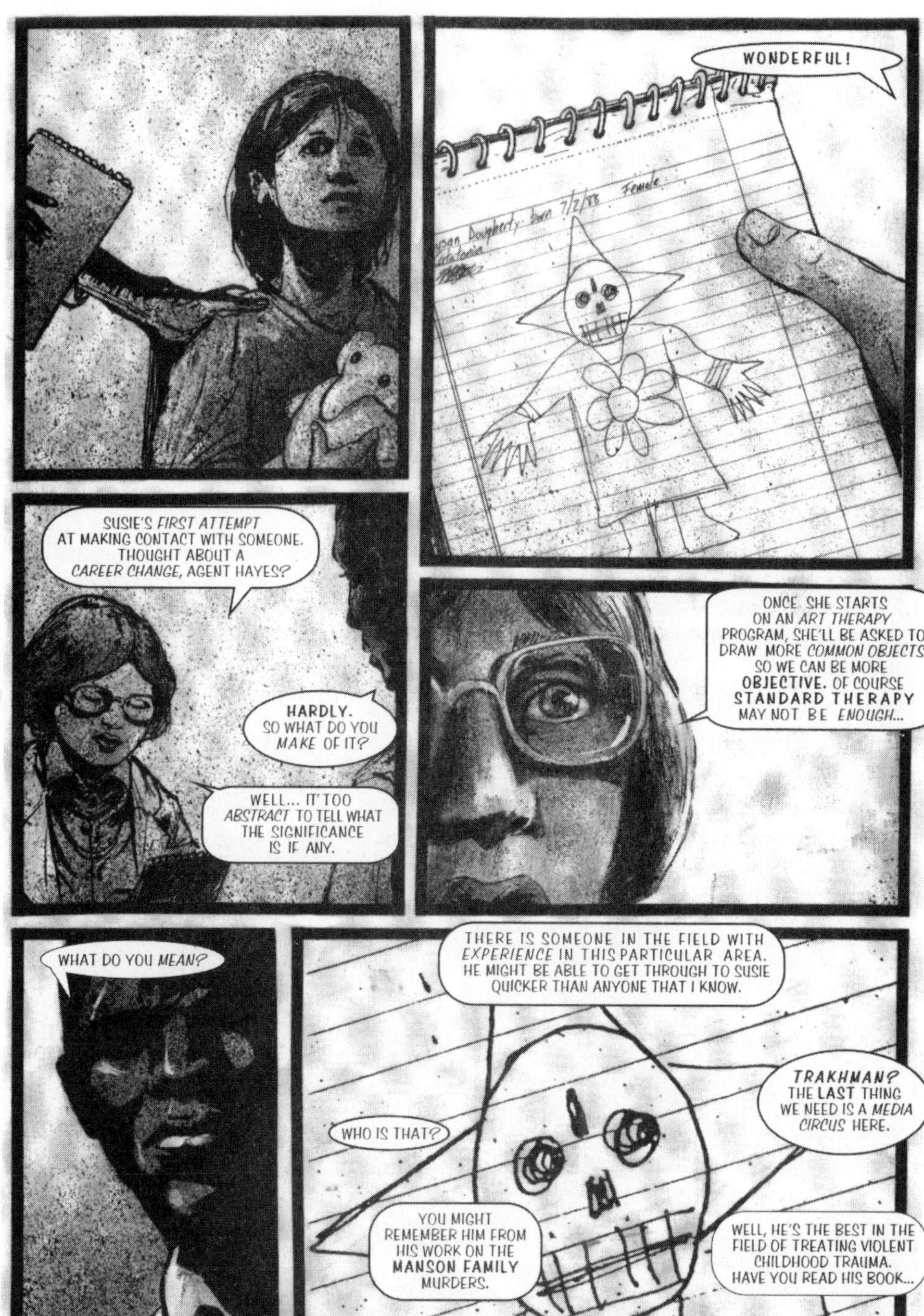
WONDERFUL!
SUSIE'S *FIRST ATTEMPT* AT MAKING CONTACT WITH SOMEONE. THOUGHT ABOUT A *CAREER CHANGE,* AGENT HAYES?
HARDLY. SO WHAT DO YOU *MAKE* OF IT?
WELL... IT'TOO *ABSTRACT* TO TELL WHAT THE SIGNIFICANCE IS IF ANY.
ONCE SHE STARTS ON AN *ART THERAPY* PROGRAM, SHE'LL BE ASKED TO DRAW MORE *COMMON OBJECTS* SO WE CAN BE MORE **OBJECTIVE.** OF COURSE **STANDARD THERAPY** MAY NOT BE *ENOUGH...*
WHAT DO YOU *MEAN?*
THERE IS SOMEONE IN THE FIELD WITH *EXPERIENCE* IN THIS PARTICULAR AREA. HE MIGHT BE ABLE TO GET THROUGH TO SUSIE QUICKER THAN ANYONE THAT I KNOW.
TRAKHMAN? THE **LAST** THING WE NEED IS A *MEDIA CIRCUS* HERE.
WHO IS THAT?
YOU MIGHT REMEMBER HIM FROM HIS WORK ON THE **MANSON FAMILY** MURDERS.
WELL, HE'S THE BEST IN THE FIELD OF TREATING VIOLENT CHILDHOOD TRAUMA. HAVE YOU READ HIS BOOK...

OH WHAT WAS IT CALLED? I READ IT WHEN I WAS AN INTERN...
OF COURSE...
..."DEMONS IN OUR MIDST".

SOMEWHERE IN NEBRASKA.
...TWAS GRACE THAT TAUGHT MY HEART TO FEAR...

I HAVE ALREADY COME...

PRAISE THE LORD!

AWFUL LATE TA BE TA-RAVELIN', INNIT?
I WALK WITH OUR LORD JESUS. HE TAKES CARE OF ME.
WE-ELL NOW, A MAN O' FAITH. HOW RARE IN THESE TA-ROUBLED TIMES OF ARRS.
SO TRUE, SAD TO SAY.

LOOMIS. JOHN LOOMIS. MUH FA-RIENDS CALL M' BUDDY.
CARE F' SOME CANDY?

WHY, THANK YOU. I'M DONOVAN GERY.

ARE Y'ONNA PILGRIMAGE, MR. GERY?
I GO WHERE THE LORD LEADS ME, MR. LOOMIS.

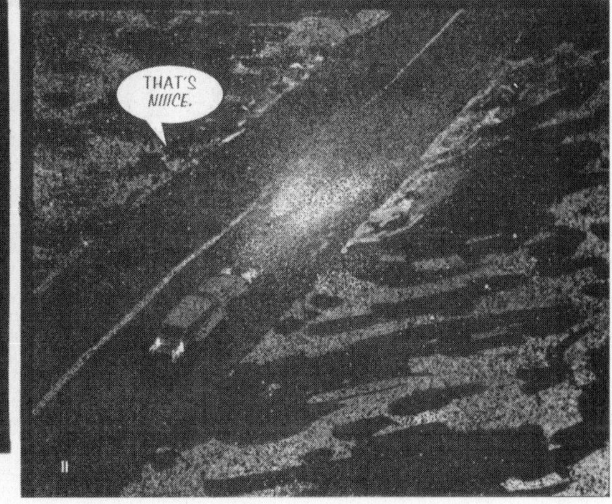
THAT'S NIIICE.

GUD MORNIN',
DONOVAN GERY.
RISE-N-SHINE!
AAR LORD HAS GA-REAT P-LANS F YA TA'DAY.
UHHN...
WHAT?...
(KOFF!)
WHAT'S...

SSSHHH... THERE, THERE. LET ME EXPA-LAIN. ST. MICHAEL DA-ROVE THE BEAST FROM TH' URTH.
Y'SHID KNOW THIS. ENNA GUD CUH-RISTIAN SHUD. ST. MICHAEL EMP-ALOYED A MORTAL MAN TUH HEP STAY BACK TH' DEMONS FROM URTH.
HE IS ST. GERHAINE, TH' CONFESSERR. Y'ULL MEET' IM SOON' NUFF.
WH- WHAT ARE...? WHY...?
IT'S A RITE OF PASSAGE, DONOVAN GERY.
Y'GOTTA SHED YER TIES TA YER WEAK FLESH.
NUH- NO! THIS IS... IS EVIL, WRUH-WRONG!
A MOST HOLY SACRIFICE!
JES' THINK OF IT. ALL WILL SING PRAISES T'ARR NEW SAVIORR.
PLEASE DON'T KUH-KILL ME! OH GOD!
YER GONNA GAIN A WHOL NEW VISION, DONOVAN GERY. YER GONNA KNOW TH' TA-RUTH!
13

MY, MY, SUSIE. YOU'VE BEEN VERY BUSY THIS MORNING!
MAY I SEE SOME OF YOUR PRETTY PICTURES?
...OH
...OH, my...
WELL, TH' SUN'S RIZIN'. TH' LORD'S WORK IS DONE!
Y'VE TAKEN TH' FUST STEP, DONOVAN GERY.
NUH- NO... UHH... GOD! ...UHH...
MOST FITTIN', INNIT? WHAT'S BEGUN WITH AN APPLE SHALL END IN AN ORCHURRD! HEY, I LIKE THET!

...AAA...AMAZING GRACE... H-HOW SWEET THE... SOUND...
THAT'S RIGHT, DONOVAN
BE AT PEACE. TH' LORD'S COMIN' F' YUH SOON.

THA-HAT... SAAAVED A WRETCH...LIKE MEEE..

I O-ONCE WAS LOST...

BUH-HUT...NOW... I'M FOUND...

WAS BLIIIIND BUT NOW I SEEEEE

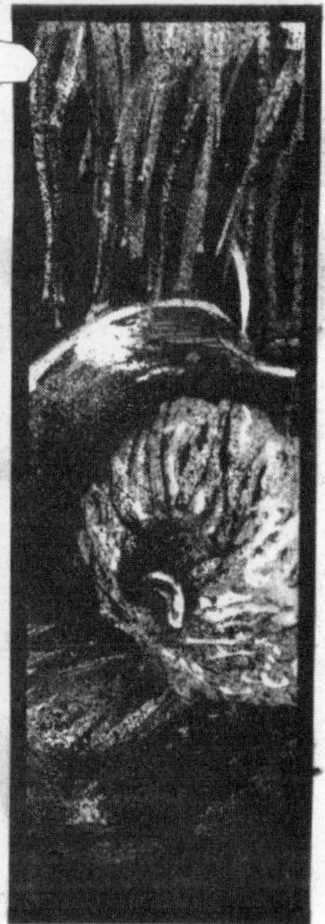

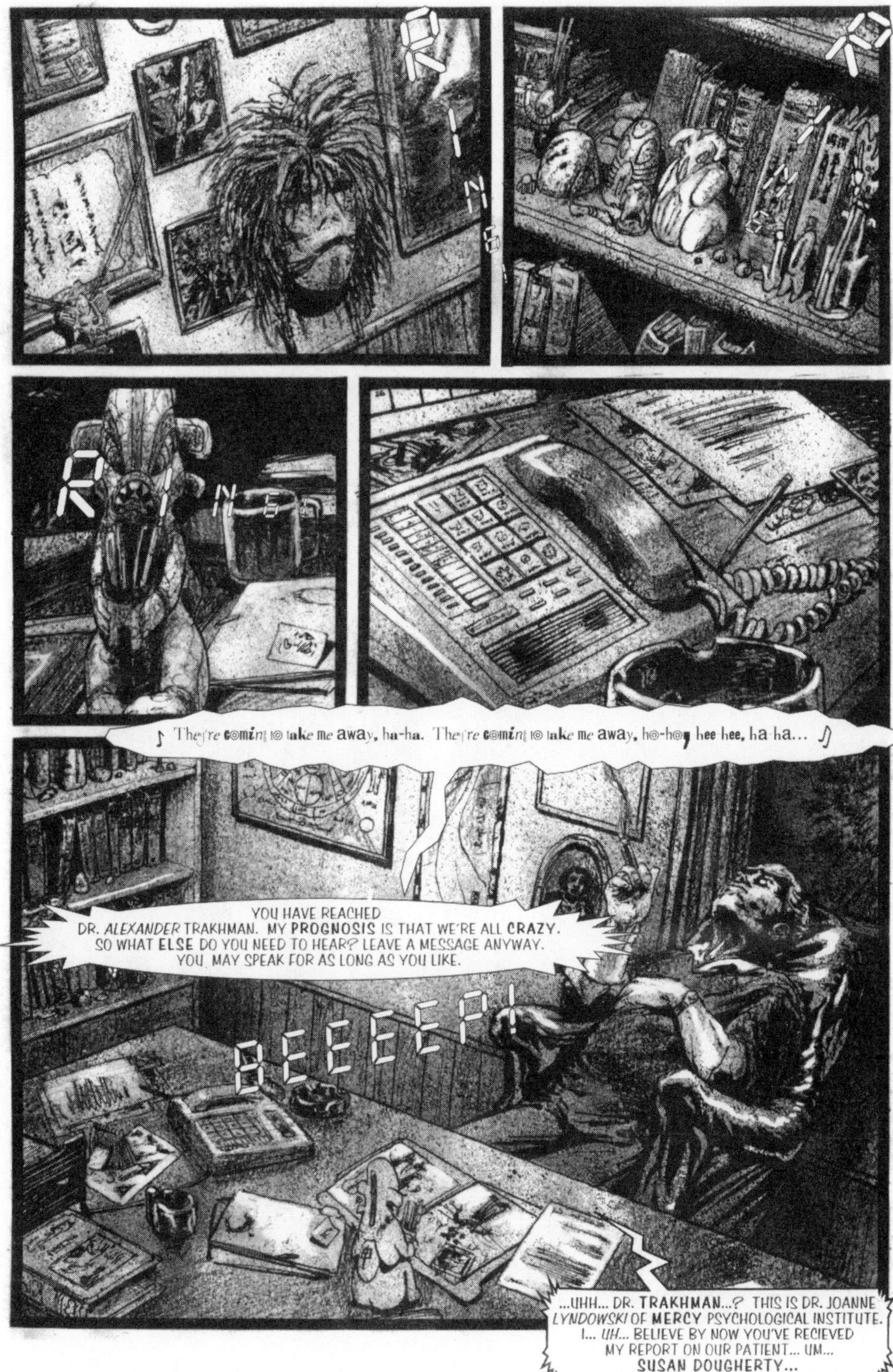
They're comin' to take me away, ha-ha. They're comin' to take me away, ho-ho, hee hee, ha ha...
YOU HAVE REACHED DR. *ALEXANDER* TRAKHMAN. MY **PROGNOSIS** IS THAT WE'RE ALL **CRAZY**. SO WHAT **ELSE** DO YOU NEED TO HEAR? LEAVE A MESSAGE ANYWAY. YOU MAY SPEAK FOR AS LONG AS YOU LIKE.
BEEEEP!!
...UHH... DR. **TRAKHMAN**...? THIS IS DR. JOANNE *LYNDOWSKI* OF **MERCY** PSYCHOLOGICAL INSTITUTE. I... *UH*... BELIEVE BY NOW YOU'VE RECIEVED MY REPORT ON OUR PATIENT... UM... **SUSAN DOUGHERTY**...

DOCTOR, I READ YOUR BOOK " DEMONS IN OUR MIDST" BACK WHEN I... UH... WAS AN INTERN. AND ALTHOUGH THE...UHMM... SO-CALLED ESTABLISHMENT OPENLY... UH... MOCKED YOUR THEORIES - WELL, SOME OF US WERE... AND ARE OPEN MINDED. YOUR IDEAS PROVIDED US WITH A... UH... PROFOUND PERSPECTIVE ON THE FACETS OF MYTHOLOGIZED SUBCONCIOUS...

I'M TRYING TO APPROACH YOU IN A PROFESSIONAL MANNER, DR. TRAKHMAN. BUT TRUTH BE TOLD, WELL... I CONSIDER YOU TO BE A MENTOR OF SORTS. YOUR BOOK IN PARTICULAR HAS HELPED ME IN MANY WAYS TO...UHHMM... DEVELOP PERSONAL MYTHOLOGIES FOR PATIENTS... OHH, FORGIVE ME FOR RAMBLING ON SO...

THE INSTITUTE WILL OF COURSE ACCOMODATE YOU FOR YOUR FLIGHT, ROOM, AND BOARD, FOR THE DURATION OF YOUR STAY, IF YOU ARE WILLING TO DO SO, SIR.
WE'RE SURE ANY INSIGHT... UH... THAT YOU COULD OFFER IN THIS CASE WOULD BE A GREAT ASSET.
Dougherty, Susan

PLEASE EXAMINE THE REPORT. I HOPE YOU'LL CONSIDER ASSISTING US.
THANK YOU AGAIN, DR. TRAKHMAN. GOODBYE.
BEEP.

THE MORE I TRY TO FACE YOU... THE MORE OBVIOUS IT BECOMES THAT I'LL NEVER BE READY TO.
...SO LONG AGO...
I WAS ONLY EIGHT YEARS OLD WHEN I WITNESSED A... DEMON BRUTALLY SLAY MY FOSTER PARENTS.
I LOOKED AT MADNESS IN ITS MOST FEROCIOUS FORM AND WAS... FASCINATED!
MY GOD, I COULDN'T HELP BUT WATCH AS THIS CREATURE CLUBBED THE WOMAN I NOW CALLED MY MOTHER UNTIL SHE WAS UNRECOGNIZABLE - NOT ONLY AS MY MOTHER, BUT EVEN AS BEING HUMAN. THE... BEAST WAS ABSOLUTE IN HIS VIOLENCE.
THE BODY OF MY NEW FATHER CAUGHT MY NOTICE ONLY PERIPHERALLY.
WHEN I REALIZED THE BEAST HAD SEEN ME, I FELT ASTHOUGH I'D INTERRUPTED SOME SACRED, PRIVATE RITUAL.
BUT IT SEEMED THAT HIS FERAL DANCE HAD NOT YET COME TO AN END...

THAK THAK THAK THAK THAK
AFTER THE FLASHES FROM EACH BLOW STOPPED, I REMEMBER A WARM TINGLING PEACE...THEN BLACKNESS AND FLOATING...
FREEZE!
DROP YOUR WEAPON!
NOW!
DROP IT DAMN YOU!
BLAM BLAM!

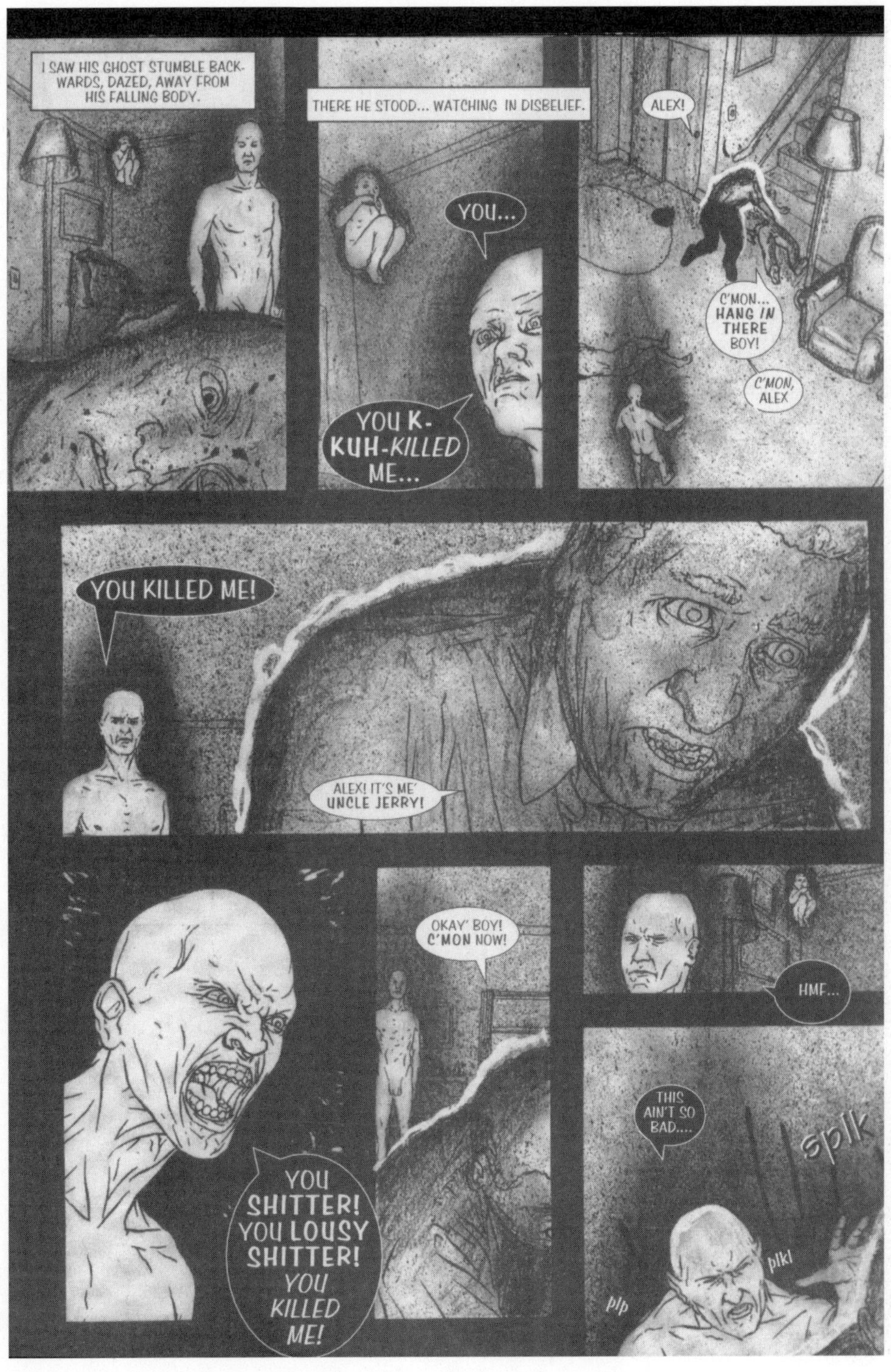
I SAW HIS GHOST STUMBLE BACKWARDS, DAZED, AWAY FROM HIS FALLING BODY.
THERE HE STOOD... WATCHING IN DISBELIEF.
YOU...
YOU K-KUH-KILLED ME...
ALEX!
C'MON... HANG IN THERE BOY!
C'MON, ALEX
YOU KILLED ME!
ALEX! IT'S ME' UNCLE JERRY!
YOU SHITTER! YOU LOUSY SHITTER! YOU KILLED ME!
OKAY' BOY! C'MON NOW!
HMF...
THIS AIN'T SO BAD....
splk
plkl
plp

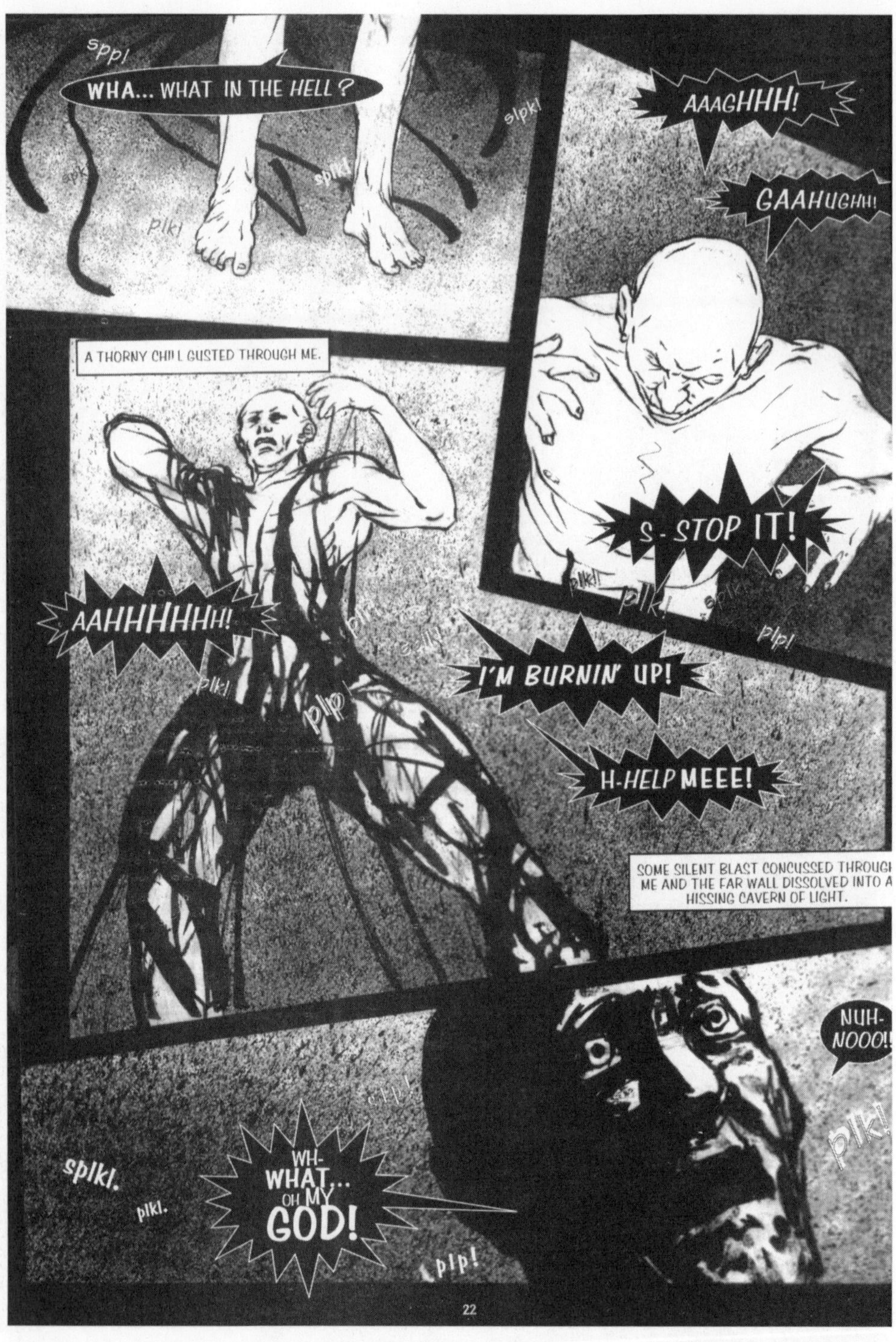
WHA... WHAT IN THE HELL?
AAAGHHH!
GAAHUGHH!
A THORNY CHILL GUSTED THROUGH ME.
S-STOP IT!
AAHHHHHH!
I'M BURNIN' UP!
H-HELP MEEE!
SOME SILENT BLAST CONCUSSED THROUGH ME AND THE FAR WALL DISSOLVED INTO A HISSING CAVERN OF LIGHT.
NUH-NOOO!
WH-WHAT... OH MY GOD!
22

OH MY GOD!
THE SMELL OF MOSSY STONE HIT ME.
NO! NO NO!
plk!
plp!
plk!
THIS CREATURE WAS FAR OLDER THAN ANYTHING I COULD FATHOM.
THE AIR BECAME THICK AND STILL LIKE THE OCEAN FLOOR AS THE KILLER STRUGGLED AGAINST HIS BONDS, LETTING OUT A FEW PATHETIC SQUEEKS OF EFFORT BETWEEN HIS HOWLS OF FEAR.
23

ITS APPROACH FROZE THE KILLER IN A SPOTLIGHT OF TERROR. THE SILENCE WAS ENDED WHEN HANDS, MADE SPINELIKE OVER TIME, GRATED LIGHTLY OVER CARAPACE-LIKE ARMOR SCARRED LIKE THE MOON.
NO! GEDAWAY FRUH-FROM ME!
plip
splk!
plk
slpk
plp!
THE MOVEMENT WAS SLOW AND DELIBERATE. THOSE HANDS FOUND A HOLD UNDER ITS RIBCAGE.
NO! GOD NO!
WITH GREAT EFFORT I INTERPRETED AS TREMENDOUS PAIN, THE SOUND OF CRACKING LOBSTERS PAINTED THE ROOM AND THE CREATURE BARED ITS PHOSPHORESCENT INTERIOR.

IN A SECOND, WHITE HOT TONGUES SHOT FROM THE CREATURES CHEST. WAVES OF FEAR FLASHED FROM THE ENSNARED KILLER AS HE TRANSFORMED INTO A TORTURED INFANT...WAILING.
YAAGHH!!
NO!
25

GOD!
OH GOD!
PLEASE GOD!
HELP ME...
HELP!
PLEASE!
PLEASE!
NO!

IT'S ME, ALEX! IT'S UNCLE JERRY! I'M HERE! IT'S GONNA BE OKAY NOW.

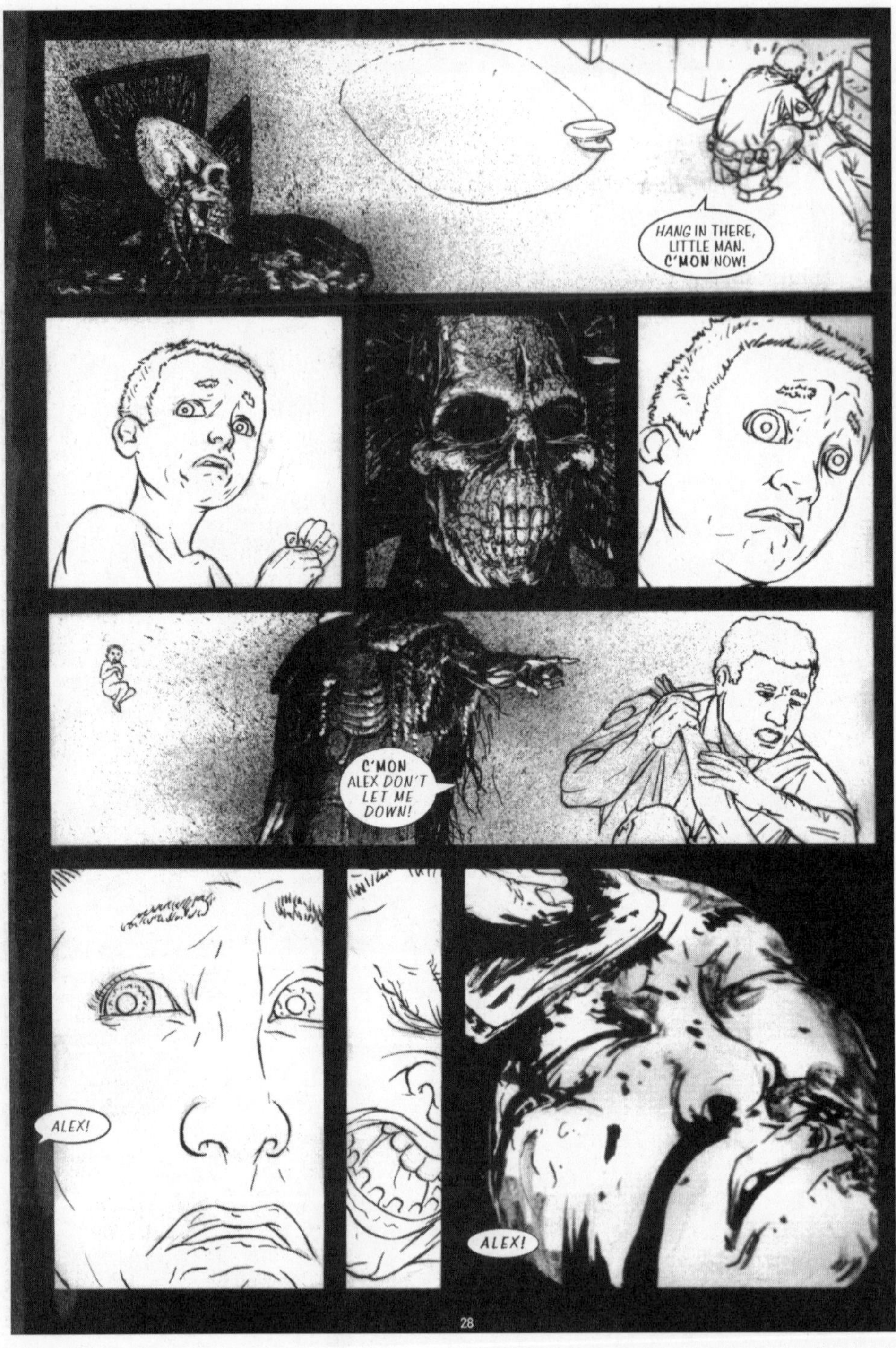
HANG IN THERE, LITTLE MAN. C'MON NOW!
C'MON ALEX DON'T LET ME DOWN!
ALEX!
ALEX!
28

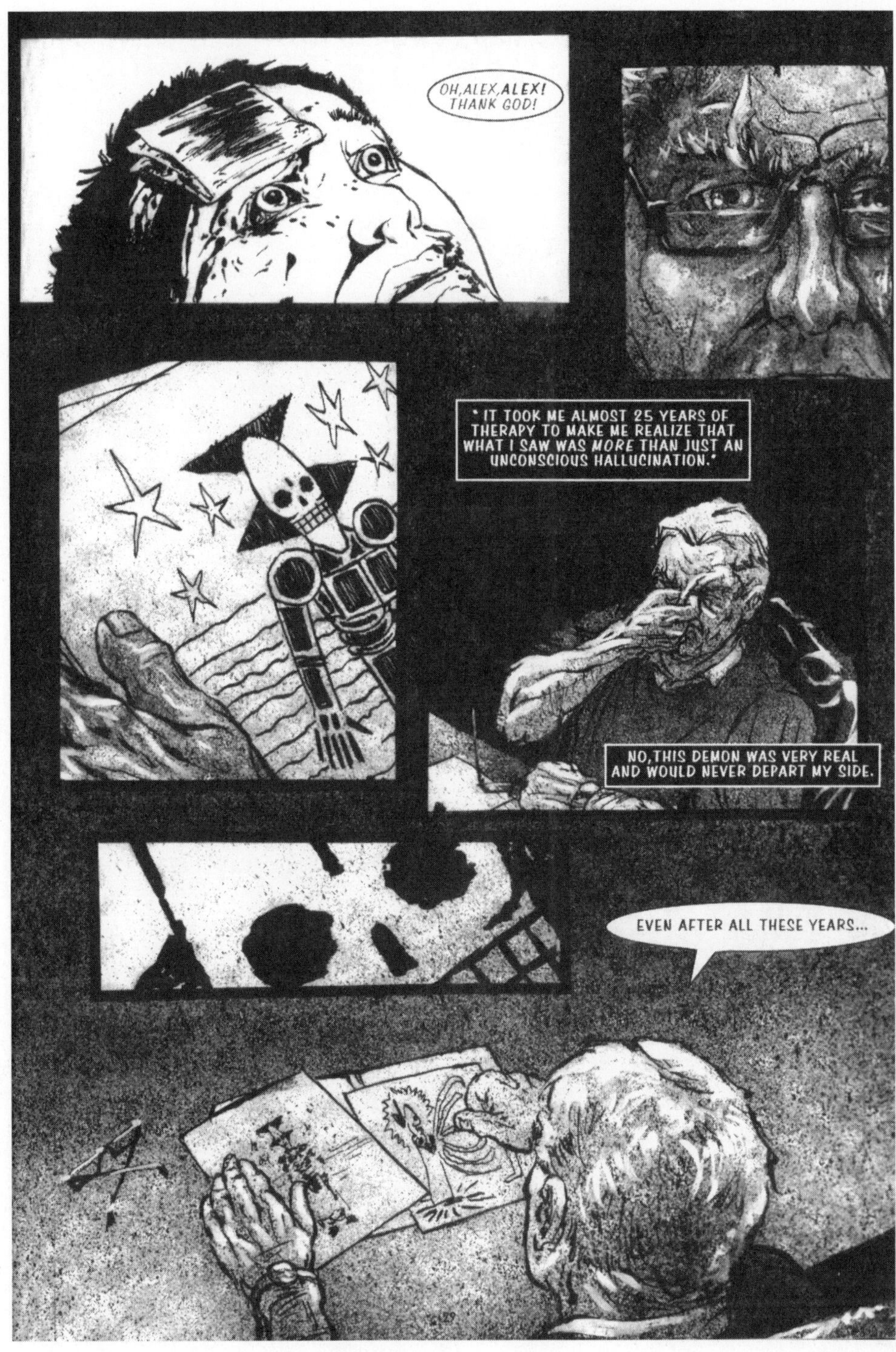
OH, ALEX, ALEX!
THANK GOD!
" IT TOOK ME ALMOST 25 YEARS OF THERAPY TO MAKE ME REALIZE THAT WHAT I SAW WAS MORE THAN JUST AN UNCONSCIOUS HALLUCINATION."
NO, THIS DEMON WAS VERY REAL AND WOULD NEVER DEPART MY SIDE.
EVEN AFTER ALL THESE YEARS...

YOU STILL
HAUNT ME.

A New Millennium for the Macabre

21st century

With the uncertainties hanging over our world in this new millennium, horror has witnessed yet another revival in comic book stores, maybe not on the same scale as the pre-Code boom and the clamour of the early Seventies, but commanding respect in the marketplace. Smaller companies continue to thrive, while larger more established publishers have also dared to explore this fear-filled domain.

DC have continued to enjoy success with the long-running *Hellblazer* and their Vertigo imprint which has consistently published comic books for a more discerning readership. *Swampthing* has made yet another return, and DC's horror titles from thirty years ago are granted the occasional limited trip around the graveyard. The psychological terror pioneered by Alan Moore twenty years before has now become the norm. Marvel has occasionally toyed with the horror medium, but recent efforts have been unusually lacklustre. Their *Marvel Zombies* was well received; and, although they chose not to promote Richard Corben's *Edgar Allan Poe Haunt of Horror* in the way that many of his fans thought they should have, this four-issue series was also the beneficiary of critical acclaim. After their financial trials and tribulations of the previous decade, Marvel prefer to stay with what they know best. The days of the House of Ideas seem long gone.

During the 1990s Dark Horse Comics made a reputation for themselves, securing the publishing rights to various films, and permission to release subsequent spin-off series – their highly successful adaptations of *Aliens* and *Predator* immediately spring to mind. Dark Horse have never turned a blind eye to the potential in comic book horror. Their *Universal Monsters* series aroused a certain interest, but it was Mike Mignola's revelatory *Hellboy* that demonstrated the potential in more offbeat horror. Monsters and demons were allowed to run amok in these pages, and the series was so successful it spawned a box office hit. So followed Eric Powell's horror pastiche *The Goon.* Set in a fictitious American town, at an undisclosed time in the past, its panels are uncannily reminiscent of Will Eisner's work from over half a century ago. It's almost as if Eric had tidied the great man's pages in a previous life and got to see his technique close at hand. The company also managed to lure Steve Niles and his Cal McDonald creation. Picture a private investigator with some pretty bad habits and all kinds of creatures trying to usurp our world, and that's only part of the story. Modern horror comics owe Steve Niles a debt, for almost twenty years he has been involved in the production of intelligent horror comics which, although not averse to dishing out the schlock of old, are character-led with stories that hold you on the very edge of your seat. Dark Horse have also had the confidence to produce experimental horror albums from creators like Pete Von Sholly, which are inspiring a new generation of enthusiasts in the construct of worlds of terrifying madness.

A more recent publisher to come to the fore has been IDW. While Dark Horse looked to the silver screen, the editorial team at IDW saw the potential in television, choosing to adapt series such as *CSI* and *24*. They also had the wisdom to support one of the great success stories of the new century, Steve Niles' quintessential terror "30 Days of Night", painted by Ben Templesmith. The previous ten years had allowed the vampire to become immersed in a tide of romanticism, but that wasn't going to happen in these pages. Steve revealed them for the evil blood-suckers they had always been and in so doing earned himself several follow-ups, each progressively more dark. His love of film is evident in these pages. The recent move to silver screen for "30 Days of Night" will only add to his and his creation's reputations. DW have not been afraid to make horror that extra bit nasty. They went as far as attempting to rekindle the spirit of the horror magazines of the 1970s in their title *Doomed*, which sadly lived up to the portent in its name, but nontheless proved a worthy attempt. Like so many of the modern publishers, they hit their readers with an excess of lavish colour; the pre-Code years were never quite like this.

Those smaller publishers who have succeeded in being able to diversify have also featured in this new decade. Joe Monks' Chanting Monks Press has released *Zacherley's Midnite Terrors* and *The Night Terrors* as part of their horror comics output while having the foresight and talent to write novels, short stories and screen plays soon to be seen on film. Similarly Slave Labour Graphics have worked with Walt Disney to expand their gothic line of horror comics and use merchandising to keep their titles on public view.

The burgeoning zombie phenomenon has been the craze of the past few years, and has helped horror comics maintain their place in our comic shops. Virtually every other horror comic has to have one of these creatures running riot if it is to sell. IDW have had their share with *Zombies*, *Eclipse of the Undead* and adaptations of *Dawn of the Dead* and *Land of the Dead*. Fright Studios tried to encourage *Living With Zombies*, and Boom Studios went for *Zombie Tales Oblivion*. Even Marvel Comics, a company not overly keen on sullying their reputation, have had their own take on zombies. The prize of the bunch has come from a publisher not always associated with horror, Image Comics. They wisely acquired the services of Gary Reed and Vince Locke's *Deadworld*, which has gone from strength to strength, maintaining a highly entertaining storyline. Prior to this they released *The Walking Dead*, another series which has had a deserved long run, written by Robert Kirkman and drawn by Adlard. Robert has distinguished himself as a writer par excellence in a gritty tale that refuses to offer any form of compromise. Thirty-five years ago it was about vampires, werewolves and swamp beasts; now it's the once-hapless zombie.

There is one other area where certain horror comics have acquired a cult following this decade, one that has been in evidence ever since the 1970s – the Lovecraft prodigy. Horror fans have never been able to escape his dark embrace. Cross Plains Publishing originally beckoned readers to hark the *Call of Cthulhu*. Alan Moore, while in the employ of Avatar, asked us to broaden our horizons with *Yuggoth Cultures*, Boom Studios now beseech us to listen to their *Cthulhu Tales*, and Slave Labour Graphics tease us with *Carl Cthulhu* and *Little Scowlie*. If only for the present, there seems to be an unusual interest in this recondite aspect of terror.

Smaller creator-owned comics continue to thrive, appearing sporadically and without the support of an established distribution network. The UK seems to have many such worthy creators, who rely on a healthy network of small-press contributors. But it is clear that once again larger publishers recognize the potential of the genre. As long as there are uncertainties in our lives, the horror comic will continue to terrorize. The spectre at your window refuses to go away.

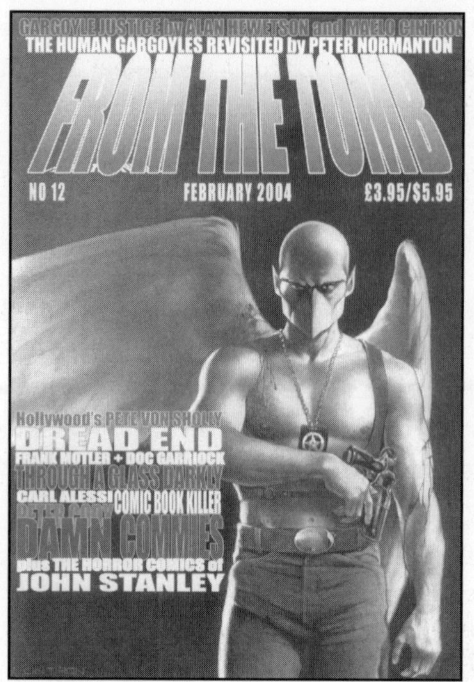

THE HUMAN GARGOYLES REVISITED by PETER NORMANTON
FROM THE TOMB
NO 12
FEBRUARY 2004
£3.95/$5.95
Hollywood's PETE VON SHOLLY
DREAD END
FRANK MOTLER + DOC GARRIOCK
THROUGH A GLASS DARKLY
CARL ALESSI COMIC BOOK KILLER
DAMN COMMIES
plus THE HORROR COMICS of
JOHN STANLEY

Dread End

From the Tomb 12, February 2004

Pete Von Sholly's photo-montage is aptly twenty-first-century in its use of technology to instil a sense of fear. It was later reprinted in his own essential collection, *Morbid,* for Dark Horse Comics. He found that, as a child, John Stanley's tale, seen earlier in this volume and originally published in Dell's *Ghost Stories 1*, scared the living daylights out of him. In its own way it inspired a creative career which has seen him work for Last Gasp, collaborate with Timothy Leary and go on to creating storyboards for films such as *Darkman*, *The Green Mile*, *James and the Giant Peach*, *Mars Attacks* and *The Shawshank Redemption.* He is also a regular contributor to *From the Tomb.*

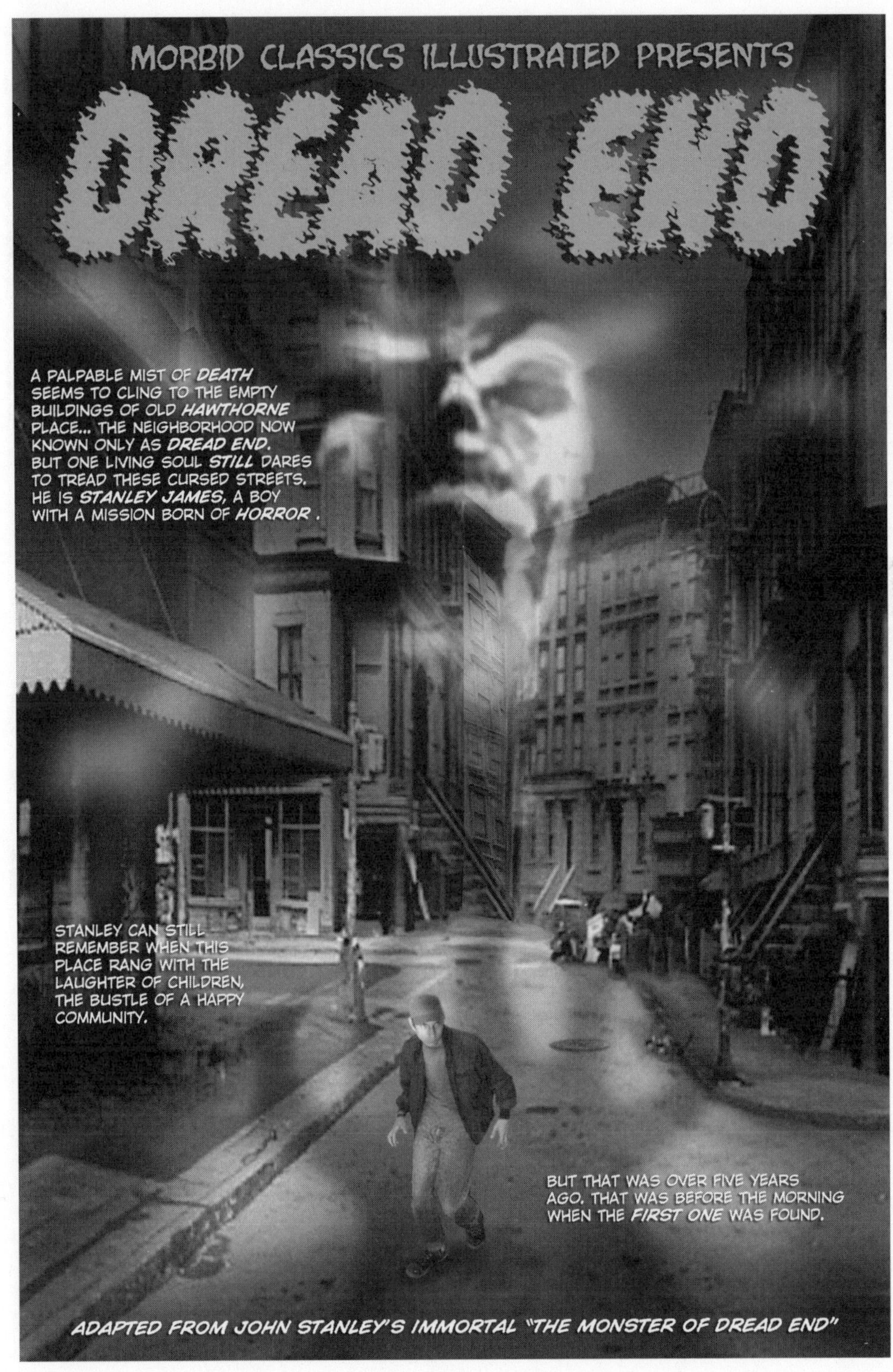
MORBID CLASSICS ILLUSTRATED PRESENTS
DREAD END
A PALPABLE MIST OF DEATH SEEMS TO CLING TO THE EMPTY BUILDINGS OF OLD HAWTHORNE PLACE... THE NEIGHBORHOOD NOW KNOWN ONLY AS DREAD END. BUT ONE LIVING SOUL STILL DARES TO TREAD THESE CURSED STREETS. HE IS STANLEY JAMES, A BOY WITH A MISSION BORN OF HORROR.
STANLEY CAN STILL REMEMBER WHEN THIS PLACE RANG WITH THE LAUGHTER OF CHILDREN, THE BUSTLE OF A HAPPY COMMUNITY.
BUT THAT WAS OVER FIVE YEARS AGO. THAT WAS BEFORE THE MORNING WHEN THE FIRST ONE WAS FOUND.
ADAPTED FROM JOHN STANLEY'S IMMORTAL "THE MONSTER OF DREAD END"

AS STANLEY SCURRIES TO HIS HIDING PLACE IN THE ALLEY, HE REMEMBERS THE MORNING WHEN IT BEGAN...

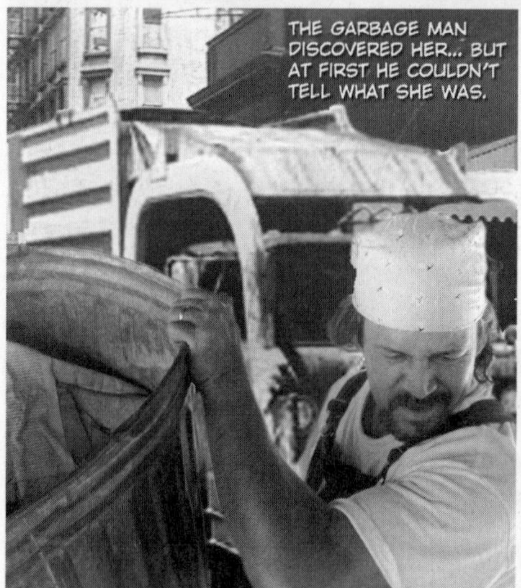
THE GARBAGE MAN DISCOVERED HER... BUT AT FIRST HE COULDN'T TELL WHAT SHE WAS.

THEN HE REALIZED SHE WAS ALL THAT WAS LEFT OF A LITTLE GIRL.

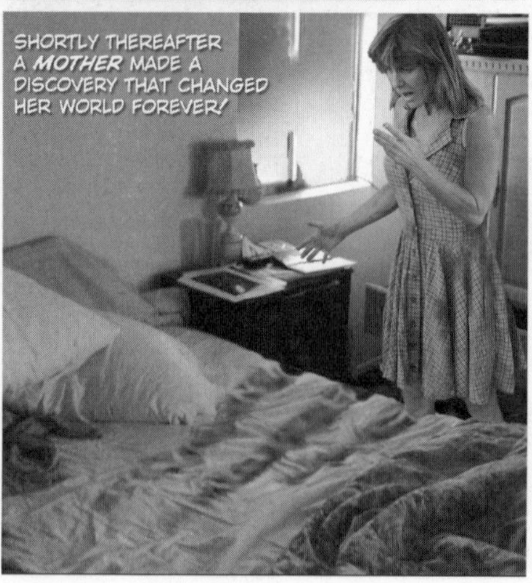
SHORTLY THEREAFTER A ***MOTHER*** MADE A DISCOVERY THAT CHANGED HER WORLD FOREVER!

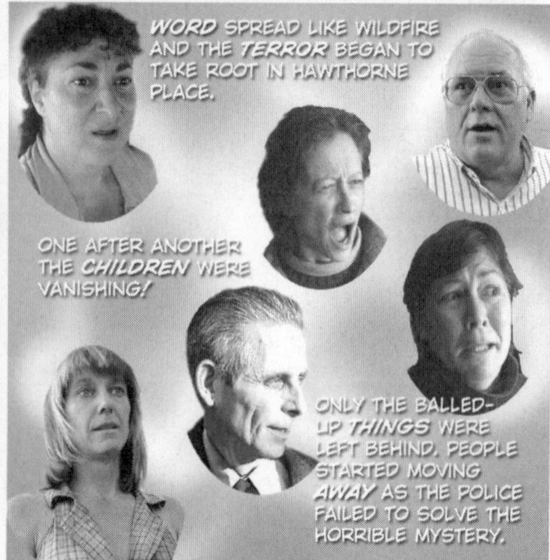
WORD SPREAD LIKE WILDFIRE AND THE ***TERROR*** BEGAN TO TAKE ROOT IN HAWTHORNE PLACE.
ONE AFTER ANOTHER THE ***CHILDREN*** WERE VANISHING!
ONLY THE BALLED-UP ***THINGS*** WERE LEFT BEHIND. PEOPLE STARTED MOVING ***AWAY*** AS THE POLICE FAILED TO SOLVE THE HORRIBLE MYSTERY.

IT WASN'T TOO LONG BEFORE EVERYBODY WAS ***GONE...*** THE BUILDINGS STOOD EMPTY AND SHUNNED. THE NEIGHBORHOOD TOOK ON THE NAME ***DREAD END!***
BUT SOMEHOW STANLEY ***KNOWS*** THAT THE KILLER ***IS STILL THERE!*** THAT'S WHY HE KEEPS A NIGHTLY VIGIL IN DREAD END, ***WATCHING... WAITING...***

WAITING FOR A CHANCE FOR ***JUSTICE;*** STANLEY'S LITTLE SISTER HAD BEEN THE KILLER'S FIRST ***VICTIM.***

AND SUDDENLY ***SHE IS THERE!*** JUST THE WAY THEY FOUND HER... A POOR MANGLED BODY! BUT SHE IS ***CRAWLING,*** DRAGGING HER BROKEN BONES ALONG THE GROUND... AND REACHING FOR HER BIG BROTHER!

"IT ***GOT*** ME, STANLEY... IT'LL GET ***YOU*** TOO! ***RUN,*** STANLEY! RUN FOR YOUR ***LIFE*** BEFORE IT COMES ***OUT*** AGAIN!"

HE AWAKENS WITH A ***GASP!*** SHE'S GONE.

ONLY A DREAM! THANK GOD. HIS HEARTBEAT SLOWS AND HIS CHEST RELAXES...

ANOTHER NIGHT OF NOTHING... ALMOST DAWN... WELL, MAYBE NEXT TIME, MAYBE...

THEN IT HAPPENS.

STANLEY SHRINKS BACK INTO THE ALLEY- UNABLE TO BELIEVE HIS EYES!

FINGERS UNDULATING LIKE THE LEGS OF A GREAT SPIDER, THE CLAW GROPES ITS WAY ALONG THE STREET... A POWERFUL SLITHERING BULK FOLLOWS THE SEARCHING TALONS...

HE FUMBLES FOR HIS CELL PHONE TO CALL THE POLICE BUT IT SLIPS FROM HIS NERVELESS FINGERS...
CLACK!
AT THE SOUND OF THE PHONE HITTING THE PAVEMENT, THE CLAW STIFFENS...
... AND VANISHES WITH BREATHTAKING SPEED!
STANLEY BEGINS TO CREEP OUT OF THE ALLEY... HIS ONLY HOPE NOW IS TO ESCAPE WITH HIS LIFE. BUT THE CLAW IS COMING OUT AGAIN, ALERTED TO HIS PRESENCE!
WITH AN INCREDIBLE BURST OF SPEED, THE CLAW IS SUDDENLY THERE, BLOCKING HIS ESCAPE.

QUICK AS A *COBRA* THE CLAW GRABS A GARBAGE CAN AND *CRUSHES* IT AS STANLEY LEAPS BACK AGAINST THE WALL!
CRUNCH!

TOSSING THE CAN ASIDE, THE MONSTER *SLITHERS* AWAY FROM THE ALLEY...

IT SEEMS *ENDLESS*... BUT AS LONG AS IT KEEPS MOVING THE *CLAW* IS GETTING FARTHER AWAY...
OR IS IT?

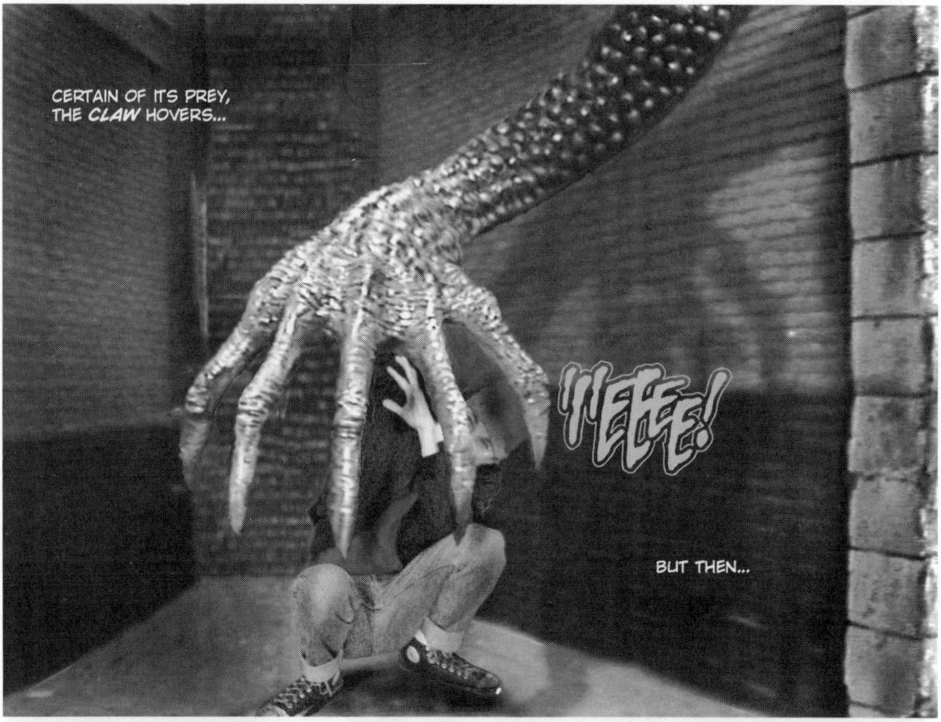

CERTAIN OF ITS PREY, THE *CLAW* HOVERS...

BUT THEN...

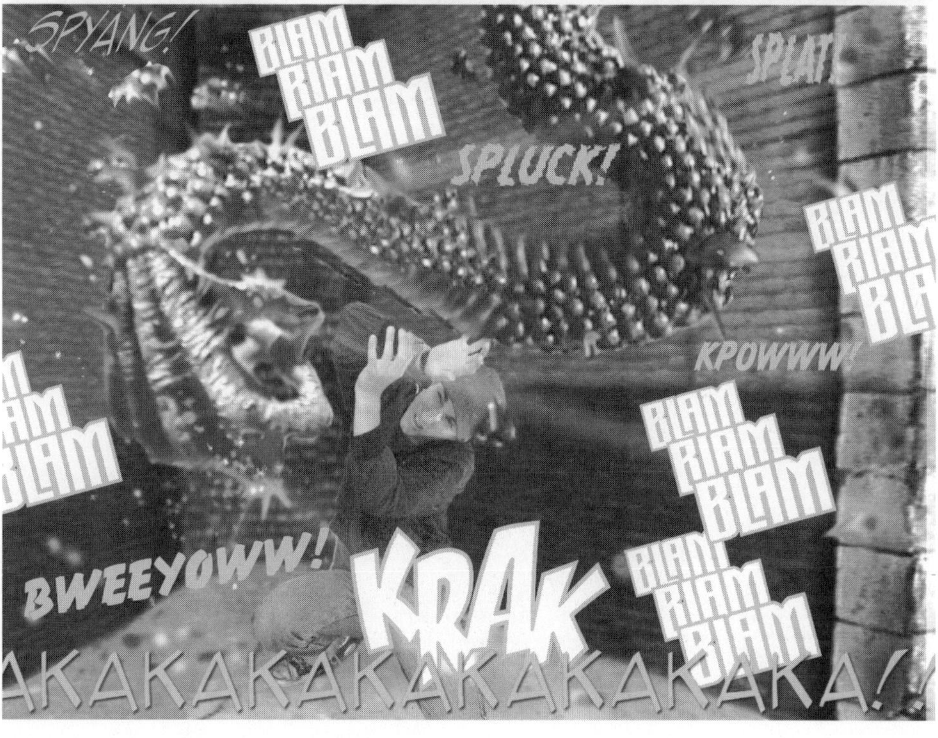

SPYANG!

BLAM BLAM BLAM

SPLUCK!

KPOWWW!

BWEEYOWW!

KRAK

AND SUDDENLY THE WORLD IS QUIET AND THE MONSTER LIES STILL. THE SOLDIERS RUSH FROM THEIR HIDING PLACES AND GAPE AT THE MOTIONLESS THING.
THE PORES IN THE CLAW SHOW HOW IT FED...
THEN COMES AN EXPLOSION OF BABBLING VOICES: "SORRY WE LET IT GET SO CLOSE"... "-KNEW IT WAS HERE BUT IT MOVED TOO FAST FOR US TO GET IT"..."-HAD TO MAKE SURE IT WAS OUT FAR ENOUGH SO IT COULDN'T GET AWAY"... "COULDN'T RISK JUST WOUNDING IT"... "BEEN HERE ALL ALONG"... "NEEDED YOU TO LURE IT OUT"...
BUT STANLEY SAYS NOTHING.
"WE'RE HERE FOR YOU, SON. EVERYTHING'S GOING TO BE- WHAT'S THAT, TOMPKINS?"
"YOU BETTER TAKE A LOOK DOWN HERE, SIR."
ONLY STANLEY DOESN'T HAVE TO LOOK. HE KNOWS THERE IS MORE...
AND DOWN IN THE SEWER, DOWN IN THE THING'S LAIR, THE SOLDIERS HAVE FOUND A HOLE...
A HOLE THAT SEEMS TO HAVE NO BOTTOM.
IN THE HEARTS AND SOULS OF THE MEN A COLD FEAR MAKES ITSELF FELT.
THE FEAR OF A DREAD END!

The Festival

Bedlam 5, July 2004

There have been several references to the gloom-ridden splendour of H. P. Lovecraft's writing in these pages; this is yet another rendition of his unworldly recital. Grant Margetts is one of the many up-and-coming talents to be found in the UK small press scene. The sombre artistry on show here is also evident in the work he scripted and pencilled for *Dead by Dawn's Dusk.*

"The Festival" was first published in *Naked 3* and soon after used by John Gallagher as the denouement to his Skywald-influenced magazine *Bedlam's* fifth appearance.

Efficiut Dæmones, ut quae non sunt, sic tamen quasi sint, conspicienda hominibus exhibeant.
I was far from home, summoned by my fore fathers.
It was the Yuletide festival, older than Bethlehem and Babylon, older than Memphis and mankind.
Beyond the hill's crest I saw Kingsport outspread in the gloaming. Labyrinths of steep, narrow, crooked streets, ceaseless mazes of colonial houses piled and scattered at all angles, and far off, the sea pounded against rotted wharves.
H.P. Lovecraft's
The Festival
Adapted by Grant Margetts
ORIGINALLY PUBLISHED IN NAKED #3 (2004)
The road was very lonely, and sometimes I thought I heard a distant horrible creaking as of a gibbet in the wind.
They had hanged four kinsmen of mine for witchcraft in 1692, but I did not know just where. The old maps still held good and I knew where to find the door of my people, the seventeenth house on the left...
..yet I heard no footsteps before the door opened.
17

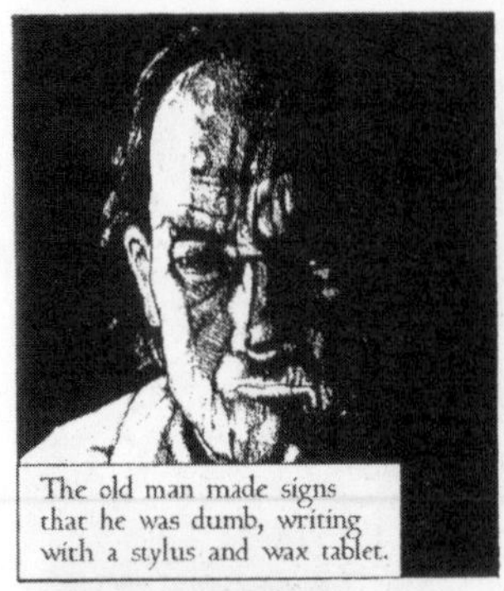
The old man made signs that he was dumb, writing with a stylus and wax tablet.

He beckoned me in.

A woman, bent, silently spinning, an indefinite dampness seemed upon the place.

The high-backed settle facing the window seemed to be occupied, though I was not sure.

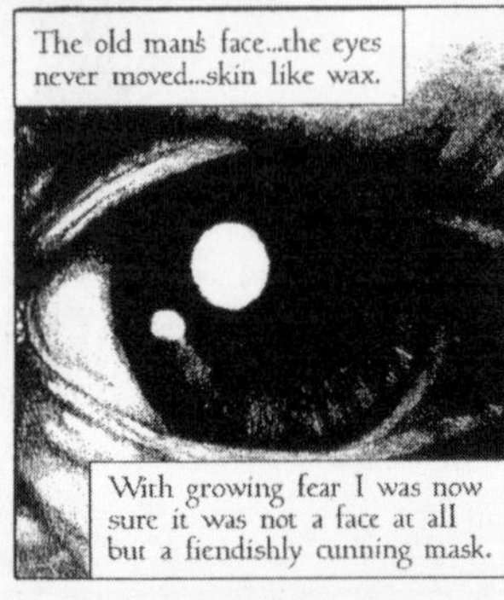
The old man's face...the eyes never moved...skin like wax.
With growing fear I was now sure it was not a face at all but a fiendishly cunning mask.

Pointing to a chair, table and pile of books, he left.

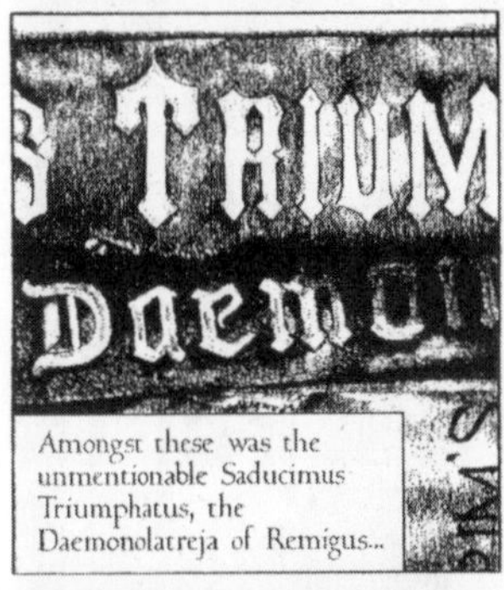
Amongst these was the unmentionable Saducimus Triumphatus, the Daemonolatreja of Remigus...

And worst of all the Necronomicon; a book I had never seen, but of which I had heard monstrous things whispered.
I tried to read and soon became terribly absorbed...

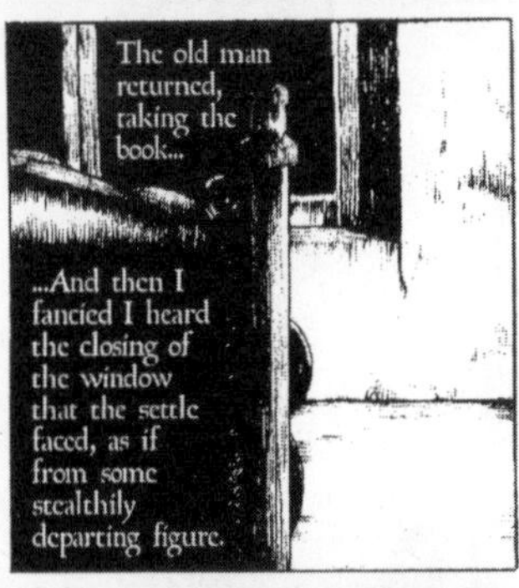
The old man returned, taking the book...
...And then I fancied I heard the closing of the window that the settle faced, as if from some stealthily departing figure.

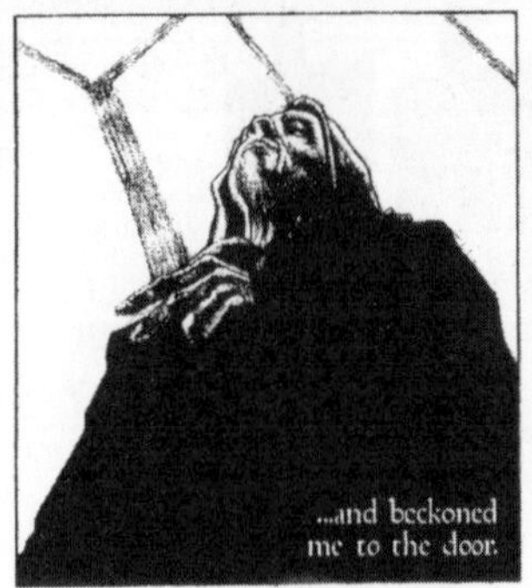
...and beckoned me to the door.

Outside a throng of cowled, cloaked figures poured silently from every doorway.

Amid these hushed figures I followed my voiceless guides, jostled by elbows that seemed preternaturally soft......pressed by chests and stomachs that seemed abnormally pulpy...
...never seeing a face....Until on a hill in the centre of town there perched a great white church.
I waited till the crowd had oozed into the black doorway, determined to be the last.
Inside most of the throng had already vanished.
I followed the trail dumbly down the foot worn steps, descending into the crypt.
After aeons of descent I knew we had passed down through the hill and beneath Kingsport itself.
A narrow staircase plunged ever further, rough and uneven as if chiselled out of the solid rock.
And then I saw the lurid shimmering of pale light, and heard the insidious lapping of sun less waters, and wished bitterly that no fore father had summoned me to this primal rite.

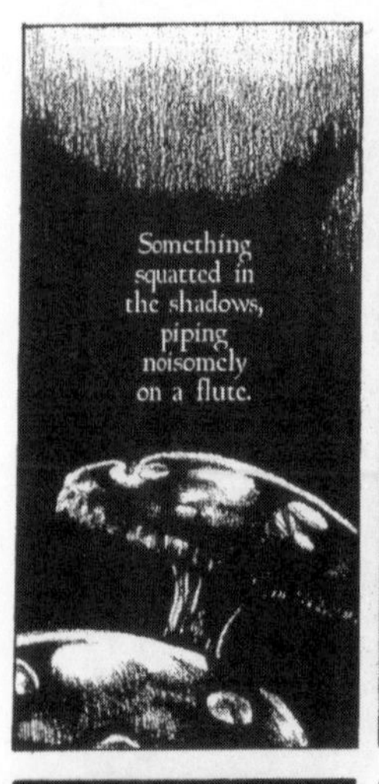

Something squatted in the shadows, piping noisomely on a flute.

The ritual was in progress.

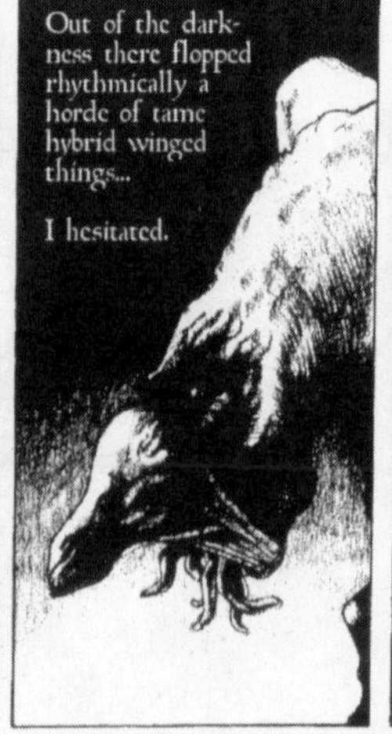

Out of the darkness there flopped rhythmically a horde of tame hybrid winged things...
I hesitated.

The old man produced a watch engraved with my family arms.
It was a hideous proof, for I knew that watch was long buried with my forefathers.

The creatures were now scratching restlessly.
He turned quickly to calm them...

And the wax... mask

I flung myself into the oily river before the madness of my screams could bring down upon me all the charnel legions these pest-gulfs might conceal.

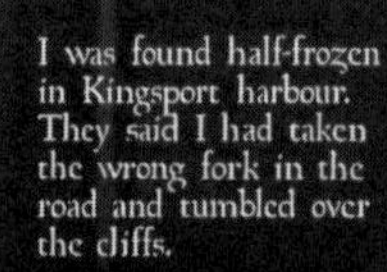

I was found half-frozen in Kingsport harbour. They said I had taken the wrong fork in the road and tumbled over the cliffs.

My outbursts ensured I was sent to St Mary's hospital in Arkham, where I would have...

...'better' care...

I agreed to get any harassing obsessions off my mind however yet I could not help but continually return to a passage from that accursed Necronomicon...

"...out of corruption horrid life springs, and the dull scavengers of earth wax crafty to vex it and swell monstrous to plague it. Great holes secretly are digged where earth's pores ought to suffice, and things have learnt to walk that ought to crawl."

The Crawlspace

From the Tomb 18, Christmas 2005

Almost ten years ago Stephen Sennitt wrote *Ghastly Terror*! "The Horrible Story of the Horror Comics" for Headpress. He followed it with a collection of some of his loathsome short stories, selected for the same publisher in 2003. This perturbing entry is adapted from his short stories by the aspiring James Fletcher. Fresh out of college, James is no stranger to the pages of *From the Tomb* and has recently been providing Oxford University Press with illustrations, along with a graphic retelling of Edgar Allan Poe's "The Black Cat".

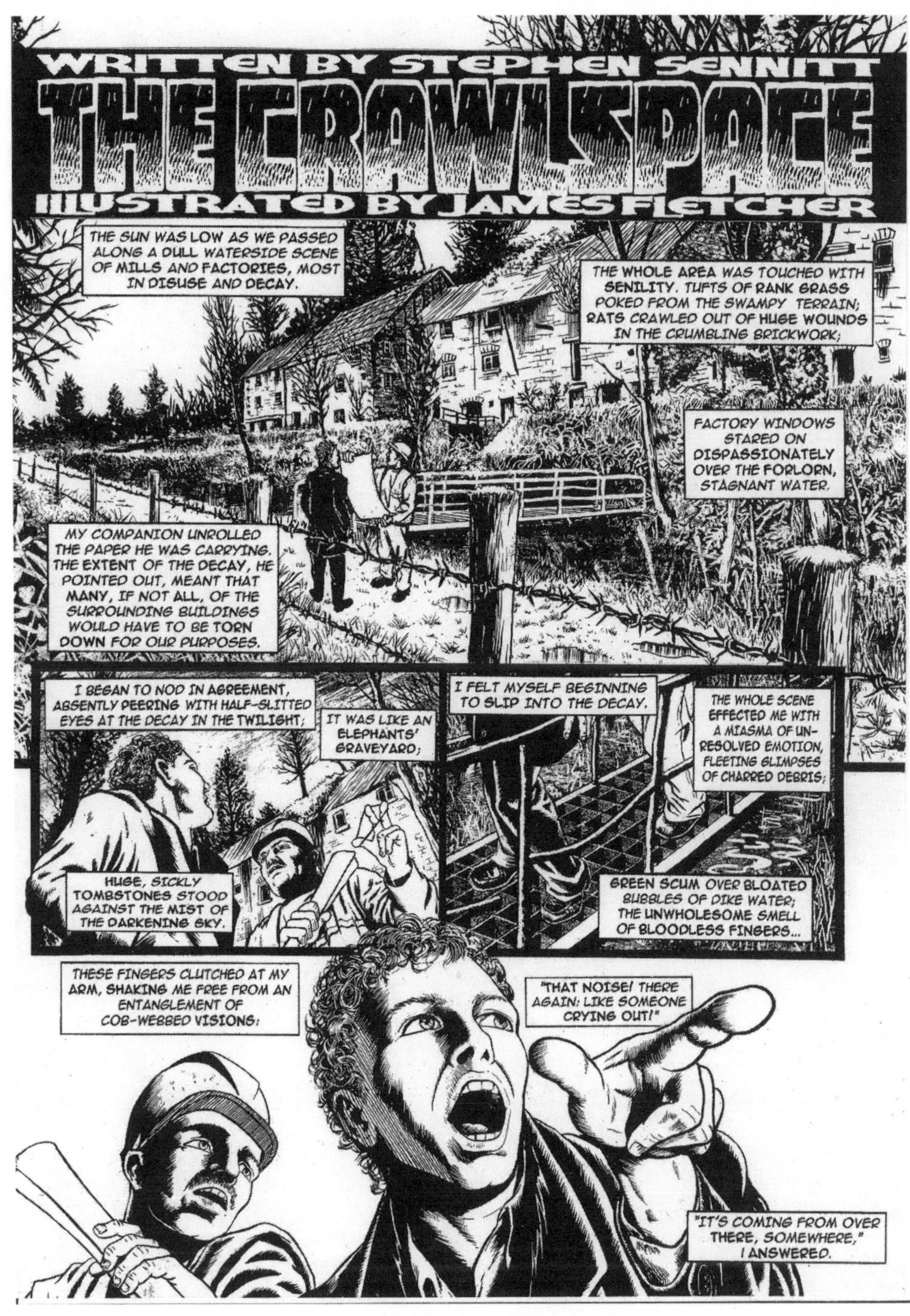
WRITTEN BY STEPHEN SENNITT
THE CRAWLSPACE
ILLUSTRATED BY JAMES FLETCHER
THE SUN WAS LOW AS WE PASSED ALONG A DULL WATERSIDE SCENE OF MILLS AND FACTORIES, MOST IN DISUSE AND DECAY.
THE WHOLE AREA WAS TOUCHED WITH SENILITY. TUFTS OF RANK GRASS POKED FROM THE SWAMPY TERRAIN; RATS CRAWLED OUT OF HUGE WOUNDS IN THE CRUMBLING BRICKWORK;
FACTORY WINDOWS STARED ON DISPASSIONATELY OVER THE FORLORN, STAGNANT WATER.
MY COMPANION UNROLLED THE PAPER HE WAS CARRYING. THE EXTENT OF THE DECAY, HE POINTED OUT, MEANT THAT MANY, IF NOT ALL, OF THE SURROUNDING BUILDINGS WOULD HAVE TO BE TORN DOWN FOR OUR PURPOSES.
I BEGAN TO NOD IN AGREEMENT, ABSENTLY PEERING WITH HALF-SLITTED EYES AT THE DECAY IN THE TWILIGHT;
IT WAS LIKE AN ELEPHANTS' GRAVEYARD;
HUGE, SICKLY TOMBSTONES STOOD AGAINST THE MIST OF THE DARKENING SKY.
I FELT MYSELF BEGINNING TO SLIP INTO THE DECAY.
THE WHOLE SCENE EFFECTED ME WITH A MIASMA OF UN-RESOLVED EMOTION, FLEETING GLIMPSES OF CHARRED DEBRIS;
GREEN SCUM OVER BLOATED BUBBLES OF DIKE WATER; THE UNWHOLESOME SMELL OF BLOODLESS FINGERS...
THESE FINGERS CLUTCHED AT MY ARM, SHAKING ME FREE FROM AN ENTANGLEMENT OF COB-WEBBED VISIONS:
"THAT NOISE! THERE AGAIN: LIKE SOMEONE CRYING OUT!"
"IT'S COMING FROM OVER THERE, SOMEWHERE," I ANSWERED.

THE SHRIEKING SOUNDED AGAIN, THIS TIME MORE LIKE A LOW GRATING MOAN.
A SHIVER RAN THROUGH MY BODY.
IN THE DISTANCE, THE SQUEALING OF RAT LITTERS OVER THE HEAVY SLUSHING OF DARK GREEN WATER AND...
AGAIN THE CRY; THIS TIME MORE URGENT.
THE SCENE WE CAME UPON WAS SO GROTESQUE I HAD TO STIFLE A PERVERSE IMPULSE TO LAUGH. OVER A SMALL, WOODEN WATERWHEEL, A VERY OLD WOMAN WAS STRETCHED,
HER LONG WHITE HAIR DRAGGED INTO THE WATER;
SPOTS OF BLOOD SPRINKLED FROM HER NOSE AND MOUTH INTO HER EYES
THE SURROUNDING DECAY SEEMED TO CLOSE IN OPPRESSIVELY;
AND, WORST OF ALL, HER SLIGHT FRAME WAS RACKED AGONOSINGLY BACK AGAINST THE SHAPE OF THE WHEEL.
BEFORE I HAD TIME TO THINK, WE WERE UNTYING HER,
BUT IT WAS TOO LATE:
SOMETHING IN HER BACK SNAPPED;
AS WE CARRIED HER FROM THE GREASY WATER SHE DIED.
BUT IN HER LAST MOMENTS, SHE LOOKED AT ME AND POINTED TO A DARK MILL ON THE BANK.
"THE...CHILDREN..." SHE SAID.
THAT WAS ALL.

I DON'T KNOW WHY I IMMEDIATELY VENTURED IN THERE.
I DIDN'T EVEN THINK ABOUT IT...
BUT AS I CLIMBED THE RUSTED IRON STAIRS
THE ROT AND DECAY OF WET WAS REPLACED BY A MUSTY SMELL OF OLD WALLPAPER.
THE PLACE WAS AWASH WITH STAGNANT BLACK SLIME,
FINALLY, I CAME INTO A DUSTY WAREHOUSE.
THERE WERE STRANGE GEOMETRICAL PATTERNS ON THE FLOOR OF THE ROOM WHERE I FOUND THEM...
BROKEN GLASS LAY ALL OVER THE FLOOR... A SMELL OF URINE IN THE DIMNESS.
IN THE CORNER, A DARK SHAPE APPEARED.
ON CLOSE INSPECTION I FOUND IT TO BE A STATUETTE IN THE SHAPE OF SOME KIND OF AMPHIBIOUS CREATURE, HIDEOUSLY BLOATED, WITH ROWS OF BIZARRE LITTLE HEADS,

EVEN THOUGH IT WAS TOO DARK TO SEE PROPERLY, I COULDN'T TAKE MY EYES FROM THE OBJECT,
THOUGH I TREMBLED NAUSEOUSLY AND DARED NOT APPROACH ANY FURTHER.
I WAS PERSPIRING AND MY FINGER-ENDS FELT WHITE AND NUMB.
AN ATMOSPHERE OF SICKENING VIOLENCE PERVADED THE WAREHOUSE, STIFLING ME.
THEN, I HEARD A MOVEMENT BEHIND ME.
LIVID PINPRICKS OF HEAT BEFORE MY EYES.
I COULDN'T MOVE, OTHER THAN TO RUB MY HANDS TOGETHER;
STOMACH CHURNING,
I TURNED AROUND SLOWLY AND SAW, THROUGH MY NAUSEA, A SMALL HAND
APPEARING FROM A SPACE IN THE FLOOR.
IN FLASHES OF PAIN, I APPROACHED VERY SLOWLY.
IT WAS A CRAWLSPACE BETWEEN THIS AND THE LOWER FLOOR.

IN IT, TWO CHILDREN, A BOY AND A GIRL (TWINS, I THOUGHT) SAT VERY STILL, EYES CLOSED.
I CANNOT EXPLAIN IT, BUT THE DARKNESS AROUND THEM SEEMED TO BE FILLED WITH MOVEMENT. IT VISIBLY CRAWLED AND FORMED STRANGE BLOTCHES, LIKE CLOUDS OF TINY FLIES.
THE CRAWLSPACE WAS FILLED WITH THE STENCH OF EXCREMENT. A TANGIBLE VIOLENCE HUNG IN THE AIR LIKE A SLAUGHTERHOUSE FULL OF ROTTEN MEAT.
EVEN SO, I PEERED IN FURTHER.
I THOUGHT I'D PUT MY HEAD INTO A HOTHOUSE; A SORT OF CLOYING, STAGNANT HEAT FLOODED OVER ME,
AND IN THE DARKNESS I SCREAMED OUT LOUD AS SOMETHING TOUCHED ME

AND AT THAT MOMENT THE CHILDREN TURNED TOWARD ME.
THOUGH RECOILING, MY LIMBS KICKING INVOLUNTARILY LIKE TWITCHING NERVES, I SAW THAT THEIR EYES WERE NOT MERELY SHUT TIGHT, BUT THAT THEIR EYELIDS HAD BEEN STITCHED TOGETHER.
AS THE THING IN THE DARKNESS FORMED ITSELF BEFORE ME, I REALISED THE CHILDREN'S EYES HAD BEEN STITCHED TIGHTLY SHUT...
...SO THAT THEY MIGHT NEVER SEE WHAT THE BLASPHEMOUS OLD WOMAN HAD CALLED...
UP FROM THE DEPTHS.

Immortal: A Vampire Tale

Black Boar Press, 2003

Dave Hitchcock is known for his signed limited edition comics; this one was limited to seventy copies, the original being printed on parchment-effect paper and in sepia. His style exudes a sense of history and provides the perfect backdrop for a veritable tale of terror. Dave is also the esteemed creator of the newspaper-sized *Whitechapel Freak*, the three-issue mini series, *Spring Heeled Jack* and *Spirit of the Highwayman.*

PRAGA
1603
The city was built within the castle walls
The town imprisoned
Much like my pitiful self
I have been here for a good many years
The Vermin have driven away my sanity

So I take life in return

Bitter as the fluid is, it has been my only nourishment for decades now

I grow weak, my time is coming and I do not fear it
I have seen many deaths, indeed I had made them

My children and I
Every fullness of the moon

Nothing could stop us

Until they came
Hussites

So I take life
in return

Bitter as the fluid
is, it has been my
only nourishment
for decades now

I grow weak, my time
is coming and I do
not fear it
I have seen many
deaths, indeed
I had made
them

My children and I
Every fullness
of the moon

Nothing could
stop us

Until they came
Hussites

I can never forget their tortured screams
I managed to flee
But in my gut instinct for survival so many of my brethren lost their lives
I left them to face the wrath of the hypocrite daydwellers

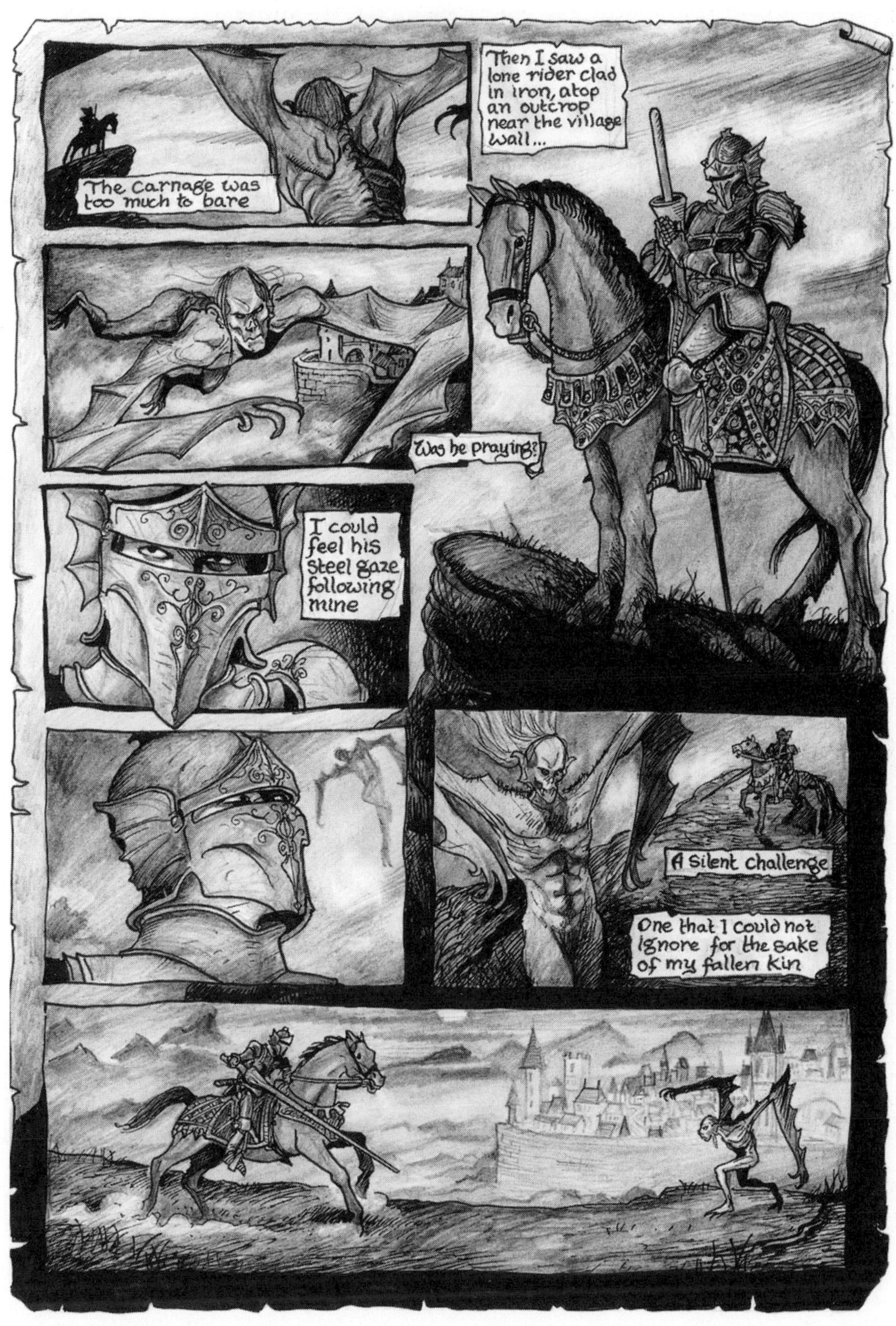
The Carnage was too much to bare
Then I saw a lone rider clad in iron, atop an outcrop near the village wall...
Was he praying?
I could feel his steel gaze following mine
A Silent challenge
One that I could not ignore for the sake of my fallen kin

The challenge will be met
By my rules of engagement...

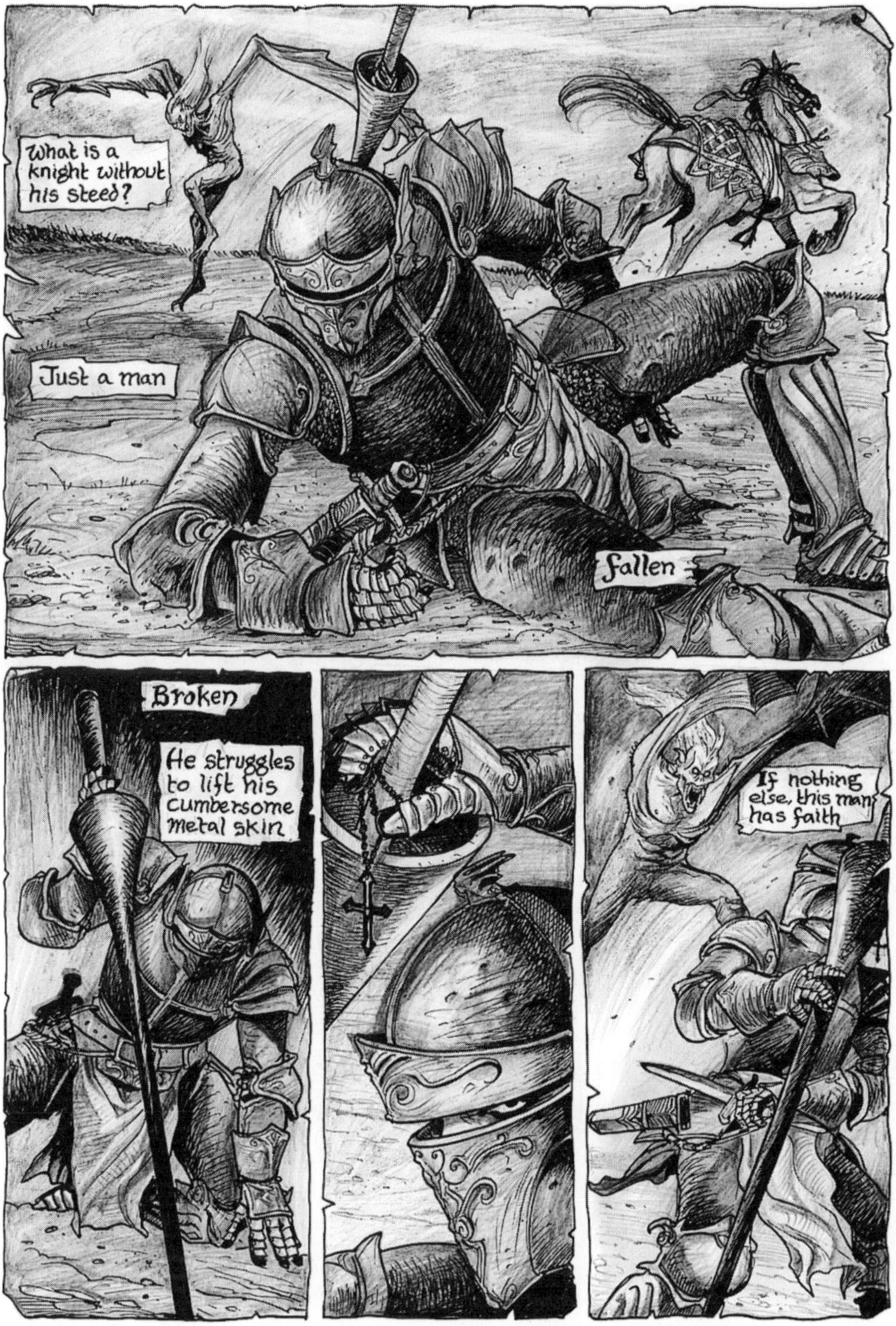

What is a knight without his steed?

Just a man

Fallen

But even if he is one of his warriors, faith alone cannot prevail
Against such as I...
Somehow he fought back
With all his heart
Try as he might I easily deflected his paltry blows
Time and again
Then I saw it
The symbol they revere
Our kind detest...

I was distracted, pain seared my nerves
My pupils left scarred by that accursed crucifix
Splinters of dawn corrode my flesh
Weak with the addition of the oncoming sunrise, I was bound
Taken prisoner
The same demise as my fellow kinsmen would not be sufficient for me...
No, they had something far worse...the tower
The town was cleansed of the plague we wrought upon it
The hussites had completed their work here
As I had mine
The few wretches who were imprisoned here have long since succumbed to my thirst

I was left to rot
But I could not die
Nor could I satisfy my hunger
The horror of that night changed me forever
I could no longer face the daydwellers
Could not bare to go amongst the crowds
Even if I could muster the strength to pass that cursed window
I would rather perish
Avoiding the rays of each new morn became a game
Stay in shadow, live another day
Not any more
It is time

There Was an Old Woman

Fleshrot Tales from the Dead 2, 2003

Vancouver's Socar Myles has the ability to merge the darkest horror with a fantasy world from which most of us would readily shy. There is a richness to her brushstrokes that takes me back to the terrors of the illustrated fairy tales of my childhood. She lives happily with her two rats, sketching and embellishing for a variety of projects. She enjoys including in her tales rats, gnarled roots and people turning into trees, amongst other things, but don't ever ask her to draw skyscrapers!

THERE WAS AN OLD WOMAN

THERE WAS AN OLD WOMAN
WHO LIVED IN A SHOE-

SHE HAD SO MANY CHILDREN
SHE DIDN'T KNOW WHAT TO DO.

THERE WAS SAMMY, THE ELDEST,
A STRAPPING YOUNG LAD;
THE TWINS, BOB AND JASON,
WHO LOOKED LIKE THEIR DAD;
THERE WERE ELSA AND CLAIRE,
WITH THE CURLY BLONDE HAIR
AND FUNNY WEE JACK,
WITH THE THOUSAND-YARD STARE.
THERE WAS METAL-MOUTHED CHRIS,
AND BESPECTACLED JANE,
AND SCREECHY WEE NELSON,
WHOSE SHRIEKS HURT YOUR BRAIN-
AND, LAST BUT NOT LEAST,,
THERE WAS NORBERT THE DOG,
WHO SLEPT IN THE TOE
OF THAT SMELLY OLD CLOG.

WHAT WITH TAXES GONE UP, AND EMPLOYMENT COME DOWN,
IT WAS ALWAYS A ROUT WHEN THE LANDLORD CAME ROUND.

AND, THOUGH THERE WAS NEVER MUCH FOOD ON THE TABLE,
THEY GOT BY ON GLUE AS BEST THEY WERE ABLE.

ONE MISERABLE NIGHT, WHEN THE CUPBOARD WAS BARE,
THAT LADY WENT BONKERS, AS MAD AS A HARE.

SHE SHUT NELSON'S MOUTH WITH A NAIL-DRIVEN BOARD,
AND SMILED IN THE SILENCE, ALL PALE AND BEGORED.

CHRIS WITH THE BRACES AND JANE WITH THE SPECS,
SHE STUFFED IN THE CRAPPER, RIGHT UP TO THEIR NECKS.

POOR STARING JACK WOULDN'T FIT IN THE BOG,
BUT, SUITABLY SLICED, HE WENT FINE IN THE DOG.

ELSA AND CLAIRE BOTH PUT UP QUITE A FIGHT,
BUT SHE FRAZZLED THEM CRISP WITH A 'LECTRICAL LIGHT.
SHE SMOTHERED THE TWINS AS THEY LAY IN THEIR BED;
WHEN SAM SAW THE CARNAGE, HE BLEW OFF HIS HEAD.
NORBERT GOT CARELESS, AND CHOKED ON A BONE,
LEAVING THAT HORRID OLD HAG ALL ALONE.

ONE NIGHT, TOWARDS MIDNIGHT, ALL ON HER TOD,
HER CHILDREN TUCKED TENDERLY UNDER THE SOD,
SHE MOUNTED HER HORSE, AND SHE RODE OFF TO NOD-
(FARTHER THAN HEAVEN, AND HIGHER THAN GOD).
AS SHE LAY WHERE SHE'D FALLEN, SNORINGLY SLEEPING,
INTO HER DREAMS, LITTLE NOISES CAME CREEPING:
A SCRATCH AT THE WINDOW, A THUMP AT THE DOOR,
A TINKLE OF GLASS, RAINING DOWN ON THE FLOOR.

SHE BURIED HER HEAD,
TO ESCAPE FROM THE DIN,
BUT, THROUGH HER THIN PILLOW,
THE SOUNDS FILTERED IN:

A TERRIBLE THUMPING
ADVANCED UP THE STAIRS;

THE KITCHEN WAS FULL OF
THE SCRAPING OF CHAIRS.

THE BREEZE BORE A
COUGHETY HOWL
IN THE DOOR,

AND, OUT IN THE HALL,
SOMETHING DRIPPED
ON THE FLOOR.

THOUGH THE HAG SQUINCHED HER EYES SHUT, AND HID HER GREY HEAD, THE NOISES CAME NEARER, RIGHT UP TO HER BED.
UP ROSE THE BLINDS, AND THE MOONLIGHT STREAMED IN, GLEAMING ON BONE POKING OUT FROM THE SKIN.
'TWAS SAMMY, HIS BRAINS TUMBLED OUT O'ER HIS BACK, AND BOBBY AND JASON, THEIR FACES ALL BLACK.
AND ELSA AND CLAIRE, WITH THEIR CURLS IN THE AIR, AND JACK, WITH HIS DOG-GOBBLED INNARDS LAID BARE.
'TWAS CHRIS AND HIS SISTER, SOGGY AND RANK, AND NELSON, HIS HEAD SPLIT IN TWO BY THE PLANK.
AND EVEN THE DOG, WITH HIS JAWS OPEN WIDE, THE BETTER TO FIT THAT OLD LADY INSIDE.

THEY FEASTED ALL NIGHT,
TILL THE MOON FLED IN FEAR.

THEY LEFT NOTHING TO WASTE,
NOT AN EYE, NOT AN EAR.

BY MORNING'S FIRST LIGHT, THAT OLD LADY WAS GONE-
-BUT NOBODY MINDED, SO THUS ENDS OUR SONG.
WRITTEN AND ILLUSTRATED BY SOCAR J. MYLES, 2003
ORIGINALLY APPEARED IN FLESHROT VOL.1,
PUBLISHED BY FRIGHTWORLD STUDIOS.

Cal McDonald: A Letter from B. S.

Drawing on your Nightmares 1, October 2003

Cal McDonald's bizarre adventures have become staple reading for countless horror fans in recent years. This is one of his more obscure appearances from a one-shot, which brought together Cal and later on Eric Powell's *The Goon*. Here Steve Niles combines a world of modern horror with the noir of the Fifties. Ben Templesmith supplied the paint job for this typically black comedic introduction. Ben was also the artist on Steve's revered "30 Days of Night" published by IDW.

Steve Niles is one of the main reasons why horror comics have once again begun to be taken seriously. He can be cruelly sardonic in his humour, even glib, but he is a formidable storyteller with a first-rate understanding of pacing and characterization. He is also a fan of the Harvey horror comics of the 1950s.

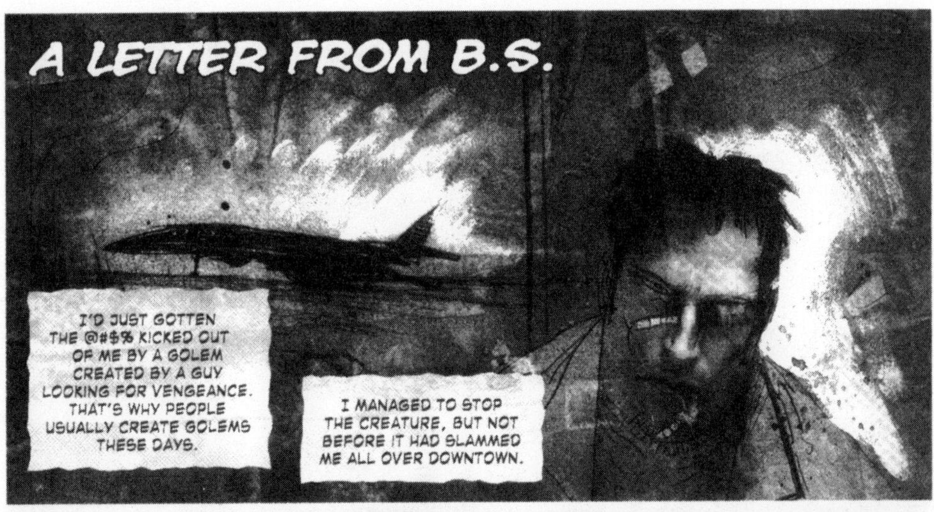
A LETTER FROM B.S.
I'D JUST GOTTEN THE @#$% KICKED OUT OF ME BY A GOLEM CREATED BY A GUY LOOKING FOR VENGEANCE. THAT'S WHY PEOPLE USUALLY CREATE GOLEMS THESE DAYS.
I MANAGED TO STOP THE CREATURE, BUT NOT BEFORE IT HAD SLAMMED ME ALL OVER DOWNTOWN.

GOOD THING I STAY WELL VERSED IN SPELLS AND INCANTATIONS. THAT'S THE ONLY WAY TO STOP A GOLEM.
PEOPLE MAKE A BIG DEAL OUT OF MAGIC SPELLS, BUT THE TRUTH IS, INCANTATIONS ARE JUST PHONE NUMBERS TO OTHER WORLDS WHICH ARE AS REAL AS THIS ONE.

I WAS PLANNING ON LAPSING INTO A DRUG-INDUCED COMA, BUT THEN I GOT THIS LETTER.
I WASN'T SCHEDULING ON A TRIP, BUT SOME THINGS CAN'T BE PLANNED.

MR MCDONALD,
I HEARD AROUND THAT YOU ARE A MAN
WHO CAN HELP A GUY LIKE ME
I'VE BEEN PATIENT SINCE THEY OFFED ME
THINK IT'S TIME THEY LET ME BACK IN. I
UNDERSTAND THE WAY THINGS WORK
IT WAS MY TIME TO GO. I SAW IT COMING IN
SOME WAYS I CAN SEE WHY I NEEDED TO BE
CLIPPED, BUT I MADE THIS PLACE.
HELL, I DIED FOR IT.
I NEED A GUY WHO CAN UNDERSTAND MY
POSITION, AND I HEARD YOU CAN DEAL WITH
SITUATIONS. I DON'T KNOW WHAT OR HOW I CAN
BUT I'LL OWE YOU MY ONE GOOD
YOU CAN GET ME BACK INSIDE
B.S.

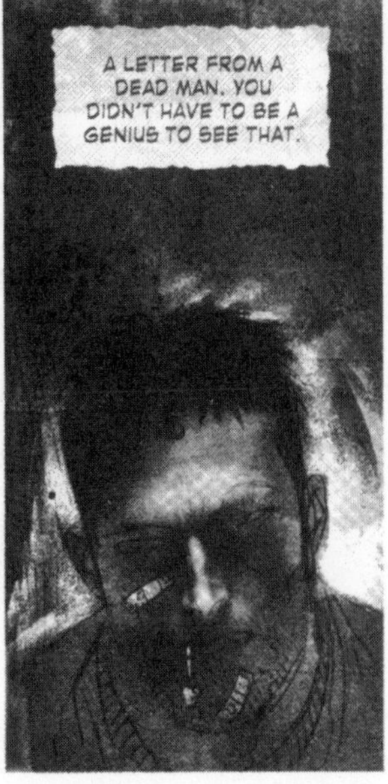
A LETTER FROM A DEAD MAN. YOU DIDN'T HAVE TO BE A GENIUS TO SEE THAT.

THE LETTER WAS POSTMARKED LAS VEGAS.
VEGAS IS A QUICK 45-MINUTE PLANE RIDE, SO I DECIDED TO CHECK IT OUT.
I LIKE IT HERE. IT'S OPEN 24-7 AND THERE AREN'T A LOT OF MONSTERS. THEY DON'T LIKE THE BRIGHT LIGHTS.
WHOEVER THIS B.S. WAS, HE DIDN'T TELL ME WHERE TO MEET HIM. IF HE WAS DEAD, HE'D FIND ME.
AND I WAS RIGHT.
CAL MCDONALD?
YIKES!

I AIN'T A PRETTY SIGHT, AM I? THEY MADE SURE I WAS DEAD, 'CUZ THEY KNEW IF I WASN'T, *THEY'D* BE.
YOU CAN SAY THAT AGAIN. CHRIST, EVER HEAR OF AN EYE PATCH?

BENJAMIN SIEGEL. THANKS FOR COMING.
NO PROBLEM. WHAT CAN I DO FOR YOU?

IT'S LIKE THIS, SEE. BEFORE I GOT OFFED--
BY MEYER LANSKY, RIGHT?
THAT'S WHAT SOME PEOPLE THINK, BUT IT WAS JUST SOME INVESTORS WHO DIDN'T WANT TO WAIT FOR THE VEGAS GRAVY TRAIN.
COME ON, LET'S WALK A BIT.

NOBODY CAN SEE YOU, RIGHT?
THAT'S RIGHT, SMART GUY. ONE OF THE FEW BENEFITS OF BEING DEAD. I CHOOSE WHO SEES ME.
SO ALL THEY SEE IS MY DUMB @%# TALKING TO NOBODY.
YEAH, THAT'S PRETTY MUCH THE CASE.

GREAT. LET'S GET ON WITH IT.
LIKE I SAID, BEFORE I GOT SPLATTERED ALL OVER MY LIVING ROOM, I HAD A GOOD THING GOING...WITH A WOMAN NAMED VIRGINIA.
SHE WAS IT, THE TOPS.

WELL, HERE'S THE THING, SEE? WHEN I GOT SMEARED I DIDN'T PASS ON. I WENT TO SYNAGOGUE, BUT I GUESS GOD THOUGHT I OFFED TOO MANY MUGS IN MY DAYS, SO HERE I AM...AND I CAN'T FIND VIRGINIA.

BUT I'M GUESSING YOU HAVE A HUNCH WHERE SHE IS.
SHE'S INSIDE THE FLAMINGO. SHE'S BEEN IN THERE SINCE SHE DIED--THEY WON'T LET HER OUT, AND THEY WON'T LET ME IN.

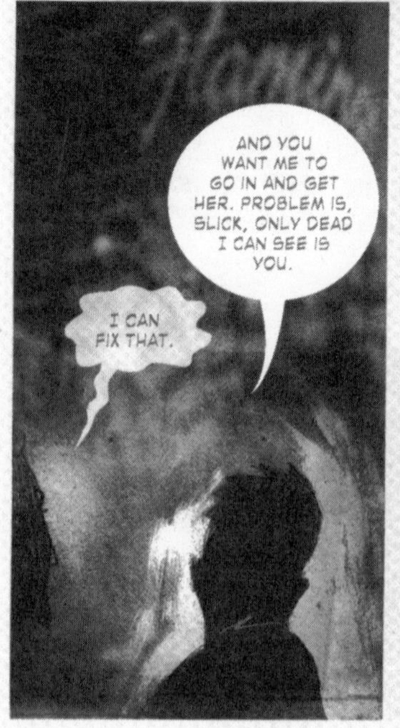
AND YOU WANT ME TO GO IN AND GET HER. PROBLEM IS, SLICK, ONLY DEAD I CAN SEE IS YOU.
I CAN FIX THAT.

THERE!
HEY!
SMACK!

WHAT THE #$%¢ WAS THAT?!

HUH?!

NOW YOUS CAN SEE EVERYTHING I SEE.
NASTY.
YEAH, IT AIN'T TOO PRETTY, I KNOW.

I'LL GIVE IT A SHOT, BUT I AIN'T MAKING NO PROMISES. WHAT'S SHE LOOK LIKE, ANYWAY?
YA CAN'T MISS HER. SHE'S BETTER LOOKING THAN CAROL LOMBARD AND JOAN CRAWFORD *COMBINED!*
OKAY.

THIS WAS OUT OF MY ELEMENT. I WASN'T SOME CRUNCHY FREAK HELPING PEOPLE CONTACT THEIR LONG-DEAD GRANNY.

I DECIDED I'D SEE WHAT WAS WHAT AND THEN FIGURE OUT AN ANGLE.

BINGO.

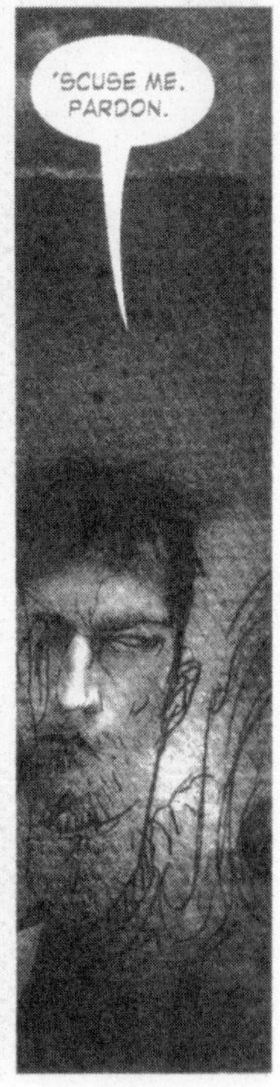
'SCUSE ME. PARDON.

I'M LOOKING FOR A WOMAN NAMED VIRGINIA HILL.
WELL, IT'S YOUR LUCKY NIGHT, MISTER. WHAT CAN A LADY DO FOR YOU?

I'M HERE AT THE REQUEST OF BEN SIEGEL.
HE AIN'T ALLOWED IN THIS JOINT.
MY BEN?!
THAT RAT!

WELL, THE WAY I SEE IT, BEN WANTS TO SEE THE LADY, BUT HE CAN'T COME IN THE PLACE HE BUILT TO SEE HER. THAT SUCKS $%@ IN MY BOOK, SO ME AND THE LADY ARE GOING TO TAKE A STROLL OUT OF HERE.
ANY OF YOU SWISS-CHEESE-LOOKING MOTHER#@$%€$# HAVE A PROBLEM WITH THAT?

YOU WANT TO SEE YOUR MAN, VIRGINIA?
YES...I DO, TERRIBLY.
THAT'S ALL I WANTED TO KNOW.

ARE YOU TALKING TO ME, SIR? WOULD YOU LIKE TO PLACE A BET?
NOT NOW.

IT'S YOUR MOVE, YEG.
OH GOOD, THE FLUNKY'S GONNA LEARN US.
LET ME TELL YOU GUYS SOMETHING YOU PROBABLY DON'T KNOW.

YOU BOYS ARE ALREADY DEAD, RIGHT? I CAN SEE THAT. YOU KNOW IT. WHAT YOU MUGS DON'T KNOW IS THAT YOU SHOULD BE IN HELL BEING ROASTED TWENTY-FOUR HOURS A DAY AND PAYING FOR THE CRIMES YOU COMMITTED AGAINST YOUR FELLOW MAN.

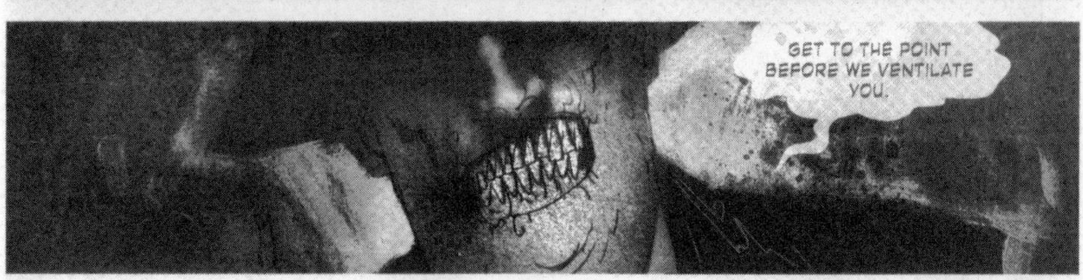
GET TO THE POINT BEFORE WE VENTILATE YOU.

THE POINT IS, I KNOW THE WORDS THAT WILL BRING A DEMON STRAIGHT UP FROM HELL AND COLLECT WHAT THEY MISSED THE FIRST TIME AROUND, SO EITHER YOU MAKE A NICE PATH FOR ME AND THE LADY, OR I START SINGING.
YOU'RE BLUFFING.
TRY ME.

SMART PLAY, BOYS. THE LAST THING YOU WANT IS A RED-HOT PITCHFORK UP YOUR #%$.

MR. MCDONALD. YOU ARE A MAN OF YOUR WORD. I WISH THERE WAS SOME WAY I COULD REPAY YOU.
YOU COULD START BY MAKING IT SO I DON'T HAVE TO LOOK AT TEN MILLION DEAD PEOPLE.

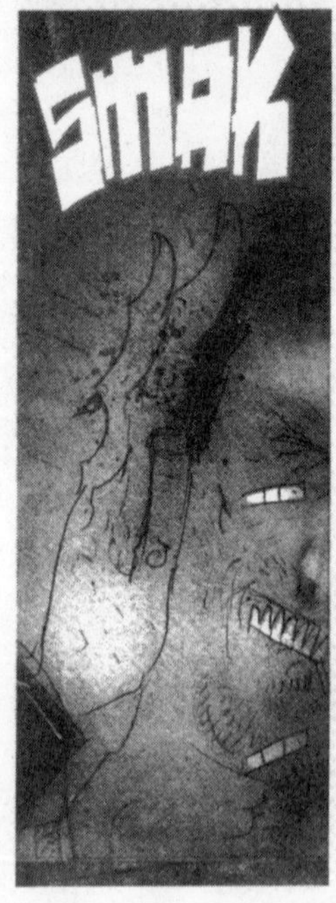
SMAK

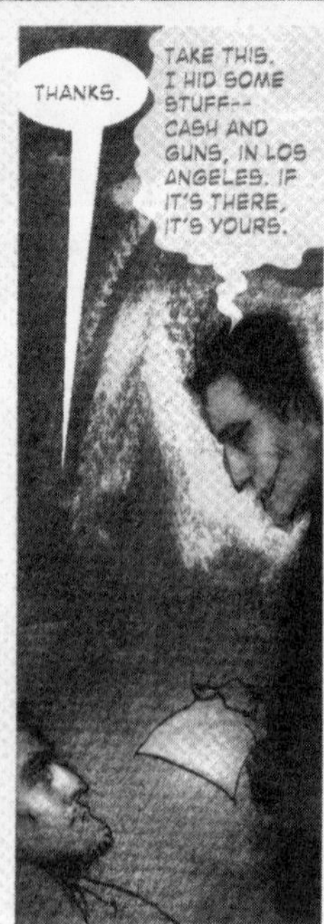
THANKS.
TAKE THIS. I HID SOME STUFF-- CASH AND GUNS, IN LOS ANGELES. IF IT'S THERE, IT'S YOURS.

The End

Luna's Story Little Red Riding Hood

Nightmares & Fairy Tales 8, March 2004

Slave Labour Graphics have done much to promote horror from the fringe, producing comics which give the impression of being aimed at younger Goths about to pursue these tenebrous passageways. When I first saw the première issue of *Nightmares* and *Fairy Tales* I was fooled into thinking it was simply one of those cute horrors. I couldn't have been more wrong. This title will no doubt interest younger readers but it has a far broader appeal. Serena Valentino has the guile to manipulate a fairy story and turn it into the terror your childhood memories have long since dispensed with. They are occasionally reminiscent of Jonathon Carroll's novels in their inclination to probe the folklore with which we were nurtured. Foo Swee Chin's artistry has child-like qualities, which complement Serena's narrative, but there are also surrealist traces deviously intended to lure the reader to the horror lying in wait.

Laura's Story: Little Red Riding Hood

Once upon a time, there was a young woman named Luna,
who found herself walking though the forest
on the way home from her grandmother's house...

Father!

Why did you kill it?

It was about to attack you, Luna!

How many times have I told you not to walk this path after dark?

I lost track of time.

Come on, your mother is worried sick about us.

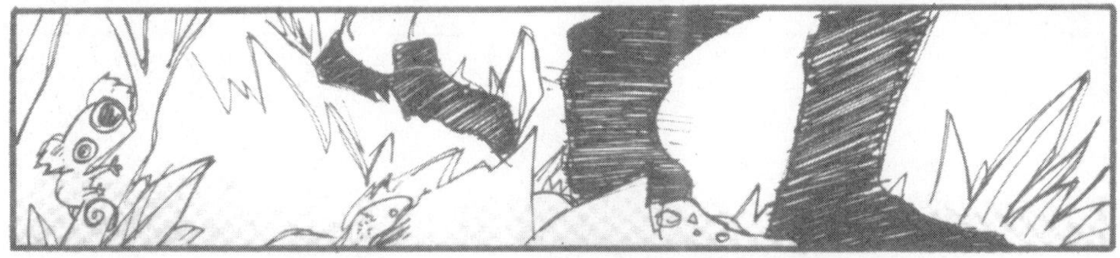

Good evening, gentlemen. I will see you at the same time tomorrow night.

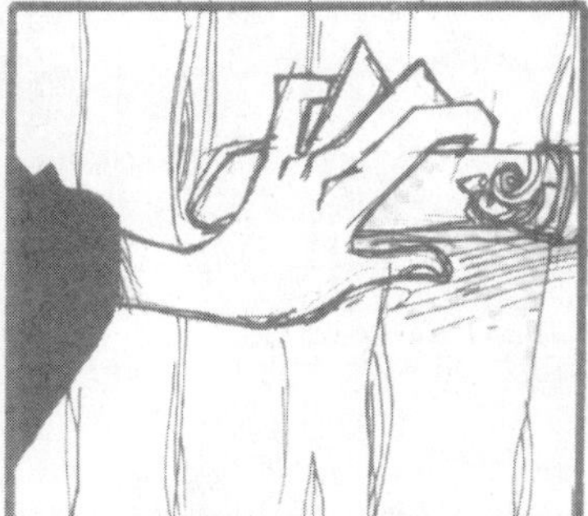

!
What in heaven's name happened?
Your feather-headed daughter almost got herself killed!
Because he almost shot me!
Don't speak ill of your father!
Look at what he did!

He is only trying to protect the village, Luna.
But the wolves have done nothing!
Why must he kill them?
They're horrible, foul,
diseased creatures!
That's not true! Grandmother said...
Your grandmother is slightly mad, Luna.
How dare you!
!

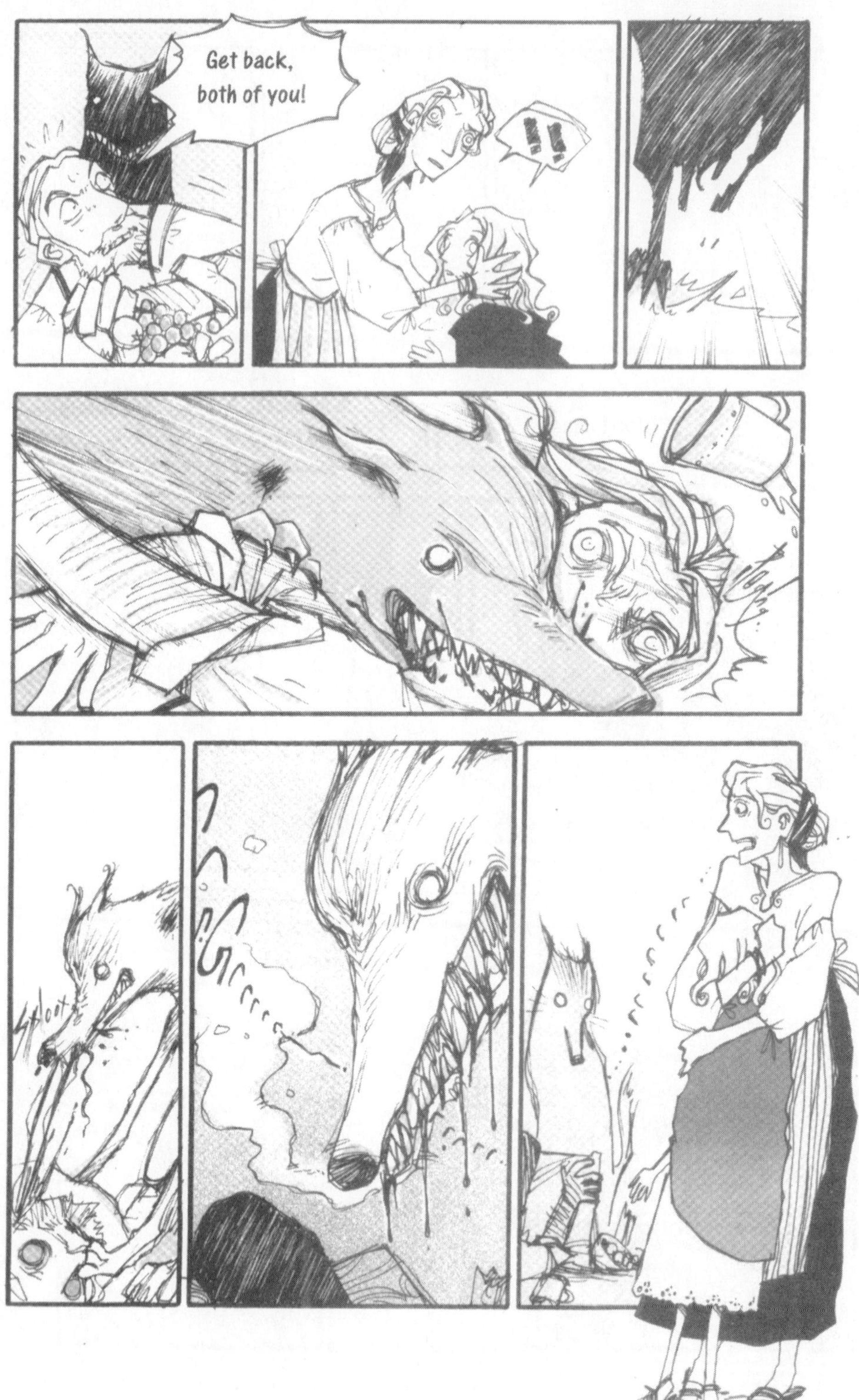
Get back, both of you!
!!
Sploot

You're hurt.
!?
Let me help you.
...Grrrrr
Sniff
... ...
Get away from me!
Flop...

Mother, what's wrong?
I can't stand the sight of you!
?
Leave now!
Mother, please!
Take your filthy hands off of me!
You're a horrible, foul creature! Leave, or I'll kill you!
!

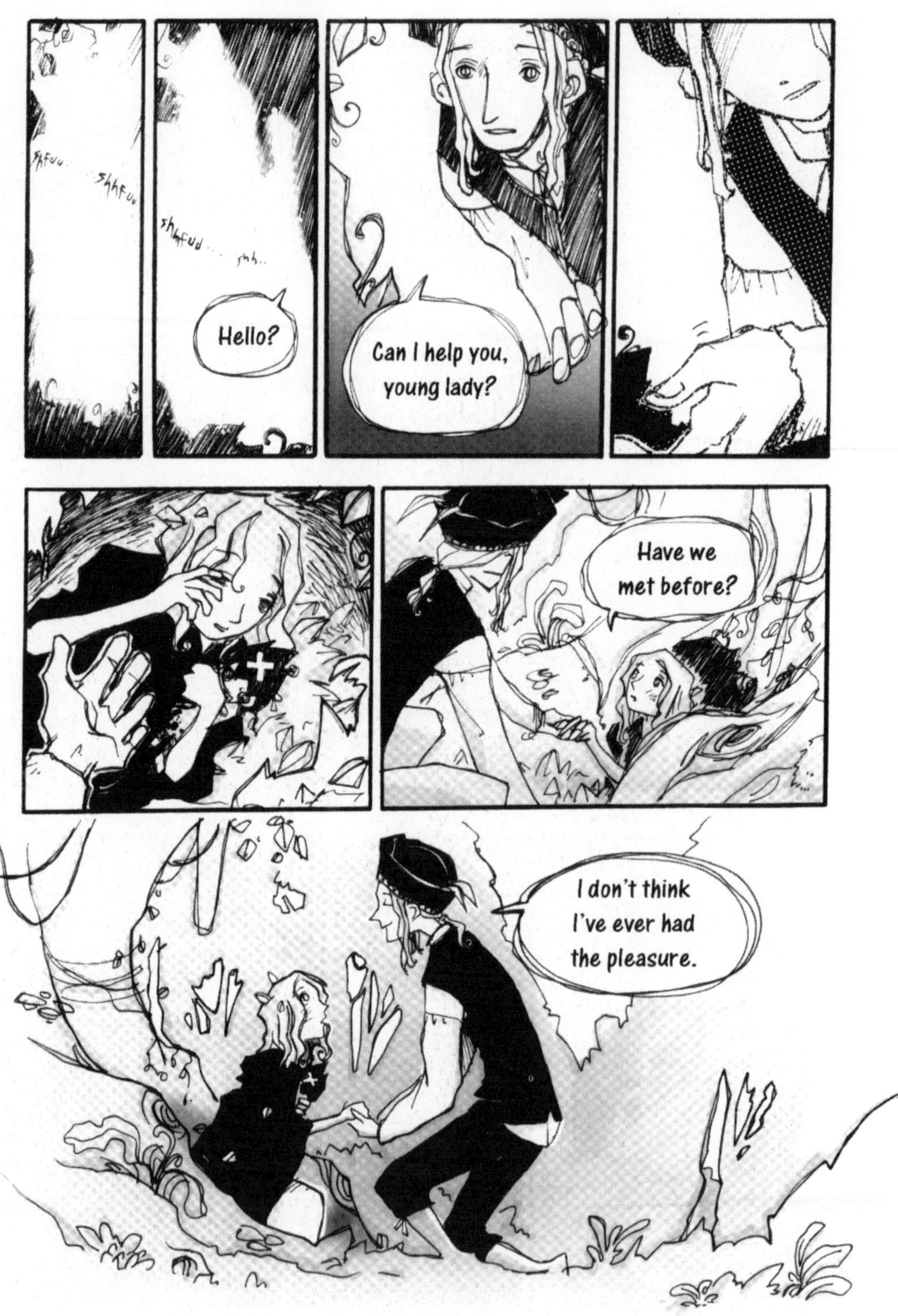
shhfuu...
shhfuu
shhfuu... shh..
Hello?
Can I help you, young lady?
Have we met before?
I don't think I've ever had the pleasure.

Oh!
Please excuse me!
I must have fallen asleep on the way to my grandmother's house.
I better get there before she starts to worry.
Would you like me to accompany you?
That won't be necessary, but I thank you all the same.
... ...
I think I had better, just to make sure you get there safely.
Thank you.

I didn't realize
how close by I was.
It was so dark,
I couldn't see.

May I call
on you in
the future?

!!

Are you
feeling
well?

I'm quite
fine...

...not
to worry.
Oh my
goodness!

Grandmother!
Please help!

Who's this?
He walked me here. he's sick!

Quick...
...let's get him to bed.

Drink this. You will feel better.

Luna, please leave the room.

Will he be okay, grandmother?
Do what I say and let me tend to this boy!

I've done all I can.
Thank you, dear.
What's wrong with him?
What happened?
Nevermind that. What are you doing here?
... ...

Luna's grandmother was shocked after hearing what happened the previous night...

I think your mother has gone insane!
Poor dear.

Well, hello! It's nice to see you up and about.
How are you feeling?

Much better. Thank you.

Please, sit down. We're about to have dinner.

I really must be going. My family will be worried.

Are you sure you are okay? Perhaps you should rest a while longer.

Really, I'll be fine.

Thank you both for everything.
You're welcome, dear boy.

I would like to
see you again—that is,
if your grandmother
permits.

By all means!
We look forward to your
next visit!

I think
he fancies
you.

Do you
really think
so?

Don't be
silly.
Didn't you
see the way
he looked
at you?

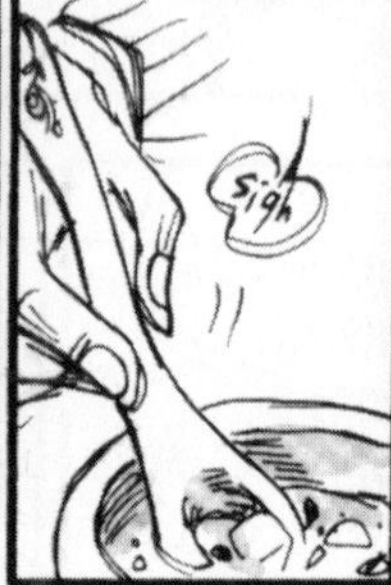
Sigh

We've lost all sense of time. It's late. I think I had better go to bed.

But you haven't finished your dinner!
It's been a long day, dear heart, and I'm not all that hungry.

Good night, then.
I love you.

I love you, too, my sweet little girl.
... ...

Don't worry, my darling. All will seem better tomorrow, I promise you.

clang
clang
clang

clang
clang

Z

FLOP

Good morning, Luna dear.

I've always loved your name, child. Do you know what it means?

I think it has something to do with the moon.

I'm surprised your mother told you that much.
She'd given up on most of the old traditions by the time she married your father.

It's a wonder she didn't name you something common, like the rest of the horrible women in that wicked village.

Why does she hate wolves so much?
Fear, my dear. It's what feeds most forms of hatred.

Well, I suspect your gentleman caller will be arriving soon. You better hurry on up and get yourself ready.
What?

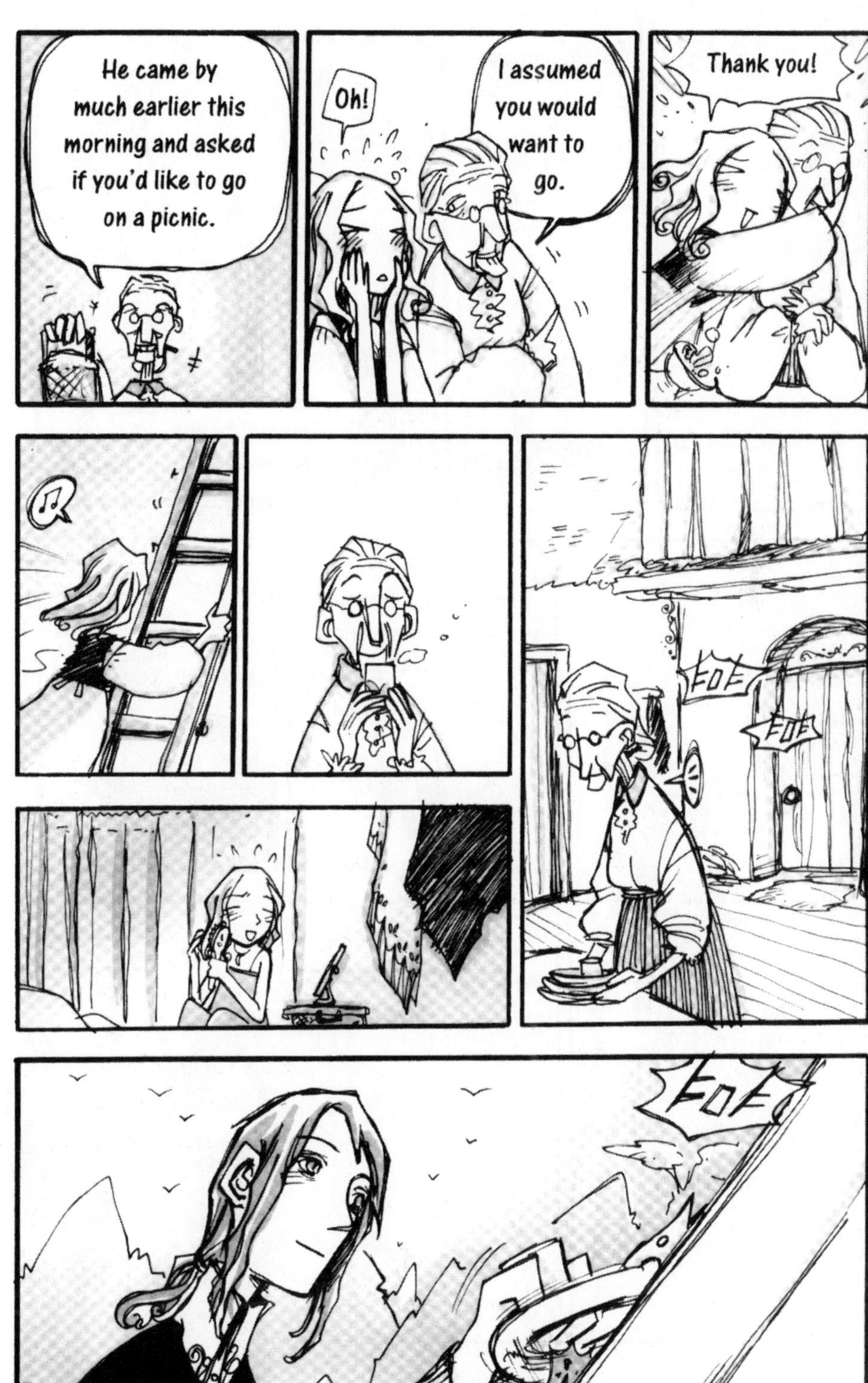
He came by much earlier this morning and asked if you'd like to go on a picnic.
Oh!
I assumed you would want to go.
Thank you!

Hello, my boy.
You're looking quite well today.
!

Thanks to you.
Think nothing of it. Luna will be out momentarily.

Here you go, my dear. This will keep you warm.
?

It's so beautiful!

Have a lovely day my dears. Goodbye.

I thought this would be a perfect spot.
It's wonderous. Almost magical.
!
I'm sorry, I wasn't thinking. Perhaps this wasn't the best of spots.
Because of the statue?
It's beautiful.
I couldn't help but overhear the story you told your grandmother yesterday.
We can pick another place if you like.

Wolves don't frighten me.
?
I hope you like what I brought.
I'm just happy to be here with you.
chip
chip

I want you to have this.
Thank you.
It's breathtaking! I could sit here all day.
And indeed we have. It's getting dark.
But we don't have to leave just yet, do we?
Your grandmother will be worried.
I promised that I would have you home before dark.
Come, my darling.
But I would like to look upon the moon with you.

Grandmother?

That's strange. Perhaps she's out.

SNFF

SNFF
Oh
I think she must be sleeping.

Thank you for a wonderful day.

Goodnight, my darling.

Grandmother...
...eeee
...are you asleep?
Gasp!?
!
Grandmother?

!
It's me! Luna!
Don't be frightened!
!!

You killed her!
How could you?!
She's a horrid creature, just like you!
Mother, Look at me! I'm your daughter!
What's started?
You take after her!
It's already started.
!

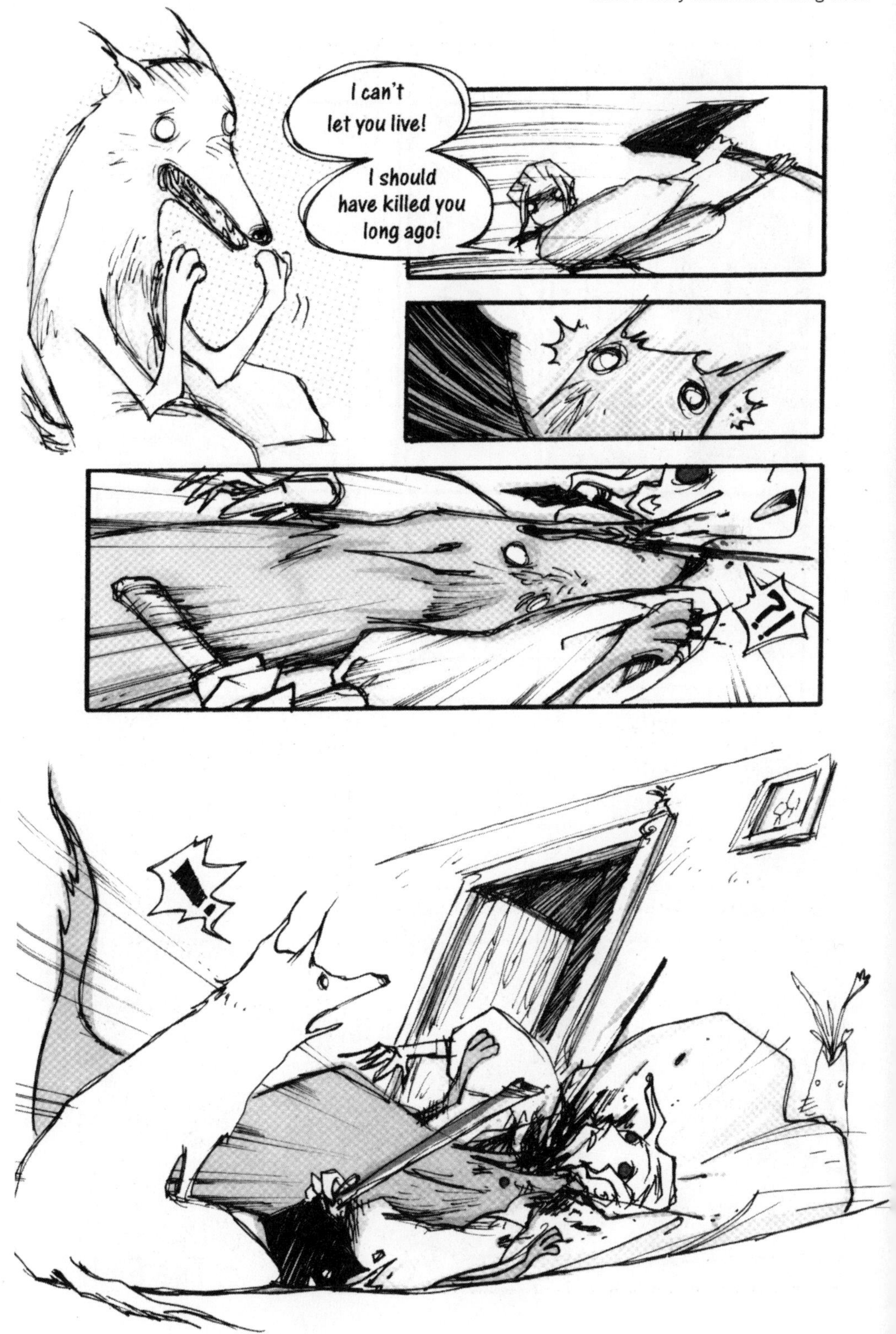
I can't
let you live!
I should
have killed you
long ago!
?!
!

The End

The Graveswellers

Morbid 2, February 2005

The release of Pete Von Sholly's second collection from Dark Horse was eagerly awaited. True to form, Pete did not disappoint. This issue once again used the photographic manipulation seen in the first compilation – at least, I hope he was manipulating these images. Elements of H. P. Lovecraft are in evidence as this story unfolds, releasing foul manifestations from beyond to menace the hapless individuals in a feature-length presentation. Enthusiasts of Ray Harryhausen's cinematic monsters will also find much to admire in these pages as well as the previous *Morbid* collection and the more recent *Extremely Weird Stories*.

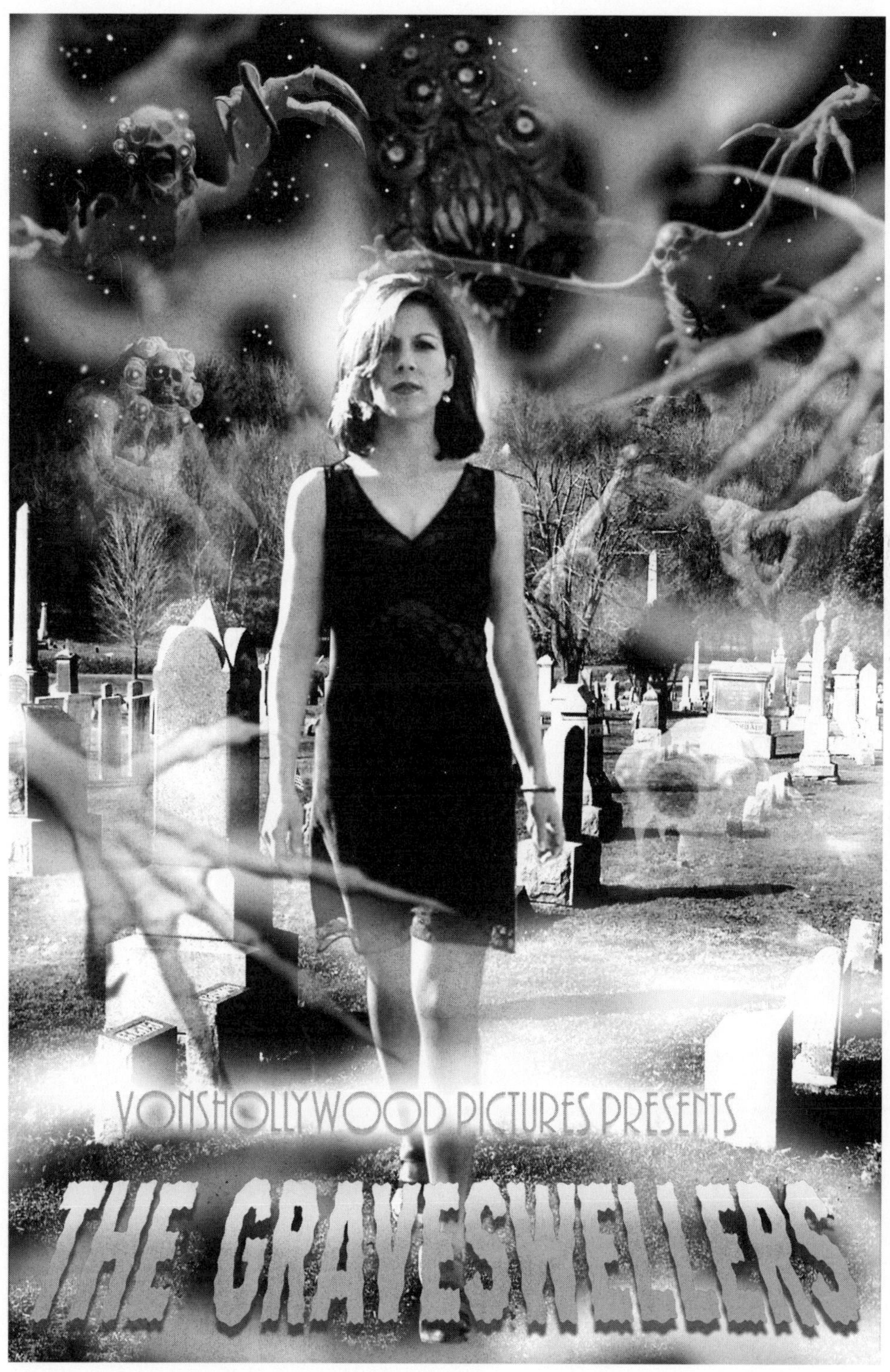
VONSHOLLYWOOD PICTURES PRESENTS
THE GRAVESWELLERS

I'M AMANDA DARKHAUS, YES, FROM THE FUNERAL HOME IN DUNWICH. I HAVE SOMETHING IN THIS BOX AND I HAVE SOMETHING I NEED TO DO. IF YOU'D LIKE TO COME WITH ME I'LL TELL YOU MY STORY.

MY STEPFATHER, DARIUS, STARTED THE FAMILY BUSINESS, BUT THEY SAID HE ONLY USED IT AS AN EXCUSE TO GET CORPSES FOR HIS OCCULT INTERESTS. MAYOR MASON THREATENED TO SHUT HIM DOWN, AND DARIUS SAID SOMETHING ABOUT MASON'S MOTHER'S BODY... SO MASON HIT HIM AND LATER HAD HIM JAILED FOR TAMPERING WITH THE DEAD. I WAS JUST A YOUNG GIRL WHEN ALL THIS HAPPENED.

DARKHAUS
FUNERAL HOME
est. 1923

I'LL NEVER FORGET THE *LOOK* DARIUS GAVE MASON WHEN HE WAS SENTENCED TO PRISON...

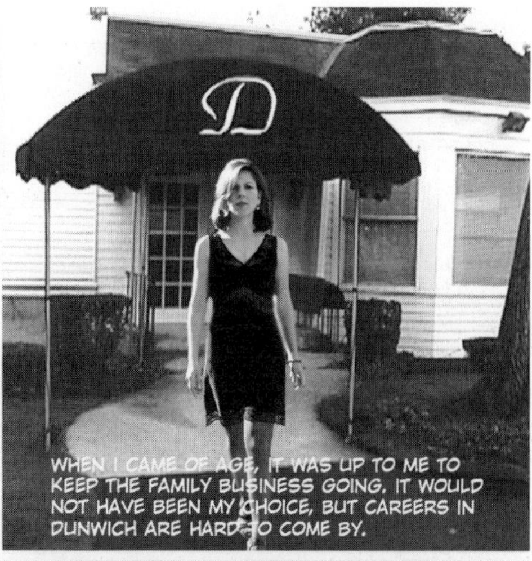
WHEN I CAME OF AGE, IT WAS UP TO ME TO KEEP THE FAMILY BUSINESS GOING. IT WOULD NOT HAVE BEEN MY CHOICE, BUT CAREERS IN DUNWICH ARE HARD TO COME BY.

THEN THEY LET HIM OUT.
Dunwich Mirror
DARKHAUS FREE

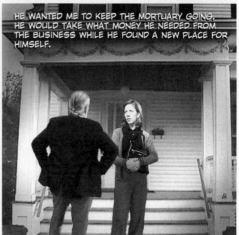

HE WANTED ME TO KEEP THE MORTUARY GOING. HE WOULD TAKE WHAT MONEY HE NEEDED FROM THE BUSINESS WHILE HE FOUND A NEW PLACE FOR HIMSELF.

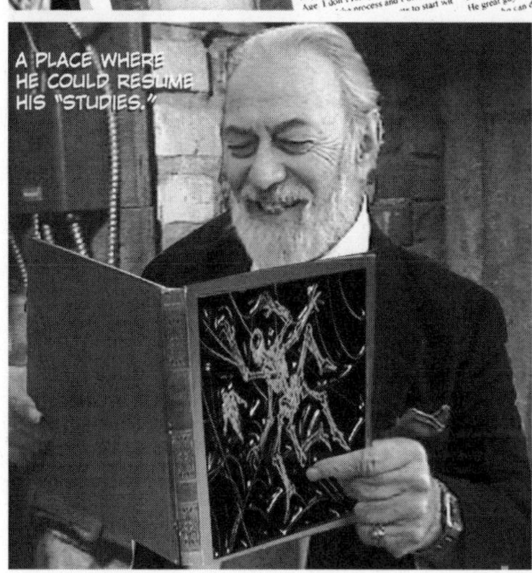
A PLACE WHERE HE COULD RESUME HIS "STUDIES."

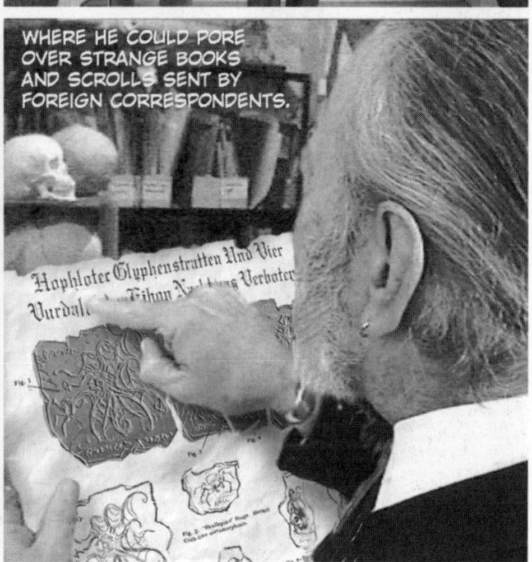
WHERE HE COULD PORE OVER STRANGE BOOKS AND SCROLLS SENT BY FOREIGN CORRESPONDENTS.
Hophloter Glyphenstratten Und Vier

DUNWICH HAD BECOME A FAIRLY QUIET LITTLE TOWN IN RECENT YEARS... TOM MASON, NOW RETIRED FROM POLITICS, OFFERED ME HIS HELP IF I NEEDED IT... IN CASE DARIUS MADE ANY TROUBLE OR CAUSED ME WORRY.
STOP

"AMANDA, CHERYL AND I WANT YOU TO KNOW YOU CAN COME TO US ANYTIME IF HE CAUSES YOU UNHAPPINESS. I'M SORRY TO SAY IT, BUT I WISH WE COULD HAVE KEPT HIM LOCKED UP!"

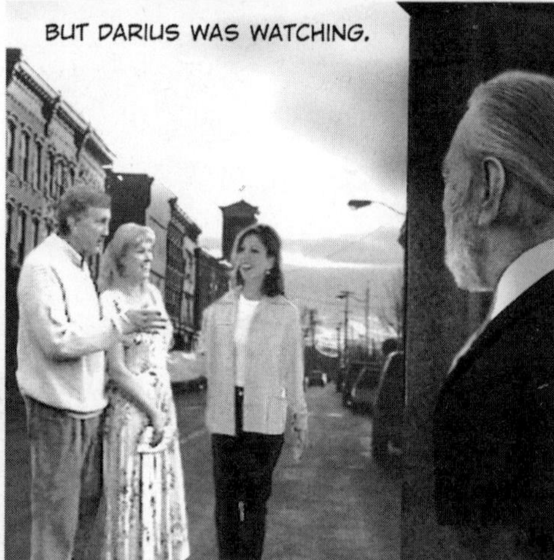
BUT DARIUS WAS WATCHING.

AND DARIUS DID NOT FORGET.

HE WORKED A SECRET SPELL ON THE BODY OF POOR AUGUST DERBY... AND PUT SOMETHING HORRIBLE IN HIS COFFIN!

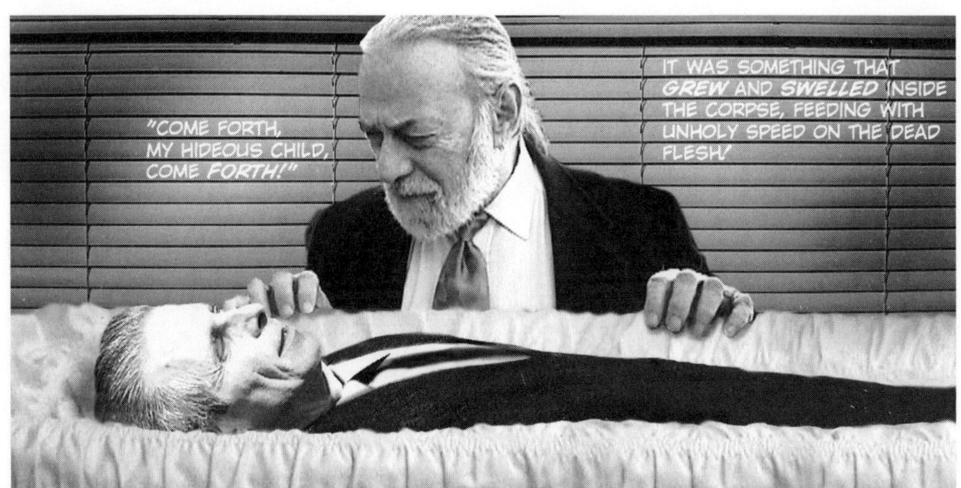
"COME FORTH,
MY HIDEOUS CHILD,
COME FORTH!"
IT WAS SOMETHING THAT GREW AND SWELLED INSIDE THE CORPSE, FEEDING WITH UNHOLY SPEED ON THE DEAD FLESH!

THE TRANSFORMATION WAS OVER QUICKLY, AND DERBY'S BODY HAD BECOME SOMETHING ELSE! IT BECAME A NIGHTMARE INSTRUMENT OF VENGEANCE.

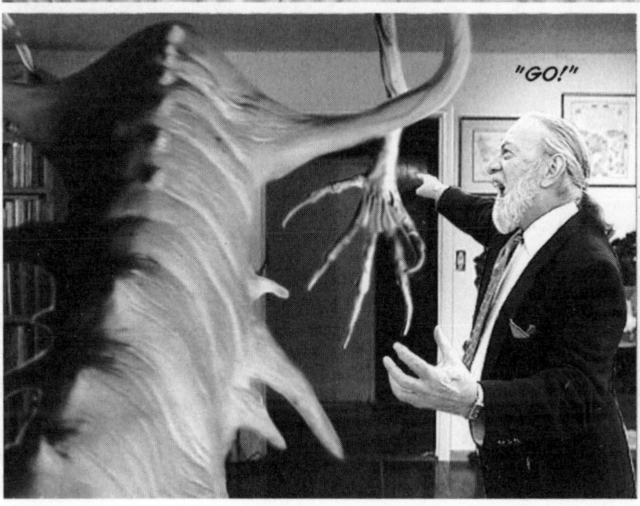
"GO!"

AND IT WENT...

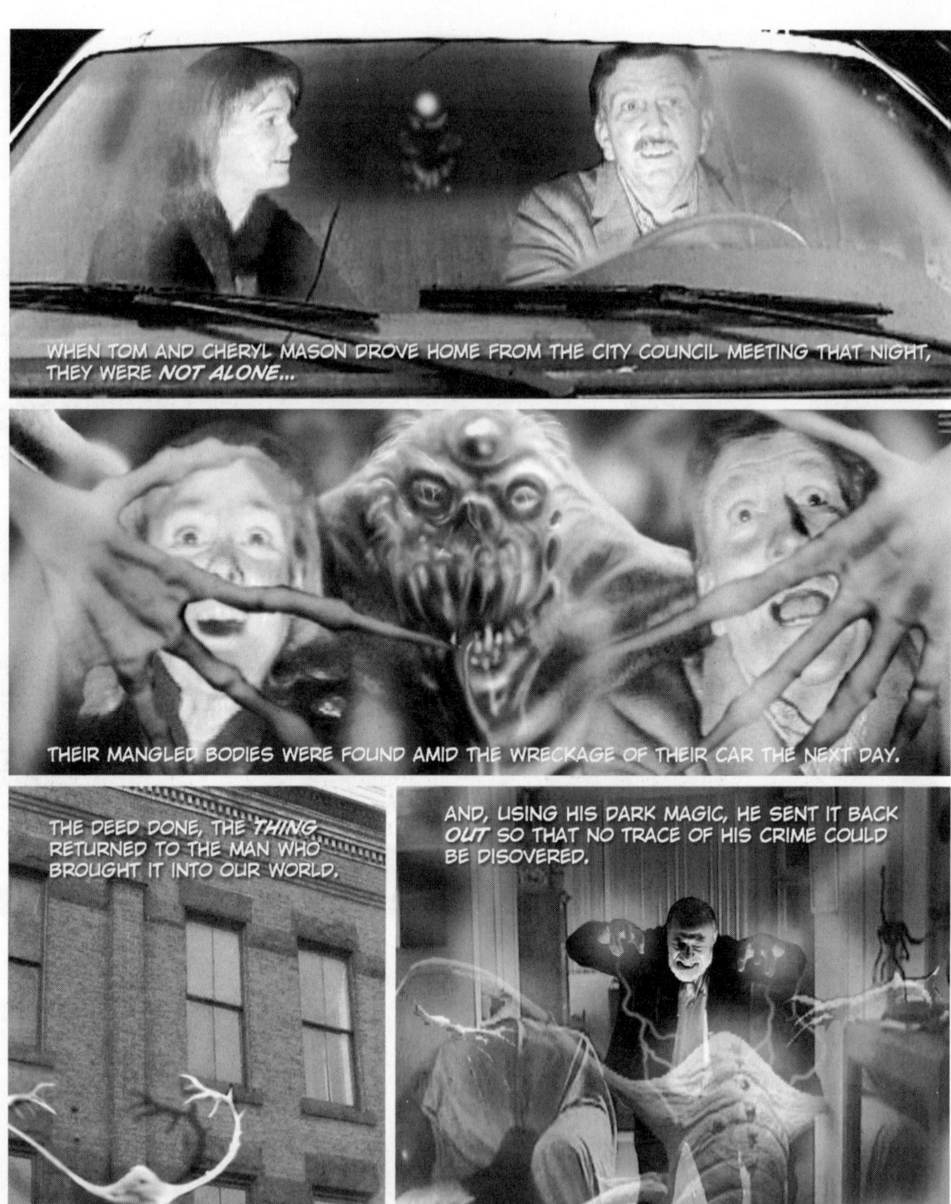
WHEN TOM AND CHERYL MASON DROVE HOME FROM THE CITY COUNCIL MEETING THAT NIGHT, THEY WERE *NOT ALONE...*
THEIR MANGLED BODIES WERE FOUND AMID THE WRECKAGE OF THEIR CAR THE NEXT DAY.
THE DEED DONE, THE *THING* RETURNED TO THE MAN WHO BROUGHT IT INTO OUR WORLD.
AND, USING HIS DARK MAGIC, HE SENT IT BACK *OUT* SO THAT NO TRACE OF HIS CRIME COULD BE DISOVERED.

OF COURSE AT THE TIME I HAD NO WAY OF KNOWING WHAT DARIUS HAD DONE... AND ALL THE LOCAL GIRLS TALKED LIKE THEY WILL, ABOUT THE WEIRD GHOUL GIRL AND HER EVIL FAMILY OF MURDERERS!

I COULDN'T REALLY BLAME THEM BUT IT STILL HURT.

THEIR NASTY SNEERS AND HATEFUL WHISPERS WERE GETTING TO ME. I WENT BACK TO THE HOUSE BUT IT WASN'T EMPTY!
ENTRANCE
THERE WAS SOMEBODY WHO WASN'T SUPPOSED TO BE THERE AND WHO RESENTED MY BARGING IN ON HIM!

"HOW DARE YOU SNEAK UP ON ME LIKE THIS?"
"WHAT... WHAT ARE YOU..."

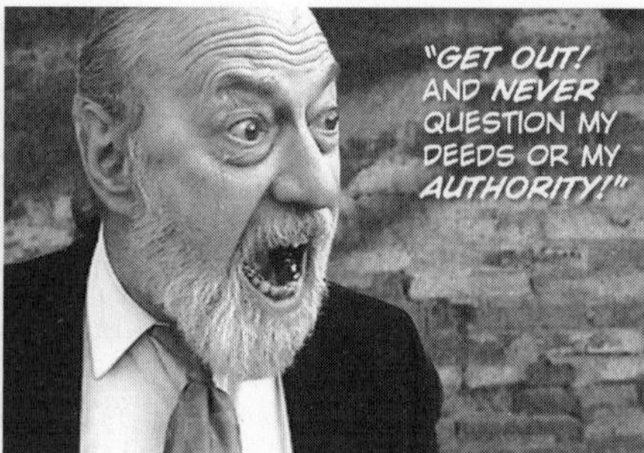
"GET OUT! AND NEVER QUESTION MY DEEDS OR MY AUTHORITY!"

I RAN FROM THE FUNERAL PARLOR IN TEARS, FILLED WITH LOATHING AND TERROR! I DIDN'T EVEN NOTICE HER WATCHING.

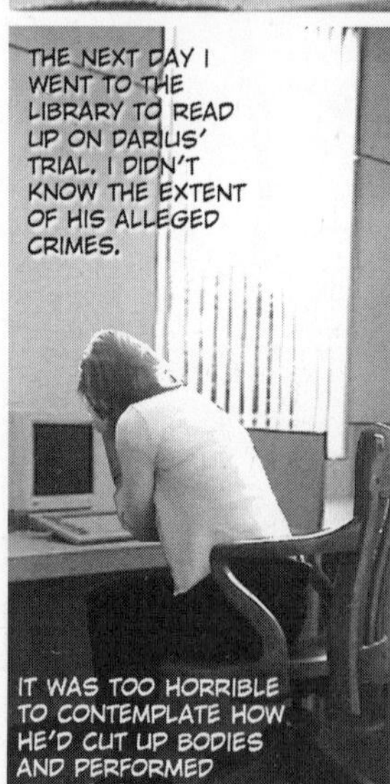
THE NEXT DAY I WENT TO THE LIBRARY TO READ UP ON DARIUS' TRIAL. I DIDN'T KNOW THE EXTENT OF HIS ALLEGED CRIMES.
IT WAS TOO HORRIBLE TO CONTEMPLATE HOW HE'D CUT UP BODIES AND PERFORMED OBSCENE RITES UPON THEM.

AND SUDDENLY KARLA WAS THERE.
SHE WAS HIS REAL DAUGHTER, BACK FROM WHERE HER MOTHER HAD HIDDEN HER.

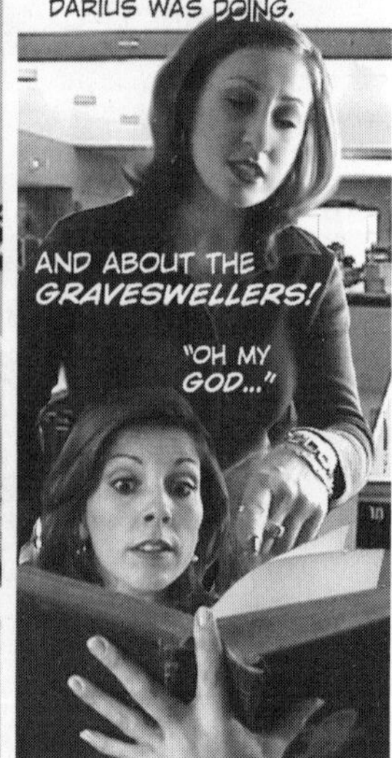
SHE SHOWED ME THE BOOKS ON MAGIC AND WE FOUND OUT WHAT DARIUS WAS DOING.
AND ABOUT THE GRAVESWELLERS!
"OH MY GOD..."

THERE WAS A PICTURE OF THE VERY BOX I SAW HIM WITH. THE BOX THAT HELD THE HEAD OF THE SORCEROR, IBNZAK!

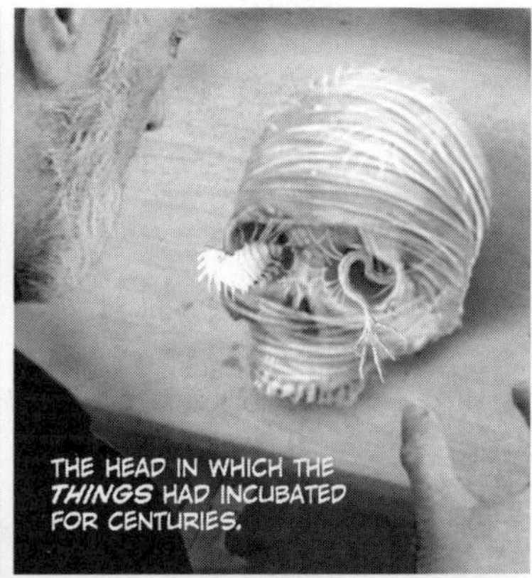
THE HEAD IN WHICH THE THINGS HAD INCUBATED FOR CENTURIES.

ALL ONE HAD TO DO, PROVIDING ONE POSSESSED THE REQUIRED FORMULAE, WAS ALLOW THEM TO EMERGE, NOURISH THEM ON CARRION, AND PLANT THEM IN A PLACE WHERE THEY COULD THRIVE!

THEY WOULD GROW IN THE CORPSE-FILLED EARTH, AWAITING THE NIGHT OF ARISING WHEN THEY COULD EMERGE AND DESTROY THE ENEMIES OF THEIR GUARDIAN!
IT WAS TO BE THE NIGHT OF THE DEAD MOON... THAT VERY NIGHT! BY MORNING ALL OF DUNWICH WOULD BE WIPED OUT. THE THINGS WOULD BE FIERCELY LOYAL TO DARIUS AS LONG AS HE SERVED AND PROTECTED THEM. IF WE COULD GET HIM TO TURN AGAINST THEM, THERE WOULD BE HOPE, BUT HOW COULD WE DO THAT?

THE NIGHT WAS VERY COLD AND QUIET...

THEN YOU COULD HEAR THE STIRRINGS BELOW.

THEN...

SCHWARTZ
THEY BEGAN TO CLAW TO THE SURFACE, SURROUNDED BY PLUMES OF FOUL DEATH-VAPORS, THE FORMER *CITIZENS* OF DUNWICH... THEIR REMAINS SHEATHED IN PULPY GRUB-FLESH... ALIVE WITH A HIDEOUS ALIEN AWARENESS...

...AND *HUNGER!*

KARLA SAID THAT *FIRE* COULD KILL THEM WHILE THEY WERE FRESHLY EXPOSED TO THE SURFACE, SO WITH *FIRE* WE CAME TO THE OLD *BARLOWE CEMETERY*...

THEY WERE SWARMING THERE TO MEET US.

FORMER MAYOR MASON WAS AMONG THEM...

AND THE GAMWELL SISTERS... TWINS WHO WERE BURIED TOGETHER.

KARLA SWUNG INTO INCREDIBLE ACTION!

SHE TORCHED THE THINGS LEFT AND RIGHT!

THE FLAMES SEEMED TO ATTACK THEM.

NGAAAAAAAAA!
-UFFF!
COLTER
SOME OF THEM, SENSING DANGER PERHAPS, BEGAN TO MOVE *FAST!*

MISTER KARSWELL, MY SIXTH GRADE MATH TEACHER, WAS HAPPY TO SEE ME AGAIN. STILL AN OLD LECHER, TOO!
HE HADN'T CHANGED ALL THAT MUCH!

NOT WANTING TO USE FIRE FOR FEAR OF INJURING ME, KARLA FOUND ANOTHER WAY.
WHUNTCH!

SHREEEEE!
THE THINGS WERE GETTING KIND OF *MAD* NOW!

BUT *SO WERE WE!*

SHSSSSSSSSS!

AT LAST THERE WAS NOTHING MOVING IN THE CEMETERY BUT FIRE AND SMOKE... WE HAD *WON*.

WE STUMBLED AWAY FROM THE STINKING SCENE OF BATTLE JUST AN HOUR BEFORE DAWN, SISTERS WHO HAD DONE A GREAT THING TOGETHER... BUT THE PROBLEM OF DARIUS DARKHAUS STILL LOOMED AHEAD.

"OH SHIT, AMANDA! LOOK!"
"WHAT IS THAT?"

"IT'S A TRAIL."
"M- MEANING?"
"MEANING WE DIDN'T GET THEM ALL."

THE TRAIL OF CRUSTY DRIED SLIME LED RIGHT TO THE OLD PICKMAN HOUSE, A HOTEL LONG ABANDONED BY ITS OWNERS.

KARLA HEADED FOR THE CELLAR... I WANTED TO GO WITH HER...

...BUT SHE TOLD ME TO STAY UPSTAIRS AND SEARCH THE MAIN FLOOR. I THINK SHE THOUGHT I'D BE *SAFER* THERE.

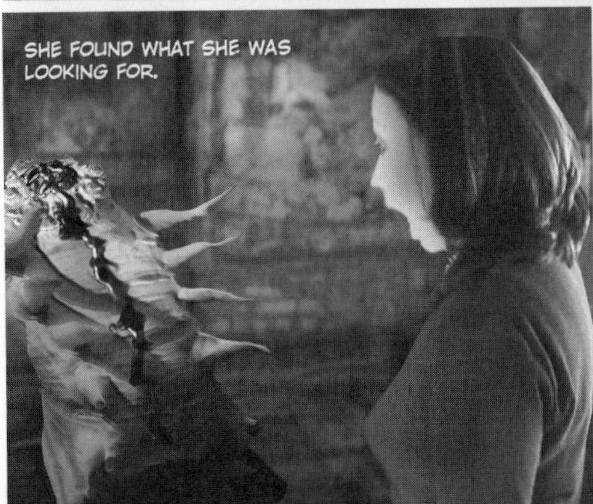
SHE FOUND WHAT SHE WAS LOOKING FOR.

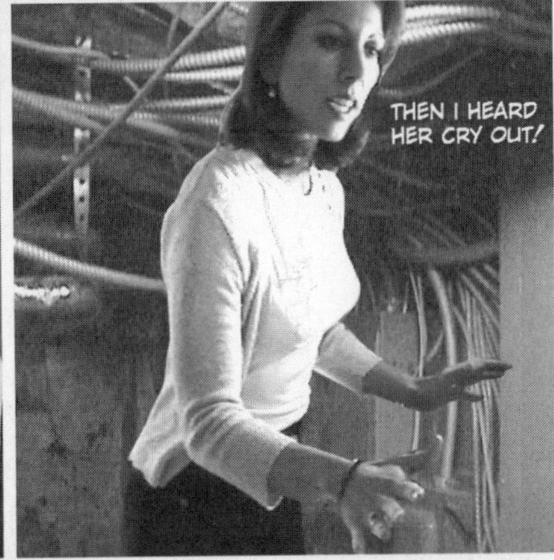
THEN I HEARD HER CRY OUT!

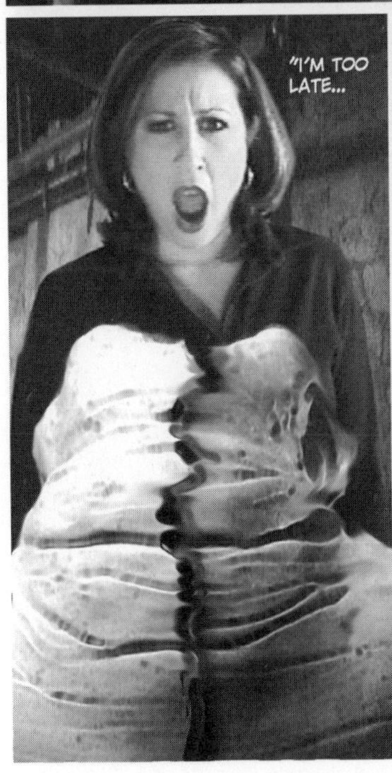
"I'M TOO LATE...

IT'S *EMPTY!* THAT MEANS... OH, NO...
AMANDA! LOOK OUT! IT'S HATCHED!"

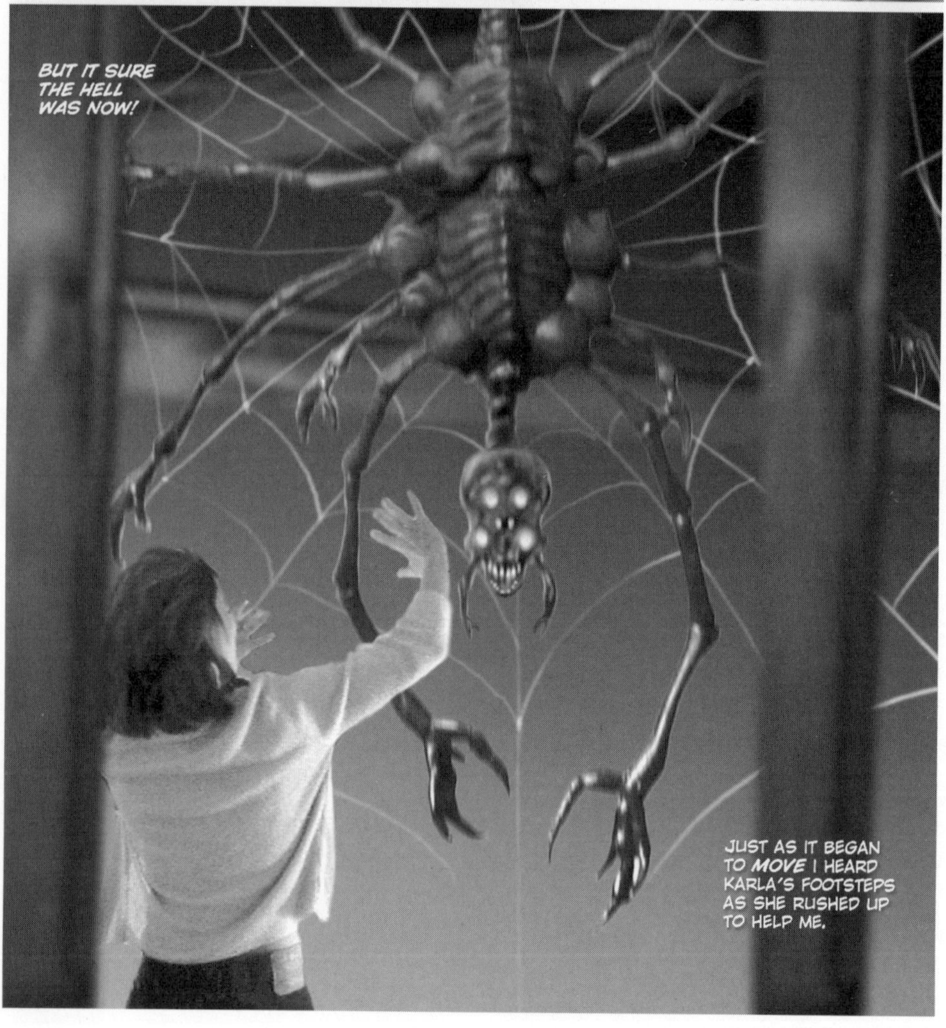

BUT IT SURE THE HELL WAS NOW!

JUST AS IT BEGAN TO ***MOVE*** I HEARD KARLA'S FOOTSTEPS AS SHE RUSHED UP TO HELP ME.

KARLA CHARGED INTO THE ROOM CARRYING A BROKEN PUSH-BROOM HANDLE! THE CREATURE WHIRLED AT THE SOUND OF HER VOICE--
KHHHSSSSAA!
"KARLA, DON'T!"
"DON'T PANIC! I'LL TRY TO..."
-GEK!
"YOU CAN'T..."
GROOOAAR!
"OKAY, PANIC!"
KRAK
EEEEEEEEEEEEEEEEEEEEEEEEE
RRMMMBLL

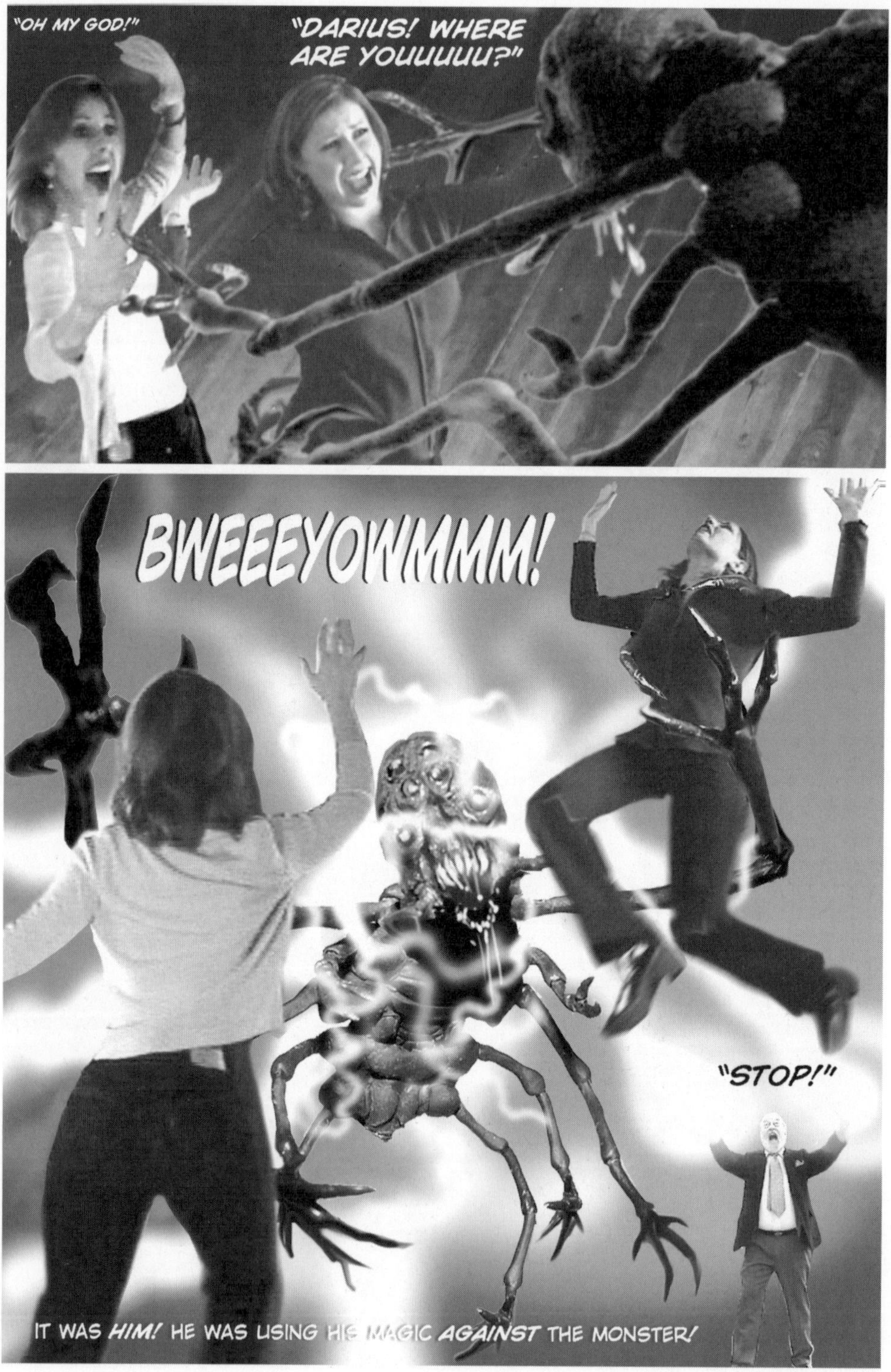

BWEEEYOWMMM!

"STOP!"

IT WAS *HIM!* HE WAS USING HIS MAGIC *AGAINST* THE MONSTER!

EEEEEE
HE WAS TRYING TO SAVE HER! THE ENERGY BEING RELEASED MADE THE AIR SUDDENLY DRY AND HOT!
THEN EVERYTHING SEEMED TO HAPPEN IN MUTE SLOW-MOTION...
KARLA WAS ON THE FLOOR, NOT MOVING.
I COULDN'T HEAR MYSELF CALLING TO HER.
BUT HER WORDS SOMEHOW CAME TO ME...
SHE SAID "IT'S OVER. THEY'LL GET HIM NOW," ALTHOUGH HER LIPS DIDN'T MOVE AND HER HEART NO LONGER BEAT.
I FOLLOWED HIM OUT INTO THE COLD DAWN.
HE WAS SCREAMING "FORGIVE ME! I SWEAR I'LL KILL THEM ALL FOR YOU!" AS HE RAN FOR HIS HOTEL IN A MAD PANIC.
KARLA WAS RIGHT. THERE WAS SOMETHING WAITING IN HIS ROOM.

HE WAS WEAK, DISLOYAL!
HE DIDN'T WANT KARLA TO DIE, AND HE WOULD HAVE TO PAY FOR THAT.
HIS HEAD WAS SEEDED, REMOVED, WRAPPED IN SILK AND PUT INTO THE BOX! ITS WORK FINISHED, ITS LINK TO EARTH DESTROYED, THE LAST GRAVESWELLER VANISHED. THE OLD BOOKS TOLD ME THIS.
AND NOW TO DO WHAT I MUST DO. THANKS FOR COMING ALONG.
IT'S A LONG WALK TO POINT WILBUR.
DARIUS' BRAIN IS THEIR HOME NOW. THERE THEY WILL THRIVE AND BIDE THEIR TIME. SOMEONE WILL FIND THEM AGAIN.
BUT IT WILL TAKE A LONG TIME. AND DARIUS WILL WAIT AT THE BOTTOM OF THE SEA FOR THE DAY.

Shuteye

Zacherley's Midnite Terrors 2, 2004

James Helkowski's rendition of Joe Monks' tale here held me spellbound. It's very rare that you see a tale of this kind. Sadly James is no longer with us, a talent who died far too soon. His work found its way into many horror magazines published in the United States. With Chanting Monks Press, Joe Monks worked alongside Bernie Wrightson, Basil Gogos, William Stout and Ken Kelly. A film written by Joe in the wake of the success of his *Flowers on the Razorwire* DVD is about to follow.

WHAT'S THE MATTER, KIDS? NOT SLEEPY? WELL TUCK YOURSELVES IN AND PULL THE BLANKETS TIGHT, THIS LITTLE BEDTIME STORY IS FOR ALL OF YOU WHO HAVE A HARD TIME GETTING TO SLEEP AT NIGHT.

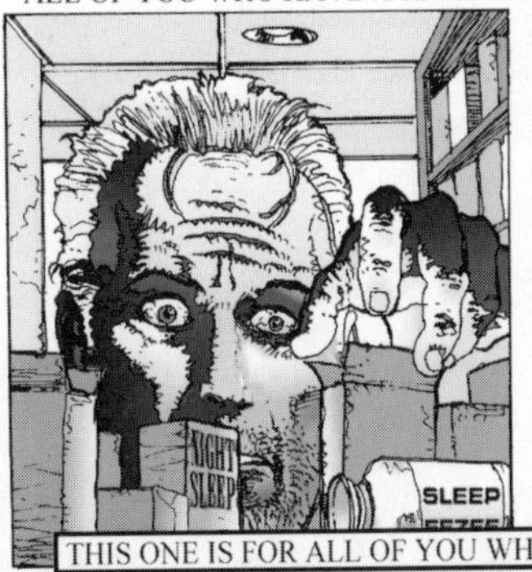

THIS ONE IS FOR ALL OF YOU WHO COULD USE A LITTLE BIT OF...

SHUTEYE

STORY BY JOE MONKS ART BY JAMES HELKOWSKI

YOU WANTIN' A DOUBLE, CHARLIE?
THE GIN MILL IS CALLED DOOLEY'S. BEFORE GETTING SENT TO THE 'HAMMER, HE WAS A REGULAR. DOOLEY HAD HAD HAIR BACK THEN. IT WAS A QUIET BAR, ASIDE FROM THE SHOUTING, THE BRAGGING...
UNLESS YOU GOT A DEEPER SHOT GLASS, DOOLS...
...THE GAMBLING, THE NIGHTLY DRUNKEN FIST-FIGHT OR BRAWL, OR THE OCCASIONAL WET SPLATTER OF VOMIT ONTO HARDWOOD.
IT IS HIS KIND OF PLACE. DOOLEY, WHO POURS LIKE A TRADITIONAL IRISHMAN, IS HIS KIND OF BARTENDER.

WHAT'S IN THE BAG? YOU BRINGING YOUR LUNCH OUT DRINKIN' NOW, ARE YOU?

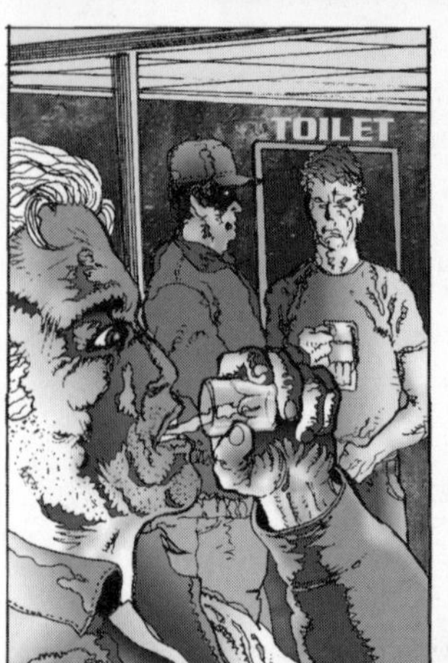
TOILET

THIS HERE'S LEGIT STUFF...WHAT'S THE SCAM?
SET ME UP AGAIN, DOOLS
...NO SCAM. I GOTTA GET SOME SHUT EYE.
BEER

BEEN HAVIN' CRAZY DREAMS...NIGHTMARES OUGHT'A FIND ME A LAWYER, SUE THE 'HAMMER.

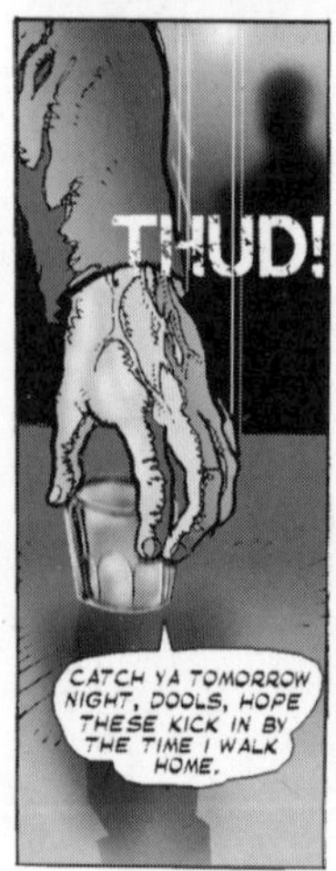
THUD!
CATCH YA TOMORROW NIGHT, DOOLS, HOPE THESE KICK IN BY THE TIME I WALK HOME.

EXIT
PSSST!

FORGET THE PILLS, SON. WHAT YOU WANT YOU NEED REAL HELP FOR. YOU KNOW OLD ROSIE? LIVES JUST OUTSIDE A' TOWN?
I HEARD OF HER.
GO SEE HER. SHE'LL PUT YOU RIGHT AGAIN.
YEAH? HOW DO YOU KNOW?
I DONE 27 YEARS IN STARKHAMMER, BOY... I KNOW ALL ABOUT LIVIN' WITH DEMONS.
YOU GO...SEE OLD ROSIE. TRUST ME...

THE SMALL HOURS...2:00, 3:00, 4:00 O'CLOCK. THESE ARE THE HOURS THAT HAUNT HIM...THE HOURS THAT EVEN HANDFULLS OF PILLS CANNOT GET HIM THROUGH...
3:27 AM
YOU DO REMEMBER ME, RIGHT CHARLIE? I REMEMBER YOU...
AND I BROUGHT SOME FRIENDS WHO REMEMBER YOU, TOO...
F-F-FRIENDS?
Y-YOU'RE DEAD, BEN, YOU AIN'T GOT NO FRIENDS NO MORE...
DO YOU?
COME ON, CHUCKY-BOY.
YOU DIDN'T THINK ALL OF US WOULDN'T BECOME FAST FRIENDS ON THE OTHER SIDE, DIDJA?
ALL OF YOU?
WHAT DO YOU MEAN, ALL OF YOU?
CHARLIE SEES, AND REMEMBERS ...HE REMEMBERS THEM ALL. THE ONES NOBODY ELSE KNEW ABOUT BUT HIM...THE ONES THE AUTHORITIES HADN'T BEEN ABLE TO PIN ON HIM.
WILEY CULLEN...RAN THE AUTO SHOP WHERE CHARLIE HAD WORKED FOR TWO MONTHS AFTER A STINT IN DELMAR CORRECTIONAL. HE'D TAKEN $230 FROM THE GARAGE'S REGISTER AND STABBED WILEY USING KNIVES STOLEN FROM A DINER UP THE STREET--
ANNIE PATTON. CHARLIE REMEMBERED SHACKING UP WITH HER AT A BAR IN DENTON. HE'D KILLED HER BEFORE SHE COULD FINISH A WATER COLOR FOR HER UNCLE.
TED. NO MORE. CHARLIE HADN'T BOTHERED TO FIND OUT BEFORE STABBING HIM AND STEALING HIS WALLET AND THE LAST $12 HE HAD. HE HAD ROLLED THE CAR INTO A DITCH AND SET IT ON FIRE. HE DIDN'T KNOW TED HADN'T BEEN DEAD WHEN HE HAD LIT HIM UP...
LEE? LYLE? CHARLIE COULDN'T REMEMBER. HE'D SNUCK UP BEHIND HIM AT A HONKEY TONK AND STOLEN HIS CAR AFTER FOLLOWING HIM DRUNK OUT OF THE JOINT. THE CAR HAD BEEN LOW ON GAS. CHARLIE HAD DITCHED IT ONLY EIGHT MILES AWAY.
GURGLE...GLOOD TOG SGEE YGOU AGGAIN, CHARGLIE...
THEY TREAT YOU NICE UP AT THE 'HAMMER, CHARLIE? NICE AS WE'RE GONNA TREAT YOU?
CHARLIE...READY TO GO FOR A RIDE WITH US?

GAK!
SWOOOOSH!
PLINK!
ROSIE...OL' ROSIE OUT BY THE EDGE OF TOWN...YOU WIN, OLD MAN... I'LL PAY THE OLD CRONE A VISIT...

THE EDGE OF TOWN IS FAMILIAR TO CHARLIE. AS A BOY HE'D GROWN UP ON THE OUTSKIRTS, SCROUNGING TO SURVIVE. SO TOO, HE KNOWS ALL ABOUT OL' ROSIE, THE ANCIENT GYPSY WHO OFFERED HELP TO THOSE DESPERATE ENOUGH TO COME TO HER...
FOR A PRICE.
BANG! BANG! BANG!

NOT SO LOUD, EH.
YOU AIN'T TRYIN' TO RAISE THE DEAD ARE YOU?

THE OLD MAN, THE ONE FROM DOOLEY'S SENT--
SHUT YER YAP ABOUT DOOLEY'S.
BUT HE TOLD ME--
GET INSIDE AND CLOSE THE DOOR...
I KNOW ALL ABOUT DOOLEY'S AND WHO SENT'CHA.

CHARLIE TELLS THE OLD CRONE WHAT HE HAS COME FOR. HOW THE NIGHTMARES COME NO MATTER WHAT HE DOES.
HOW THEY COME AND ROB HIM OF SLEEP...AND WORSE.
HOW HE DOES NOT BELIEVE HE CAN GO ON MUCH LONGER.
HOW IT IS KILLING HIM...

THESE CRITTERS WILL HELP YOU SLEEP, AND KEEP YER FROM DREAMING,
BUT--YOU GOTTA FOLLOW THE RULES CAREFULLY.

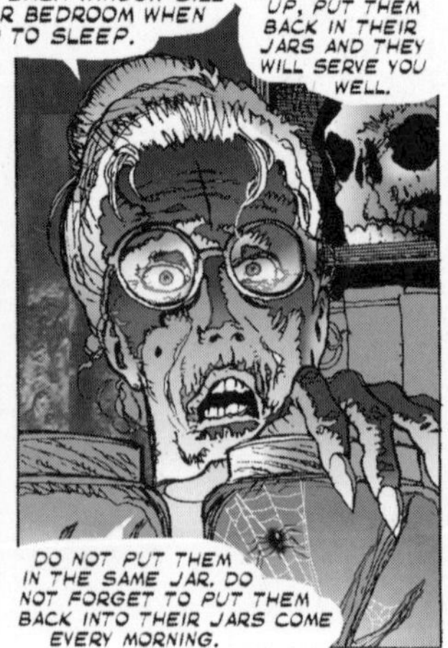
KEEP THEM APART. PUT ONE ON EACH WINDOW SILL IN YOUR BEDROOM WHEN GO TO SLEEP.
WHEN YOU WAKE UP, PUT THEM BACK IN THEIR JARS AND THEY WILL SERVE YOU WELL.
DO NOT PUT THEM IN THE SAME JAR. DO NOT FORGET TO PUT THEM BACK INTO THEIR JARS COME EVERY MORNING.

AND CLEAR AWAY THEIR WORK EACH MORNING. DO NOT LEAVE THEIR WEBS BEHIND FOR THE NEW DAY.
THEIR WEBS? BUT WHY?
THEIR WEBS WILL CAPTURE YOUR DREAMS, AND SO EACH DAY THEY MUST BE ERASED SO THEY CAN BEGIN ANEW
IF YOU DON'T FOLLOW THAT ...THINGS MAY NOT GO WELL

"DO THEY BITE? WILL I BE SAFE WITH THEM OUT?"
"JUST FOLLOW THE RULES...THEN THEY'LL HAVE NO REASON TO BITE."

EAGER TO TEST THE OLD WOMAN'S PROWESS, CHARLIE PUTS HIS NEW COMPANIONS TO WORK...
THERE YA' GO, LEGS. YOU STICK TO THE WINDOW LIKE OL' ROSIE SAID AND WE'RE GONNA GET ALONG JUST FINE...

THE EIGHT-LEGGED CRITTERS APPEARED TO CHARLIE CONTENT TO STICK TO THE WINDOW SILL, WHICH IS FINE BY HIM. CHARLIE HAD NEVER BEEN TERRIBLY FOND OF SHARING HIS DIGS WITH BUGS.

STILL, THE SPIDERS ARE A STEP UP FROM THE ROACHES WHICH HAD INFESTED HIS CELL AT STARKHAMMER,
GONNA WORK...THIS IS GONNA WORK... JUST TWO LITTLE SPIDERS...NOTHING TO WORRY ABOUT... FOLLOW THE RULES ...JUST FOLL---
AND FAR LESS LIKELY TO WIND UP IN HIS MASHED POTATOES.

URNGK...
YAWN.
KRACK
5:10

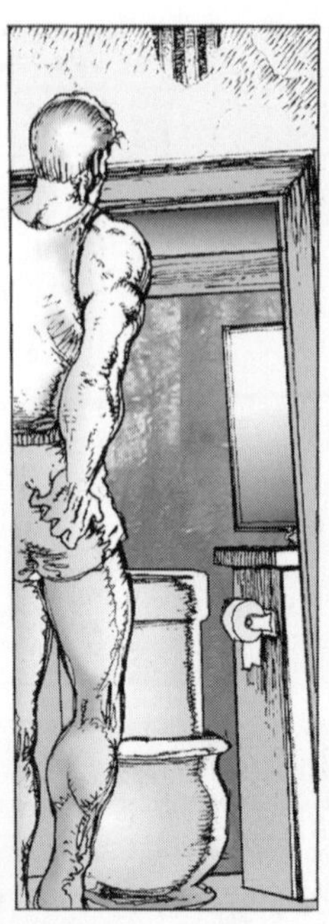

PSSSSSSSSSSSSSS

IT TAKES A MOMENT, BUT THE REALIZATION STRIKES CHARLIE LIKE A THUNDERBOLT: IT ISN'T THE SUNRISE HE IS STARING AT, IT IS THE SUN SET.

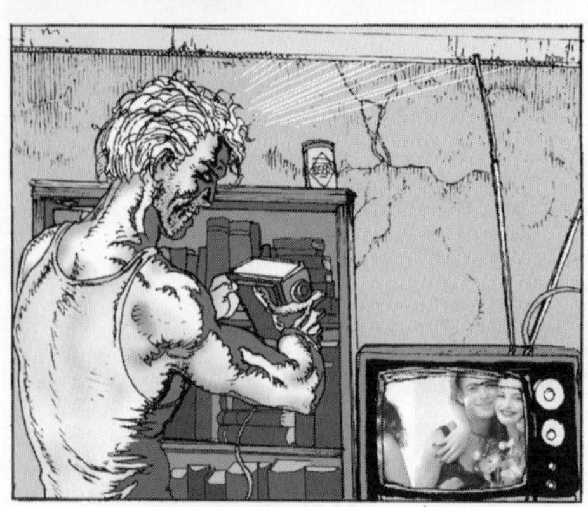

SONOFAGUN, YOU GUYS REALLY WORK!
I'M GONNA HAVE TO GO DOWN AND BUY YOU BOYS SOME GOURMET FLIES!

WHOOPS--

SEE YOU LATER, BOYS. AFTER A GOOD DAY'S SLEEP, I DESERVE A GOOD NITE'S FUN!
WOULDN'T WANNA LEAVE THOSE AROUND.

AND SO IT STARTS.
WITH THE RETURN OF SLEEP TO CHARLIE'S LIFE--
COMES MUCH OF HIS OLD LIFESTYLE.
THE BOOZE, THE BUDDIES, THE BROADS...
THE RECIPE THAT PUT HIM IN STARKHAMMER IN THE FIRST PLACE...

NO KIDDIN', BEEN BEEN ITCHIN' FOR A JOB EVER SINCE I STARTED GETTING SOME SL...GOT OUT'A THE JOINT.
OH YEAH...S'LONG AS THERE'S MONEY THERE, I'M IN.
ITS A BUSY DAY AT FIRST UNION FEDERAL.
FREE CHECKING=FRE
NATIONBANK
recording 11:44 am
THE LAST FRIDAY OF EVERY MONTH ALWAYS IS. IT'S PAY DAY.
recording 11:45 am
THIS BUSY FRIDAY, THOUGH, DOESN'T QUITE GO AS PLANNED--FOR ANYBODY.
BLAM!
BLAM!
Y'HEAR ABOUT WHAT HAPPENED TO TURK AND DENNY? I HEAR THEY CAUGHT A CASE O' LEAD POISONING..
NAW, MISSED THAT. BUT I SEE SOMETHING I WANNA PLUG RIGHT RIGHT ABOUT NOW...

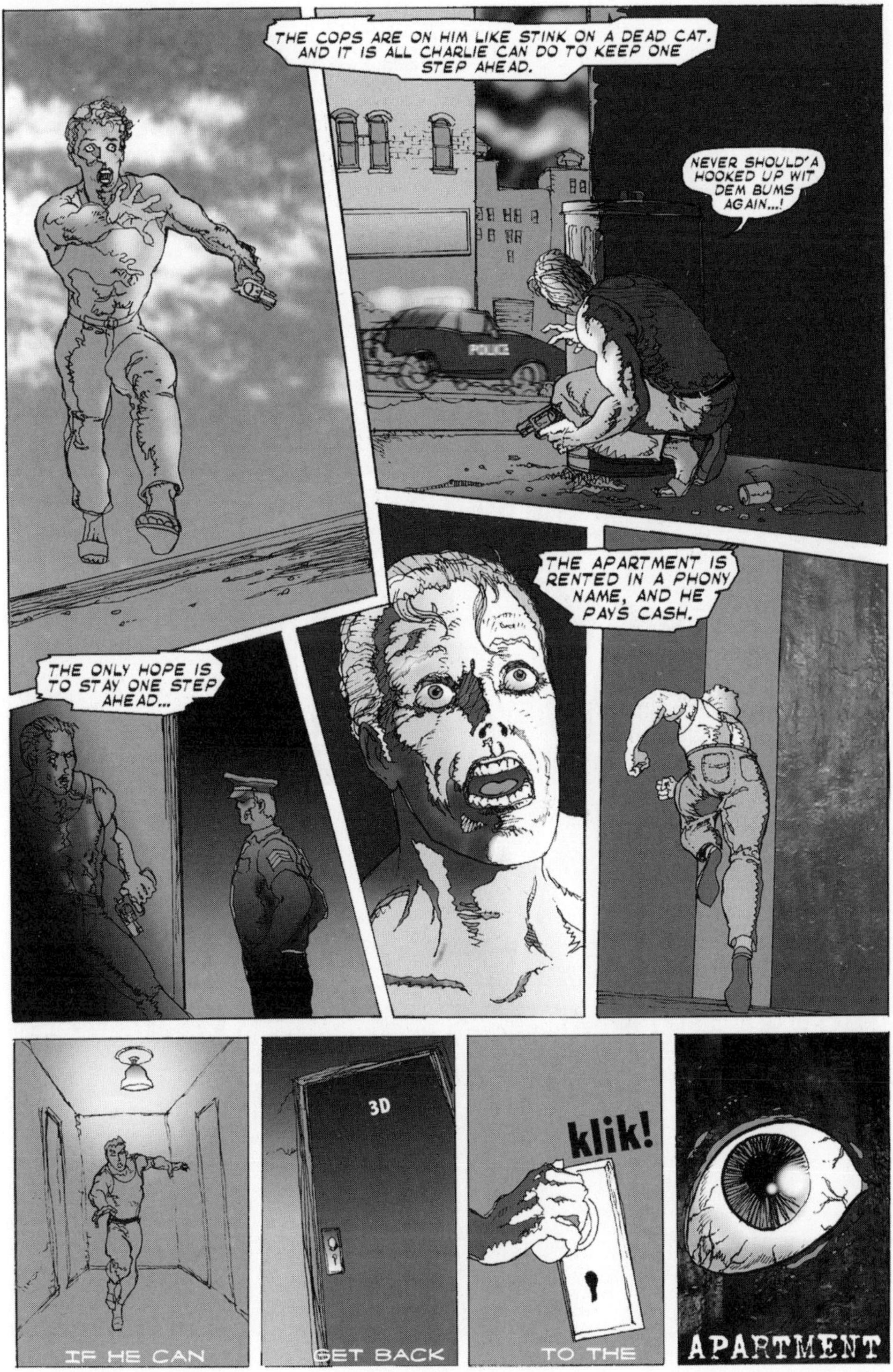

THE COPS ARE ON HIM LIKE STINK ON A DEAD CAT. AND IT IS ALL CHARLIE CAN DO TO KEEP ONE STEP AHEAD.

NEVER SHOULD'A HOOKED UP WIT DEM BUMS AGAIN...!

POLICE

THE ONLY HOPE IS TO STAY ONE STEP AHEAD...

THE APARTMENT IS RENTED IN A PHONY NAME, AND HE PAYS CASH.

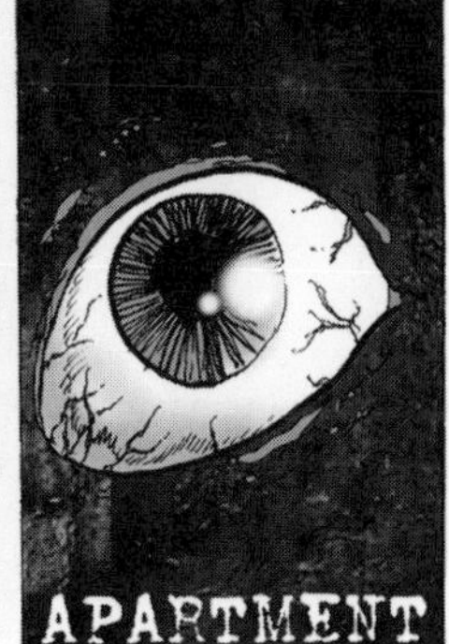

THE COPS ARE ON HIM LIKE STINK ON A DEAD CAT. AND IT IS ALL CHARLIE CAN DO TO KEEP ONE STEP AHEAD.
NEVER SHOULD'A HOOKED UP WIT DEM BUMS AGAIN...!
POLICE
THE ONLY HOPE IS TO STAY ONE STEP AHEAD...
THE APARTMENT IS RENTED IN A PHONY NAME, AND HE PAYS CASH.
IF HE CAN
3D
GET BACK
klik!
TO THE
APARTMENT

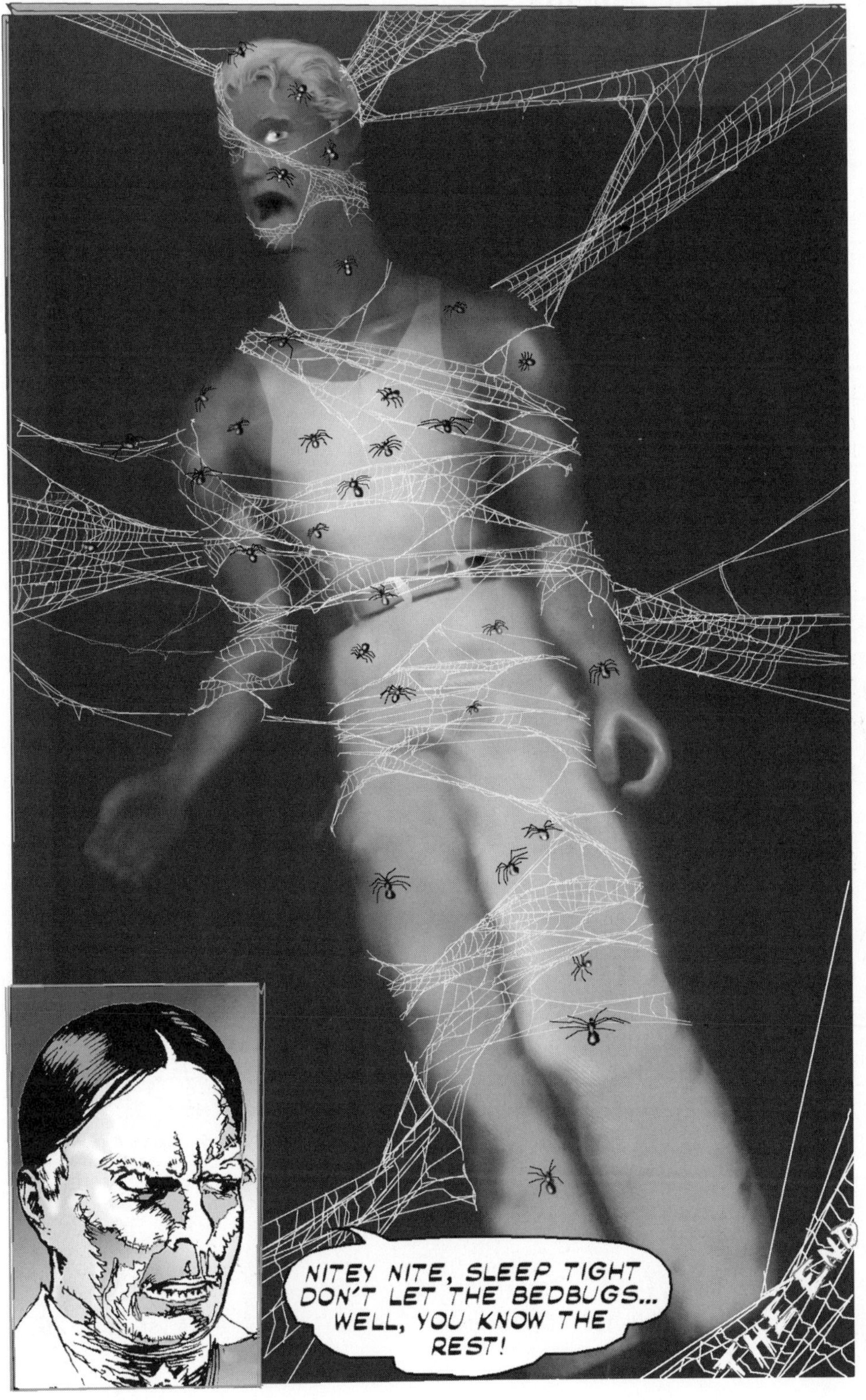

NITEY NITE, SLEEP TIGHT DON'T LET THE BEDBUGS... WELL, YOU KNOW THE REST!
THE END

Acknowledgments

"Famous Tales of Terror", copyright © 1944 by E. A. Poe. Originally published by E. Levy in *Yellowjacket Comics 1*, September 1944.

"Hitler's Head", copyright © 1952 by Don Heck. Originally published by Comic Media in *Weird Terror 1*, September 1952.

"No Rest For the Dead", copyright © 1953 by Iger Studios. Originally published by Superior Comics in *Journey into Fear 12*, March 1953.

"He", copyright © 1952 by Rudy Palais. Originally published by Harvey Comics in *Black Cat Mystery 38*, August 1952.

"The Secret Files of Dr Drew", copyright © 1949 by Jerry Grandenetti. Originally published by Fiction House in *Rangers Comics 49*, October 1949.

"The Corpse That Wouldn't Die", copyright © 1952 by Jack Cole. Originally published by *Quality in Web of Evil 2*, January 1952.

"Bride of Death", copyright © 1952 by Jack Katz. Originally published by Standard in *Adventures into Darkness 7*, December 1952.

"Dungeon of Doom", copyright © 1952. Originally published by Harvey Comics in *Chamber of Chills 6*, March 1952.

"Terror of the Stolen Legs", copyright © 1954 by G. Altman. Originally published by Master Comics in *Dark Mysteries 18*, June 1954.

"Den of Horror", copyright © 1953. Originally published by Comic Media in *Weird Terror 3*, January 1953.

"The Living-Dead", copyright © 1954 by John D'Agostino. Originally published by Master Comics in *Dark Mysteries 20*, October 1954.

"Marching Zombies", copyright © 1952 by Rudy Palais. Originally published by Harvey Comics in *Black Cat Mystery 35*, May 1952.

"Grave Rehearsal", copyright © 1953. Originally published by Ajax-Farrell Publications in *Strange Fantasy 7*, August 1953.

"A Glimpse of the Pit", copyright © 1954 by Pete Morisi. Originally published by Comic Media in *Horrific 9*, January 1954.

"The Horror of the Walking Corpse", copyright © 1954 by A. C. Hollingsworth. Originally published by Master Comics in *Dark Mysteries 16*, February 1954.

"The Thing That Walked at Night", copyright © 1953 by Bill Benulis and Jack Abel. Originally published by Fiction House in *Ghost Comics 9*, Winter 1953.

"Partners in Blood", copyright © 1952. Originally published by Superior Comics in *Journey into Fear 6*, May 1952.

"Dead Man's Revenge", copyright © 1952 by Jay Disbrow. Originally published by Star Comics in *Shocking Mystery Cases 50*, September 1952.

"The Hand of Glory", copyright © 1952 by Matt Fox. Originally published by Youthful in *Chilling Tales 13*, December 1952.

"The Man Who would be Fate", copyright © 1954 by Lou Cameron. Originally published by Ace Magazines in *Hand of Fate 21*, August 1954.

"The Monster of Dread End", copyright © 1962 by John Stanley. Originally published by Dell Comics in *Ghost Stories 1*, September 1962. Reprinted by permission of John's son, Jim Stanley.

"Santa's Claws", copyright © 1970 by Frank Brunner. Originally published by Major Magazines in *Web of Horror 3*, April 1970. Reprinted by permission of Frank Brunner.

"The Game Keeper", copyright © 1974 by Tom Sutton. Originally published by Charlton Comics in *Ghostly Haunts 40*, September 1974.

"Fatal Scalpel", copyright © 1966 by unknown. Originally published by Eerie Publications in *Weird* Vol. 2 No. 1, December 1966.

"The Weirdest Character I've Ever Known", copyright © 1974 by Tom Sutton. Originally published by Charlton in *Ghostly Haunts 38*, May 1974.

"Now... Another Maniac!", copyright © 1974 by Maelo Cintron. Originally published by Skywald in *Psycho 18*, May 1974.

"Through a Glass Darkly", copyright © 1975 by Tom Sutton. Originally published by Charlton Comics in *Ghostly Tales 113*, February 1975.

"Ghouls Walk Among Us", copyright © 1973 by Augustine Funnell and Ferran Sostres. Originally published by Skywald in *Psycho 15*, November 1973.

"Tradition of the Wolf", copyright © 1975 by Ed Fedory and Roberto Martinez. Originally published by Skywald in *Nightmare 23*, February 1975.

"Sea of Graves", copyright © 1970 by Michael W. Kaluta. Originally published by Major Magazines in *Web of Horror 2*, February 1970. Reprinted by permission of Michael W. Kaluta.

"Killer Planet", copyright © 1978 by Rand Holmes. Originally published by Stampart in Fog City Comics 2, 1978; reprinted in *Death Rattle 1*, October 1985. Reprinted from *Death Rattle 1* by permission of Denis Kitchen.

"Over His Head", copyright © 1983 by Mike Ploog. Originally published by Pacific Comics in *Twisted Tales 2*, April 1983. Reprinted by permission of Mike Ploog.

"Christmas Carol", copyright © 1984 by Arthur Suydam. Originally published by Pacific Comics in *Demon Dreams 1*, February 1984. Reprinted by permission of Arthur Suydam.

"Mr Monster: His World", copyright © 1988 by Michael T. Gilbert. Originally published by Dark Horse in *Dark Horse Presents 14*, January 1988. Reprinted by permission of Michael T. Gilbert.

"Home Ties", copyright © 1984 by Mike Hoffman. Originally published by Pacific Comics in *Twisted Tales 6*, January 1984. Reprinted by permission of Mike Hoffman.

"One of these Days", copyright © 1987 by Gary Reed. Originally published by Arrow Comics in *Deadworld 6*, December 1987. Reprinted by permission of Gary Reed.

"The Dunwich Horror", copyright © 1999 by John Coulthart. Originally published by Oneiros Books in *The Haunter of the Dark and Other Grotesque Visions*, 1999. Reprinted by permission of John Coulthart.

"Dream Snake", copyright © 1999 by Robert E. Howard. Originally published by Cross Plains in Robert E. Howard's *Myth Maker*, 1999. Reprinted by permission of Robert E. Howard Properties Inc.

"Purgation", copyright © 1996 by Chuck Regan. Originally published by Dark Matter Press in *The Confessor Demonicus-ex-Deo*, 1996. Reprinted by permission of Chuck Regan.

"Dread End", copyright © 2003 by Pete Von Sholly. Originally published by Soaring Penguin in *From the Tomb 12*, February 2004. Reprinted by permission of Pete Von Sholly.

"The Festival", copyright © 2004 by Grant Margetts. Originally published by Chimera Arts in *Bedlam 5*, July 2004. Reprinted by permission of Grant Margetts.

"The Crawlspace", copyright © 2005 by Stephen Sennitt and James Fletcher. Originally published by Soaring Penguin in *From the Tomb 18*, Christmas 2005. Reprinted by permission of Stephen Sennitt and James Fletcher.

"Immortal: A Vampire Tale", copyright © 2003 by Dave Hitchcock. Originally published by Black Boar Press, 2003. Reprinted by permission of Dave Hitchcock.

"There Was an Old Woman", copyright © 2003 by Socar Myles. Originally published by Fright Studios in *Fleshrot Tales from the Dead 2*, 2003. Reprinted by permission of Socar Myles.

"Cal McDonald: A Letter from B. S.", copyright © 2003 by Steve Niles and Shawna Gore. Originally published by Dark Horse in *Drawing on your Nightmares 1*, October 2003. Reprinted by permission of Steve Niles and Shawna Gore.

"Luna's Story Little Red Riding Hood", copyright © 2004 by Serena Valentino. Originally published by Slave Labour Graphics in *Nightmares & Fairy Tales 8*, March 2004. Reprinted by permission of Serena Valentino and Dan Vado.

"The Graveswellers", copyright © 2005 by Pete Von Sholly. Originally published by Dark Horse in *Morbid 2*, February 2005. Reprinted by permission of Pete Von Sholly.

"Shuteye", copyright © 2004 by Joe Monks. Originally published by Chanting Monks Press in *Zacherley's Midnite Terrors 2*, 2004. Reprinted by permission of Joe Monks.